Michigan
Wildflowers

Dwarf Lake Iris

Michigan Wildflowers

Helen V. Smith

Illustrations by Ruth Powell Brede

CRANBROOK INSTITUTE of SCIENCE

1966

Bulletin 42
REVISED

Library of Congress Catalog Card Number: 66-19039
Printed by The Cranbrook Press
Color printing by University Microfilms, Inc.
Binding by the Kingsport Press

*Dedicated to my parents
who encouraged my early interest in plants
and to my husband and daughter
whose aid and forbearance have made it possible
for me to devote myself to Michigan wildflowers*

Michigan Wildflowers
was published with financial support from
The Edwin S. George Publication Fund

TABLE OF CONTENTS

LIST OF COLOR PLATES

PUBLISHER'S NOTE

Michigan is unlike any other state in its combination of extensive forests of broad-leaved trees, vast areas of jack-pine plains, bits of prairie, and a shoreline unique in length. Its wilderness, lakes and streams, beaches, and sand dunes, its woods, meadows, and abundance of wildflowers and wildlife, bring pleasure each year both to its year-round residents and to hundreds of thousands of visitors.

But residents and visitors alike who have gone afield in Michigan during the blooming season have often felt the lack of a good flower book especially adapted to the Michigan scene.

Michigan Wildflowers has been prepared and published to meet this need. In it are described and illustrated almost every wildflower which attracts attention through charm, abundance, or rarity. Cranbrook Institute of Science takes pride in making available a handbook that we believe will have wide and continued use.

The Institute is grateful to the author and the illustrator, both well qualified for their tasks. The design of the book is by William A. Bostick. Thanks are due also to many others, both on the Institute staff and elsewhere, who have contributed to the final fashioning of this book.

R. T. H.

June, 1961

PREFACE

A book on the wildflowers of Michigan has been discussed by various groups for a number of years. There was obvious need for one which would include most of the wildflowers that one might encounter in the ordinary course of outdoor activities in the state. The larger publications are too technical and difficult for any but the trained botanist and are too large to carry about. The general handbooks include too many species not found in Michigan and too few species that are; in addition, the descriptions are often so sketchy that one cannot be sure of correct identification. It was to fill this need that Dr. Robert T. Hatt, Director of the Cranbrook Institute of Science, asked me to undertake a book on Michigan wildflowers. While I was extremely pleased, I felt considerable hestitation about accepting the task because of a realization of the difficulties which had to be overcome. However, I have had a lively interest in wildflowers most of my life. In pursuing this interest many manuals have been used as well as many of the small, limited guides designed to give quick identification of a few species. I have experienced much difficulty in trying to make identifications and consequently have developed a number of ideas as to just what is important to one who wants to learn the wildflowers. Hence writing such a book as this was a challenge too great to resist.

This work is offered with many misgivings. I find it much easier to criticize what others have done than to do a better job myself. If this publication enables the hobbyist to learn the names and something about the wildflowers of the state, my aim will have been accomplished.

Nearly 500 kinds of plants are included, most of which are herbaceous. Since there are excellent books on Michigan shrubs, trees, and weeds, few of these plants are treated here; even the showy Dogwood has been omitted. The plants to be included were selected by the Cranbrook Institute of Science, with the advice of members of the Herbarium Committee of the Institute.

The Institute was also responsible for the execution of the drawings, the author acting in an advisory capacity. The majority of the drawings are from freshly collected plants, a few from Kodachrome slides, and a very few from dried herbarium material. The drawings were made by Mrs. Ruth Powell Brede, under the direction of Dr.

Marion Trufant Hall. They were made, primarily from specimens collected in southeastern Michigan, while Dr. Hall was Associate Botanist of Cranbrook Institute of Science. However, to be sure of a more adequate representation of the interesting northern flowers, Mrs. Brede spent one summer at the University of Michigan Biological Station, near Cheboygan, making drawings under my direction.

The majority of the descriptions likewise were written up from living plants. The aim has been to give, through descriptions and illustrations, the picture of the plant as it appears in nature, coupled with such technical details as are essential in identifying it. One species of each kind of plant is quite fully described; for closely similar kinds merely the identifying or distinguishing characters are given. The general aspect and most easily seen characteristics of the plant as a whole are given first, followed by a description of the flowers, the nature and arrangement of the leaves, the habitat, and the flowering time. In many cases interesting notes on the plant under discussion are added.

No book of any size can be prepared without assistance; this one has been no exception. The late F. C. Gates, of Kansas State College and the University of Michigan Biological Station, gave me much interesting and helpful information based on his more than forty summers of work with Michigan plants. Professor Volney H. Jones of the University of Michigan made available to me the Museum of Anthropology file on the uses of native plants by Indians of the Great Lakes region. Professor Rogers McVaugh of the University of Michigan Herbarium has given advice on all phases of the work. Dr. E. B. Mains, Director of the University of Michigan Herbarium, offered access to the collection of Michigan flowering plants. Dr. Lloyd Shinners aided in some of the identifications, particularly in the Compositae. Throughout the course of the work Professor Alexander H. Smith of the University of Michigan Herbarium and Department of Botany has collected material for my use and has read the manuscript. Professor A. H. Stockard, Director of the University of Michigan Biological Station, provided me with facilities at the Station during the three summers I worked on the project there. Dr. Edward G. Voss of the University of Michigan Herbarium was most helpful in obtaining material for drawing and providing information on the distribution of species in the state; he also read the proofs. To all these I offer sincere gratitude.

H.V.S.

INTRODUCTION

CONSERVATION OF WILDFLOWERS

In the not very distant past Michigan had a wealth of wildlife habitats where anyone might enjoy nature in its several aspects. However, with our greater population, more rapid transportation, and increased hours of leisure, pressures on our wild lands make it more and more difficult to find unspoiled tracts for the enjoyment of animals and plants in their native haunts. Further, a large proportion of the population is turning to nature to find a release from the nervous tension engendered by the fast pace of industrial and city life. Thus we have two opposing forces, the increasing, more widespread, desire to enjoy the out-of-doors, and the constantly decreasing space in which to do so.

Fortunately, several groups of people are aware of the importance of saving some areas from further change. The State Conservation Department is buying large tracts of marginal land to be used for recreation by the public, part of which will be kept in the natural state for hiking, bird-watching, and nature study in general. Other governmental agencies, such as the Huron-Clinton Metropolitan Authority, and several nongovernmental organizations—sportsmen's groups, spearheaded by the Michigan United Conservation Clubs, the Michigan Natural Areas Council, the Michigan Botanical Club, the Federated Garden Clubs of Michigan, and others—are working for the preservation of natural areas. On the national level there are several conservation organizations; many, such as Nature Conservancy and the Audubon Society, have state and other local branches.

Many of our native species are disappearing so rapidly that in some states endangered species are protected by law. In Michigan it is now unlawful, without written permission from the owner of the land, to pick or dig up the following species:

Trailing Arbutus (*Epigaea repens*)
Prince's Pine (*Chimaphila umbellata*)
Bird-foot Violet (*Viola pedata*)
Climbing Bittersweet (*Celastrus scandens*)
Flowering Dogwood (*Cornus florida*)
Mountain Holly (*Nemopanthus mucronata*)
Michigan Holly (*Ilex verticillata*)
American Lotus (*Nelumbo lutea*)

Orchid Family—all members:
  Lady's-slipper or Moccasin Flower (*Cypripedium*)
  Orchis (*Orchis*)
  Rein-orchid, Fringed Orchid (*Habenaria*)
  Pogonia (*Pogonia, Isotria,* and *Triphora*)
  Grass Pink (*Calopogon*)
  Arethusa (*Arethusa*)
  Lady's-tresses (*Spiranthes*)
  Rattlesnake Plantain *or* Orchid (*Goodyera*)
  Twayblade (*Listera* and *Liparis*)
  Coral-root (*Corallorhiza*)
  Adder's-mouth (*Malaxis*)
  Putty-root (*Aplectrum*)
  Calypso, Fairy Slipper (*Calypso*)
  Cranefly Orchid (*Tipularia*)
Trillium (*Trillium*)—all species
Gentian Family—all members:
  Rose-pink (*Sabatia*)
  Centaury (*Centaurium*)
  Gentian (*Gentiana*)
  Columbo (*Swertia*)
  Spurred Gentian (*Halenia*)
  Buckbean (*Menyanthes*)
  Floating-heart (*Nymphoides*)

GROWING WILDFLOWERS

Growing wildflowers is one of the most fascinating of hobbies. The equipment and materials used can be very simple, and only a small plot of ground is needed. Wild plants have special requirements as to soil type, acidity, moisture, sun, shade, etc; it is futile to try to grow them under conditions radically different from those in nature. One should choose species for a wildflower garden according to the kind of habitat available. They can be found for almost any kind of habitat: a sunny or shady rock garden, a sandy spot in the sun, a wet or boggy garden, an open sunny field, or a woodland setting—which may be simply a shady spot under a tree or beside a building. Wildflowers for the garden should be grown in a naturalistic setting, in clumps, never in formal rows.

I derived great pleasure from a small "backyard woodland garden," which was merely a small area under an apple tree and some shrubs. The tree had been trimmed high enough to provide head room and some sun. The drainage was good, but the soil was a rather poor clay, with a small amount of ashes, sand, and humus in the form of grass clippings and peat worked in. The garden received little attention except for weeding in the spring and watering when it was very dry. About forty kinds of native plants were grown there, and most of these multiplied.

A fairly large number of species of wildflowers can be grown in a relatively small area. A half acre, partly wooded, partly open and sunny, now has growing on it about 125 (over one-fourth) of the species described in this book. The majority of these are growing there naturally, and more can probably be introduced without much difficulty.

Material for the garden can be obtained in several ways. If specimens are to be transplanted from the wild, one must have permission from the owner of the land and a certificate of inspection from the State Department of Agriculture to transport them. The plants should be dug when the soil is moist and a good ball of earth can be secured. Actually, in Michigan it is quite difficult to meet all the requirements for getting plants from the wild, and many of the more attractive species are either on the protected list or should be. Most plants, therefore, should be grown from seed. For best results, seed of most species should be planted soon after it ripens. Some plants can be purchased from dealers. Several dealers specialize in wildflower plants and seeds, and some of the larger nurseries also offer a few of the showier species. Anyone planning to grow wildflowers would do well to consult the books on that subject listed on page 446.

The following list of plants is suggested for the person starting out in this fascinating hobby. As previously stated, for a spot with special conditions one must select species adapted to those conditions; the wildflowers in the list are for the woodland garden or open sunny places. Asterisks indicate the dozen woodland genera I especially recommend for the core of this relatively simple type of garden because they are quite easy to grow and, for the most part, not difficult to obtain.

LIST OF PLANTS FOR THE
HOME WILDFLOWER GARDEN

Aster (*Aster*). Sunny location needed for most species, but some grow in woodlands; be sure to obtain a species adapted to the conditions in your garden.

Baneberry (*Actaea pachypoda* and *rubra*). Woodland. Both species are attractive for foliage and berries, but they should not be planted where children can reach them because the berries are poisonous.

Beard-tongue (*Penstemon digitalis* and *pallidus*). Sunny Places. *P. hirsutus* grows in light shade or sun.

Bedstraw (*Galium*). Woodland. Various species are useful for their foliage.

3

Bishop's-cap (*Mitella diphylla*). Woodland. Easily grown in a cool, moist, shady place.

Black-eyed Susan (*Rudbeckia hirta*). Sunny places. Attractive but short-lived.

Blazing Star (*Liatris*). Sunny places. Very attractive.

*Bloodroot (*Sanguinaria canadensis*). Woodland. Most attractive; usually multiplies freely; leaves are pretty and persist for some time.

Blue Cohosh (*Caulophyllum thalictroides*). Woodland. Valuable because of the interesting, though inconspicuous, flowers; the foliage is attractive.

Butterfly-weed (*Asclepias tuberosa*). Sunny places. Very attractive, but the deep roots are easily broken in transplanting and are then susceptible to attack by fungi. This species is often offered for sale by nurseries.

Canada Anemone (*Anemone canadensis*). Sunny places or light shade. Needs considerable moisture; easily grown, but has a tendency to spread and crowd out other plants.

Columbine (*Aquilegia canadensis*). Sunny places or light shade. One of the easiest wildflowers to grow; usually spreads by self-seeding, and does best in rather poor soil.

Dutchman's-breeches and Squirrel-corn (*Dicentra cucullaria* and *canadensis*). Moist woodland rich in humus. Very attractive, but flowers sparsely; the foliage soon disappears. The tubers are often eaten by mice.

*False Solomon's-seal (*Smilacina racemosa* and *stellata*). Woodland. Both kinds are hardy; they spread rapidly and are easily propagated by root divisions.

Fawn Lily, Adder's-tongue, Dog's-tooth Violet (*Erythronium americanum* and *albidum*). Very attractive, but the tubers occur deep in the soil, are difficult to transplant, and must be several years old before they will produce flowers. Both species are likely to bloom poorly, but the white one is said to flower more freely.

Fireweed (*Epilobium angustifolium*). Sunny places or light shade. Does well under a variety of conditions; may crowd out other species.

Foam Flower (*Tiarella cordifolia*). Woodland. Makes good ground cover in a moist garden.

Goldenrod (*Solidago*). Sunny places or woodland, depending on the species.

Harebell, Bluebell (*Campanula rotundifolia*). Sunny places or light shade; good in a rock garden.

*Hepatica (*Hepatica americana* and *acutiloba*). Woodland. Both the flowers and the leaves are attractive. The first species does best in a moderately acid soil; Sharp-lobed Hepatica, in a slightly acid to neutral soil.

*Jack-in-the-pulpit (*Arisaema atrorubens*). Woodland. Requires little care and multiplies freely. The flowering stage is interesting and the clusters of red berries are very attractive.

*Lungwort, Virginia Cowslip *or* Bluebells (*Mertensia virginica*). One of the most attractive species for the wild garden. Grows very well, but dies down soon after blooming. Readily obtained from nurseries.

May-apple (*Podophyllum peltatum*). Woodland. A good species for gardens where plenty of space is available. After it becomes established it may crowd out other species.

*Meadow-rue (*Thalictrum dioicum*). Woodland. The airy flower-clusters make this a desirable species.

Merrybell (*Uvularia*). Woodland. Often forms extensive patches.

Ox-eye Daisy (*Chrysanthemum leucanthemum*). Sunny places. Usually multiplies freely.

*Phlox, Wild Blue Phlox, Wild Sweet William (*Phlox divaricata*). Woodland. Very desirable and usually obtainable from nurseries. Downy Phlox (*P. pilosa*) is said to be harder to grow; it flowers a little later.

Rue-anemone (*Anemonella thalictroides*). Woodland. Does best in a slightly acid soil.

Solomon's-seal (*Polygonatum*). Woodland. Less attractive than False Solomon's Seal.

Spiderwort (*Tradescantia*). Sunny places. Well known as a garden flower; easy to grow.

*Spring-beauty (*Claytonia virginica* and *caroliniana*). Woodland. Very desirable; both species flower over longer periods than most early flowers. The plants die down completely by early summer. Narrow-leaved Spring Beauty (*C. virginica*) is the more attractive because of slightly larger and more numerous flowers.

Toothwort (*Dentaria diphylla* and *laciniata*). Woodland. After these become established, they may spread rapidly.

*Trillium, Wakerobin (*Trillium*). Woodland. All species are on the protected list in Michigan. They may be propagated by seed, but this takes several years. A number of species can be obtained from nurseries. The Large-flowered Trillium is the showiest and is one of the easiest kinds to grow.

*Violet (*Viola*). Woodland. A number of kinds can be easily grown; their requirements differ somewhat, so that the type of habitat should be noted when the plants are obtained.

*Wild Geranium (*Geranium maculatum*). Woodland. Grows well and multiplies freely—it may have to be kept in check. Both the flowers and the foliage are attractive, and the plants do not die down early.

*Wild Ginger (*Asarum canadense*). Woodland. A good ground cover.

Wild Lupine (*Lupinus perennis*). Sunny places. Very attractive. Requires dry, sandy, acid soil. Difficult to transplant, as the roots are deep. Seeds may need to be treated with a nitrogen-fixing bacterial inoculant.

Wood-poppy (*Stylophorum diphyllum*). Woodland. Beautiful, but rare in Michigan.

THE NAMING OF PLANTS

When one discovers an unfamiliar object, the first question that comes to mind is: "What is its name?" Living organisms, plants and animals alike, have two types of names. The more familiar, everyday ones are called common names. These are often descriptive, as, for example, *Blue-eyed Grass, Black-eyed Susan,* or *Milkweed.* However, a single kind of plant may be called by different common names in different countries or even in different sections of the same country. Further, the same common name, in different regions, may be applied to entirely different plants.

To avoid the difficulties arising from conflicting common names, each kind of plant is given a scientific name. This consists of two Latin or Latinized words and is the same in all countries. The first word is capitalized and is the generic name, the name of the genus. A genus is a group of closely related kinds (species) of plants. The second word, called a species epithet, indicates which particular plant in the group is designated. *Viola* is the generic name for all our native violets. *Viola canadensis* is the name for the Canadian or Tall White Violet; *Viola pedata* (*pedata* meaning "footlike") is the Birdfoot Violet; and *Viola rostrata* ("having a beak") is the Long-spurred Violet. It is customary to italicize the scientific name and to indicate the name of the person who first named the species. Thus the full designation for Birdfoot Violet would be *Viola pedata* L., the L. standing for Linnaeus. Genera (plural of genus) are grouped in families. The family names usually end in the letters *aceae*, as in Violaceae. The scientific names used for the plants in this book are, except where stated otherwise, those given in Gray's *Manual of Botany*, 8th edition, 1950, by M. L. Fernald.

THE PARTS OF A PLANT

In order to identify wildflowers it is necessary to understand a little about the plant as a whole, its parts, and the descriptive terms applied to them. The parts with which we are principally concerned are those that occur above ground; the *stem* and its branches, the *leaves,* the *flowers,* and the *fruits.* (See Figs. 1–5.)

One of the first things to notice about a plant is whether it is *herbaceous* or *woody,* i.e., whether it dies down to the ground in the winter or has a persistent woody stem. Some plants are *evergreen,* i.e., they have green leaves the year around, but most of our species either shed their leaves (are deciduous) or are herbaceous. The habit of growth of plants, the direction in which the stem grows, is easily noted and is often characteristic (Fig. 1).

The leaves are extremely important as the photosynthetic or food-manufacturing organs of the plant. All life is dependent upon the ability of green plants to combine carbon dioxide with water to form a simple sugar. This process can be carried on only by the green coloring material (chlorophyll) acting in the presence of sunlight or its equivalent. Leaves are also of importance in the classification of plants. Most of the common terms used in describing them are illustrated (Figs. 4–5). Definitions of the terms are given in the Glossary.

The flowers are the reproductive structures of the plant; their function is to produce seeds. A typical flower has four whorls or circles of parts. The outer whorl is called the *calyx.* This is composed of separate or united *sepals* and is usually green. The *corolla* is composed of separate or united *petals,* which are usually white or colored. The corolla is often lacking, and the calyx may be colored and corollalike. The calyx and corolla (Fig. 2) function as floral envelopes to protect the essential organs and/or to attract insects. The *stamens,* each consisting of an *anther* and *filament,* and the *pistil,* or pistils, are essential for reproduction. The anther is borne on the filament and produces the *pollen* grains; these contain the male reproductive elements. The pistil consists of the (usually enlarged) *ovary* at the base, the *style,* and the *stigma.* The ovary contains the ovules which, when fertilized by the male element from the pollen grain, may develop into seeds. The stigma acts as the receptive organ for the pollen and usually has a moist or sticky surface. Flowers vary greatly in arrangement on the plants, number and shape of parts, etc. These variations are important in the classification of plants. Many of the common descriptive terms applied to flowers are illustrated (Figs. 2–3), and the terms are defined in the Glossary.

The fruits are the "ultimate purpose" of a plant; they are the structures that bear the seeds. Under proper conditions seeds germinate and produce new plants. Fruits are quite diverse and are an aid in identification. Some types of fruit are hard to classify; a few of the more easily distinguished kinds are illustrated (Fig. 3).

In addition to the names and shapes of the parts of a plant it is often necessary or helpful to know the sizes. In this book the size is expressed in the metric system. The measurements, with their abbreviations and approximate equivalents in inches, are as follows:

Millimeter (mm.)	1/25 inch
Centimeter (cm.=10 mm.)	2/5 inch
Decimeter (dm.=10 cm.)	4 inches
Meter (m.=10 dm.)	39.4 inches

MATERIALS FOR COLLECTING AND IDENTIFYING PLANTS

Materials needed in collecting and identifying the plants described are few. A good hand lens or reading glass will be helpful. In collecting, a plastic bag offers the simplest way of carrying a few small specimens; a damp paper towel placed in the bag will help to retard wilting on a warm day.

BOTANICAL KEYS

IDENTIFYING A PLANT WITH THIS KEY

A few plant families are easily recognized on sight. For example, the Cruciferae, or Mustard Family, with its cross-shaped flowers and 6 stamens of unequal length, is readily recognized. However, many plants offer more difficulty, and help is needed in learning to identify them. Even if one knows the family or genus to which a specimen belongs, there may be many similar species, and some quicker method of identification is needed than that of reading through many descriptions. A botanical "key" offers such a method.

The process of "running down" a specimen in a key consists, first, of selecting from a pair of identically numbered statements the one applicable to the specimen at hand. When this choice has been made, the leaders to the right of the statement indicate either a name—in which instance identification is made—or another number. If it is a number, reference is made to the pair of statements bearing that number. Of this pair, the one best fitted to the specimen is again selected. This process is continued until selection leads to a name. Reference is then made to the description and illustration of the species, and the specimen is checked to see if the identification is correct.

The following example shows how to identify a Downy Yellow Violet, with the correct choices italicized.

1. Flowers blue to lavender 2
1. *Not as in alternate choice* 3
    2. Plants with leafy stems . . . . *Viola conspersa*, Plate 112
    2. Stemless plants . . . . *V. pedata*, Plate 111

3. Flowers white . . . . *V. canadensis,* Plate 109
3. *Flowers yellow* 4
    4. *Plants hairy* . . . . *V. pubescens,* Plate 110
    4. Plants glabrous . . . . *V. pensylvanica,* Plate 110

Thus the correct name for this violet is *Viola pubescens,* and the identification may be confirmed by comparing the specimen with the description and illustration.

If, after such a search, the characters do not match, another attempt to run the specimen through the key, selecting a different choice, may bring success. If further attempts do not succeed, either the species is not included in this book or an error in judgment has been made. Since plants vary considerably, it is often difficult to evaluate a character correctly. Nevertheless, though not infallible, a key provides both help and a short cut in identifying plants.

The keys in this book, based on the species described and illustrated, represent less than a fourth of the flowering plants growing in Michigan. For identification of the many species not included, the books cited in the Selected References may be consulted.

SECTIONS OF THE KEY
(See Figs. 1–5)

Monocots: Section A. Flower parts mostly in 3's or multiples of 3; leaves simple, margins entire, veins usually parallel, extending from base to apex; veins in stem scattered, not appearing in a ring in cross section.

Dicots: Flower parts mostly in 4's or 5's or multiples thereof; leaves simple or compound, margins entire, toothed, or lobed; veins netted, principal veins either pinnate or palmate in arrangement; veins in stem appearing in a ring in cross section.

    Section B. Perianth lacking or consisting of only one (or only one apparent) circle of parts, often colored and/or petallike.

    Section C. Calyx and corolla both present, petals distinct and separate, often falling separately. Part 1. Flowers regular. Part 2. Flowers irregular.

    Section D. Calyx and corolla both present, petals united at least at base, corolla falling as a unit. Part 1. Flowers regular. Part 2. Flowers irregular.

Some Monocots and Dicots: Section E. Flowers several to many, usually small, sessile or nearly so, borne in a structure resembling a single flower: 1, on a spadix subtended by a spathe; 2, inside a cuplike structure; 3, in heads or dense clusters subtended by at least 4 bracts.

KEY TO SPECIES INCLUDED
Section A: Monocots

1. Flowers small, several to many, in a dense, compact,
   globose or cylindrical inflorescence 2
1. Flowers often large, individual ones distinct, or,
   if borne in clusters, not densely compact 5
   2. Flower cluster with a distince leaflike or fleshy and colored
      spathe at base (if flowers blue, see *Pontederia*) . ARACEAE, p. 33
   2. Flower cluster lacking a spathe 3

3. Flowers borne in dense, terminal, brown,
cylindrical spikes .   .   .   . *Typha latifolia* or *angustifolia,* Plate 1
3. Not as in alternate choice 4

    4. Flowers greenish white, borne in dense,
      globose heads along stem .   .   . *Sparganium eurycarpum,* Plate 2
    4. Flowers yellow, borne in solitary, terminal,
      conelike heads .   .   .   . *Xyris montana,* Plate 9

5. Plant rushlike, leaves round in cross section;
flowers greenish white .   .   . *Triglochin maritima* or *palustris,* Plate 3
5. Not as in alternate choice 6

    6. Sepals green, petals white or colored 7
    6. Sepals and petals colored alike 10

7. Leaves 3, in a whorl at top of stem .   .   .   .   .   . *Trillium,* p. 55
7. Leaves not whorled 8

    8. Flowers blue .   .   .   .   .   . *Tradescantia ohiensis,* Plate 9
    8. Flowers white or sometimes pinkish 9

9. Flowers 1.5–3 cm. wide, of 2 kinds (staminate and pistillate separate),
usually 3 in a whorl; leaves usually arrow-shaped . *Sagittaria latifolia,* Plate 5
9. Flowers smaller, perfect, leaves never
arrow-shaped .   .   .   . *Alisma subcordatum,* Plate 4

    10. Flowers rose, in an umbel, leaves long
       and narrow .   .   .   . *Butomus umbellatus,* Plate 3
    10. Not as in alternate choice 11

11. Flowers regular 12
11. Flowers irregular 15

    12. Ovary superior .   .   .   . LILIACEAE, p. 41
    12. Ovary inferior 13

13. Petals and sepals similar in size, shape, and position;
flowers not over 2.5 cm. broad 14
13. Petals and sepals quite different in size and/or shape,
petals erect, sepals hanging down; flowers 3 cm.
or more broad .   .   . *Iris versicolor* or *lacustris,* Plate 21 or Frontispiece

    14. Flowers yellow .   .   .   .   .   . *Hypoxis hirsuta,* Plate 20
    14. Flowers blue
       to whitish .   .   . *Sisyrinchium albidum* or *angustifolium,* Plate 20

15. Flowers bright blue, leaves elongate
heart-shaped .   .   .   . *Pontederia cordata,* Plate 9
15. Not as in alternate choice .   .   .   .   . ORCHIDACEAE, p. 66

Section B: Dicots
(Perianth lacking or, actually or apparently,
consisting of only one circle of parts)

1. Leaves simple and not deeply cut 2
1. Leaves compound or cut nearly to base or midrib 13

    2. Nodes of stem covered by tubular sheaths . POLYGONACEAE, p. 97
    2. Nodes not covered by tubular sheaths 3

3. Plants stemless or creeping 4
3. Plants having erect leafy stems 5

4. Stems creeping; flowers brown-purple,
bell-shaped, 3-lobed . . . . . *Asarum canadense,* Plate 36
4. Plants stemless; flowers of separate white, pink, or blue sepals;
leaves 3-lobed . . . *Hepatica acutiloba* or *americana,* Plate 55
5. Juice of plant milky . . . . *Euphorbia,* p. 221
5. Juice of plant watery 6
  6. Leaves mostly in whorls . . . . *Galium,* p. 357
  6. Leaves not in whorls 7
7. Leaves opposite; stem swollen at nodes 8
7. Leaves alternate or scattered 9
  8. Flowers pink or magenta; leaves with definite
  blade and petiole . . . . . *Mirabilis nyctaginea,* Plate 42
  8. Flowers usually not pink; if pink, leaves
  apparently sessile . . . . . CARYOPHYLLACEAE, p. 109
9. Flowers white or pink 10
9. Flowers greenish, red, or yellow 12
  10. Flower clusters opposite the leaves . *Phytolacca americana,* Plate 42
  10. Flower clusters at end of stem 11
11. Leaves usually 2–3, heart-shaped at base *Maianthemum canadense,* Plate 15
11. Leaves numerous, elliptic. . . . . *Comandra richardsiana,* Plate 36
  12. Flowers bright yellow, showy . . *Caltha palustris,* Color Plate 6
  12. Flowers greenish or red, tiny,
  in dense clusters . . *Chenopodium capitatum* or *album,* Plate 41
13. Plant a vine . . . . *Clematis virginiana* or *verticillaris,* Plate 58
13. Plant an erect herb 14
  14. Flowers few, mostly solitary . . . RANUNCULACEAE, p. 123
  14. Flowers numerous, small, in clusters 15
15. Flowers in a many-branched terminal corymb;
stamens 3; leaves opposite . . . . *Valeriana uliginosa,* Plate 181
15. Flowers in umbels; stamens 5;
leaves alternate . . . . UMBELLIFERAE, p. 251

Section C: Dicots
(Sepals present; petals present, distinct from each other and usually falling separately)

Part 1. Flowers Regular

1. Leaves, flowers, or both, floating; *or* the plants insectivorous, with
hollow, pitcherlike leaves or leaves covered with sticky glands . . . 2
1. Not as in alternate choice 4
  2. Leaves or flowers floating . . . . NYMPHAEACEAE, p. 117
  2. Not as in alternate choice 3
3. Flowers large, showy, solitary . . . *Sarracenia purpurea,* Plate 72
3. Flowers small, several on a coiled stalk . . . . . *Drosera,* p. 164
  4. Flowers small, numerous, borne in an umbel 5
  4. Not as in alternate choice 7
5. Plants climbing by tendrils . . . . . *Smilax lasioneura,* Plate 19
5. Plants not climbing, lacking tendrils 6
  6. Fruit dry, splitting into 2 seedlike bodies;
  petioles enlarged and sheathing at base . UMBELLIFERAE, p. 251
  6. Fruit a berry; petioles not sheathing . . . ARALIACEAE, p. 247
7. Stem, leaves, or both, thick and fleshy; leaves lacking, scalelike,
or thick and fleshy; plants green or not 8
7. Not as in alternate choice 10

8. Plants not green; stem having small scales
   in place of leaves . . . . PYROLACEAE, p. 271
8. Plants green 9

9. Stem enlarged into fleshy, padlike sections, usually leafless, bearing
   prickles or spines; flowers large and showy . *Opuntia humifusa*, Plate 112
9. Stem bearing fleshy leaves and numerous small flowers
   up to 1 cm. wide . . . . *Sedum acre* or *purpureum*, Plate 74

   10. Erect shrub, flowers white; leaves narrow, lower surface
      covered with rusty wool . . . *Ledum groenlandicum*, Plate 135
   10. Not as in alternate choice 11

11. Sepals or calyx lobes 2, often soon falling, sometimes very small . . 12
11. Sepals or calyx lobes more than 2 15

   12. Juice of plant colored . . . . . PAPAVERACEAE, p. 147
   12. Juice of plant not colored 13

13. Leaves 2, opposite; petals 5 . . *Claytonia virginica* or *caroliniana*, Plate 43
13. Leaves usually more than 2; petals 2 14

   14. Leaves opposite . . . *Circaea quadrisulcata* or *alpina*, Plate 116
   14. Leaves alternate . . . . *Maianthemum canadense*, Plate 15

15. Sepals 3 16
15. Sepals or calyx lobes more than 3 17

   16. Leaves 3, borne in a whorl at top of stem; flowers
      large and showy . . . . *Trillium*, p. 55
   16. Leaves more than 3, mostly in a basal rosette; flowers
      tiny . . . . *Rumex acetosella*, Plate 37

17. Sepals or calyx lobes and petals 4 18
17. Sepals or calyx lobes and/or petals more than 4 20

   18. Stamens 6, 2 shorter than the other 4;
      leaves alternate or basal . . . . . CRUCIFERAE, p. 150
   18. Stamens same number or twice as many as petals;
      leaves often opposite 19

19. Stems swollen at nodes, ovary superior . CARYOPHYLLACEAE, p. 109
19. Stems not swollen at nodes, ovary inferior . . ONAGRACEAE, p. 241

   20. Leaves having translucent or black dots; stamens
      clustered in 3–5 groups; petals 5, oblique at ends,
      rolled lengthwise in bud . . . . . . *Hypericum*, p. 227
   20. Not as in alternate choice 21

21. Calyx bearing a band of hooked
   bristles . . . . *Agrimonia gryposepala* or *parviflora*, Plates 86, 87
21. Not as in alternate choice 22

   22. Stamens same number as petals 23
   22. Stamens more numerous than petals 31

23. Leaves compound or deeply lobed 24
23. Leaves simple 26

   24. Flowers rose to rose-purple . . . *Erodium cicutarium*, Plate 101
   24. Flowers white or yellowish 25

25. Flowers solitary, white . . . . . *Jeffersonia diphylla*, Plate 62
25. Flowers in clusters, yellowish to greenish or
   bronze . . . . *Caulophyllum thalictroides*, Plate 62

   26. Leaves opposite 27
   26. Leaves alternate, scattered, whorled, or basal 29

Part 2. Flowers Irregular

4. Leaves in a basal rosette . . . . *Goodyera*, p. 85
4. Leaves borne along stem . . . . *Polygala*, p. 217
5. Flowers tiny, borne in umbels; petioles enlarged
and sheathing at base . . . . . . UMBELLIFERAE, p. 251
5. Not as in alternate choice 6
  6. Sepals 2, separate . . . . PAPAVERACEAE, p. 147
  6. Sepals united into a 5-lobed calyx . . . LEGUMINOSAE, p. 189

Section D: Dicots
(*Calyx and corolla both present; petals united at least at base, and falling together*)

Part 1. Corolla Regular or Nearly So

1. Flowers few to many on a common receptacle or disk
subtended by involucre of bracts . . . . COMPOSITAE, p. 373
1. Not as in alternate choice 2
  2. Juice of plant milky 3
  2. Juice of plant not milky 6
3. Plants twining or trailing . . . . . . *Convolvulus*, p. 301
3. Plants principally erect, not twining 4
  4. Flowers blue . . . . *Campanula*, p. 367
  4. Flowers not blue 5
5. Flowers bell-shaped or tubular, white to
pinkish . . *Apocynum androsaemifolium* or *cannabinum*, Plate 145
5. Not as in alternate choice . . . . . . *Asclepias*, p. 298
  6. Plants not green; leaves reduced to scales . PYROLACEAE, p. 271
  6. Plants having normal green leaves 7
7. Plants shrubby, prostrate, creeping, or vinelike 8
7. Not as in alternate choice 13
  8. Flowers white, borne in spherical
  heads . . . . . . *Cephalanthus occidentalis*, Plate 179
  8. Not as in alternate choice 9
9. Plants climbing by tendrils . . . . *Echinocystis lobata*, Plate 183
9. Not as in alternate choice 10
  10. Leaves opposite; flowers borne in pairs 11
  10. Not as in alternate choice 12
11. Flowers joined together at base . . . . *Mitchella repens*, Plate 180
11. Flowers separate, drooping from tips of slender
stalks . . . . *Linnaea borealis*, Plate 180
  12. Flowers violet to purple . . . . *Solanum dulcamara*, Plate 165
  12. Not as in alternate choice . . . . . . ERICACEAE, p. 277
13. Leaves simple 14
13. Leaves compound or cut nearly to base or midrib 36
  14. Flowers orange, having a crownlike circle formed
  of 5 erect hoods . . . . . *Asclepias tuberosa*, Color Plate 11
  14. Not as in alternate choice 15
15. Flowers funnelform 16
15. Not as in alternate choice 17
  16. Rank, erect plants . . . . . *Datura stramonium*, Plate 166
  16. Low, weak plant, often twining
  at tip . . . . *Convolvulus spithamaeus*, Plate 147

14

15

37. Plants of bogs; leaflets elliptic,
flowers white . . . . . *Menyanthes trifoliata,* Plate 144
37. Plants of average soil; leaflets inverted heart-shaped;
flowers yellow or pink or white . . . . *Oxalis,* p. 213

    36. Flowers white; leaves opposite . . *Valeriana uliginosa,* Plate 181
    36. Flowers blue, leaves alternate 38

38. Leaves pinnately compound . . . *Polemonium reptans,* Plate 149
38. Leaves palmately compound
    or lobed . . . . . . *Hydrophyllum canadense,* Plate 149

Part 2. Corolla Irregular

1. Plants lacking chlorophyll, not green . . OROBANCHACEAE, p. 351
1. Plants having normal green color 2

    2. Plants having minute or very finely dissected leaves; growing
      in water or wet places; flowers yellow . . . . *Utricularia,* p. 353
    2. Not as in alternate choice 3

3. Flowers pealike, having wings and a keel 4
3. Not as in alternate choice 5

    4. Leaves compound . . . . LEGUMINOSAE, p. 191
    4. Leaves simple . . . . POLYGALACEAE, p. 97

5. Anthers united into a tube; juice of plant milky . . . *Lobelia,* p. 367
5. Anthers separate; juice of plant watery 6

    6. Leaves in a basal rosette; flowers borne on a scape 7
    6. Leaves borne along stem 8

7. Flowers blue to violet . . . . . *Pinguicula vulgaris,* Plate 176
7. Flowers white . . . . *Goodyera,* p. 85

    8. Fruit 1–4 seedlike nutlets 9
    8. Fruit a capsule 12

9. Stamens 5; plants covered with bristly hairs;
leaves alternate . . . . *Echium vulgare,* Plate 150
9. Stamens 2–4; plants merely hairy to glabrous; leaves opposite . . 10

    10. Flowers borne in distinct, opposite pairs; the elongate nutlet
       becoming bent down against stem . *Phryma leptostachya,* Plate 177
    10. Not as in alternate choice 11

11. Flowers blue, only slightly irregular, borne in terminal spikes;
style rising from apex of ovary; foliage not aromatic . *Verbena,* p. 313
11. Not as in alternate choice; foliage usually aromatic . LABIATAE, p. 317

    12. Flowers hanging horizontally from slender pedicels
       rising from axils of upper leaves;
       capsule opening explosively . . . *Impatiens capensis,* Plate 104
    12. Not as in alternate choice . . . SCROPHULARIACEAE, p. 337

Section E: Some Monocots and Dicots

*(Flowers several to many, usually small, sessile or nearly so, borne in
one of following ways: (1) on a spadix subtended by a spathe; (2) inside a cuplike structure; (3) in heads or clusters subtended by at
least 4 bracts—the whole structure resembling a single flower)*

1. Plants having a milky juice 2
1. Plants not having a milky juice 3

2. Flowers greatly reduced, borne in
a cup-shaped structure . . . . *Euphorbia*, p. 221
2. Flowers of normal structure, numerous in a head, with
several green or greenish bracts at base . . . COMPOSITAE, p. 373
3. Flowers borne on a spadix 4
3. Flowers not borne on a spadix 5
   4. Flowers blue . . . . *Pontederia cordata*, Plate 9
   4. Flowers not blue . . . . ARACEAE, p. 33
5. Cluster of flowers surrounded by 4 (rarely 6) large, white,
petallike bracts . . . . *Cornus canadensis*, Plate 131
5. Not as in alternate choice 6
   6. Involucre cuplike, 5-lobed, resembling a calyx;
calyx petallike . . . . *Mirabilis nyctaginea*, Plate 42
   6. Involucre composed of separate bracts; petals present 7
7. Flowers distinctly 2-lipped; foliage aromatic; stems
square . . . . *Monarda fistulosa* or *punctata*, Plate 161
7. Flowers not having 2 lips 8
   8. Heads elongate, flowers interspersed with rigid, pointed
bracts; stamens 4, separate . . . . *Dipsacus sylvestris*, Plate 182
   8. Not as in alternate choice; stamens
united by their anthers . . . . COMPOSITAE, p. 373

Figure 1

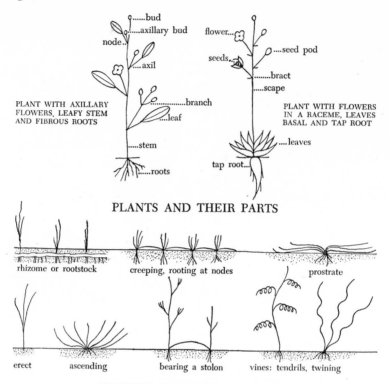

......bud

.....axillary bud

node..

....axil

flower...

....seed pod

seeds..

........bract

....scape

PLANT WITH AXILLARY
FLOWERS, LEAFY STEM
AND FIBROUS ROOTS

...............branch

....leaf

PLANT WITH FLOWERS
IN A RACEME, LEAVES
BASAL AND TAP ROOT

....leaves

.....stem

tap root...

....roots

PLANTS AND THEIR PARTS

rhizome or rootstock

creeping, rooting at nodes

prostrate

erect

ascending

bearing a stolon

vines: tendrils, twining

GROWTH PATTERNS OF STEMS

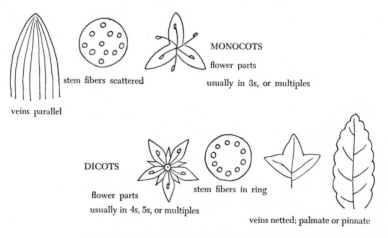

stem fibers scattered

MONOCOTS

flower parts

usually in 3s, or multiples

veins parallel

DICOTS

flower parts

usually in 4s, 5s, or multiples

stem fibers in ring

veins netted; palmate or pinnate

MONOCOT AND DICOT CONTRASTS

Figure 2

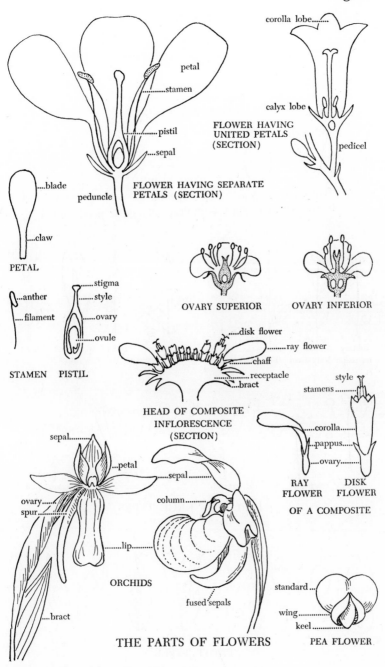

corolla lobe

petal

stamen

pistil

sepal

calyx lobe

**FLOWER HAVING
UNITED PETALS
(SECTION)**

pedicel

**FLOWER HAVING SEPARATE
PETALS (SECTION)**

peduncle

blade

claw

PETAL

anther

filament

stigma

style

ovary

ovule

STAMEN   PISTIL

OVARY SUPERIOR

OVARY INFERIOR

disk flower

ray flower

chaff

receptacle

bract

**HEAD OF COMPOSITE
INFLORESCENCE
(SECTION)**

style

stamens

corolla

pappus

ovary

**RAY   DISK
FLOWER   FLOWER**

OF A COMPOSITE

sepal

petal

ovary

spur

sepal

column

lip

ORCHIDS

fused sepals

standard

wing

keel

THE PARTS OF FLOWERS

PEA FLOWER

bract

19

Figure 3

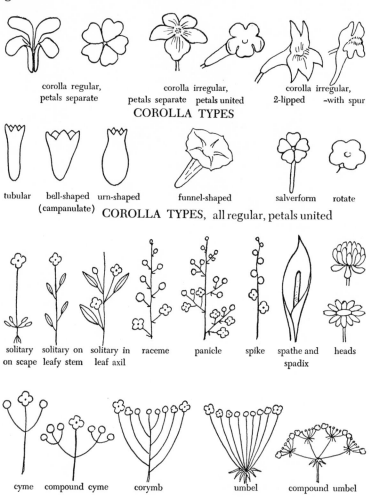

corolla regular,
petals separate

corolla irregular,
petals separate   petals united

corolla irregular,
2-lipped   –with spur

COROLLA TYPES

tubular   bell-shaped   urn-shaped   funnel-shaped   salverform   rotate
(campanulate)

COROLLA TYPES, all regular, petals united

solitary   solitary on   solitary in   raceme   panicle   spike   spathe and   heads
on scape   leafy stem   leaf axil   spadix

cyme   compound cyme   corymb   umbel   compound umbel

INFLORESCENCE TYPES

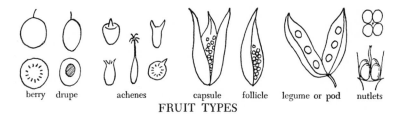

berry   drupe   achenes   capsule   follicle   legume or pod   nutlets

FRUIT TYPES

Figure 4

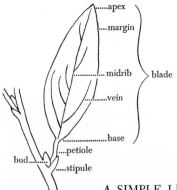

A SIMPLE LEAF

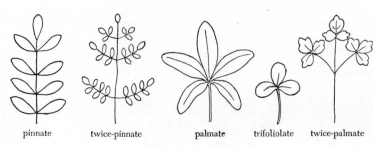

pinnate   twice-pinnate   palmate   trifoliolate   twice-palmate

COMPOUND LEAVES

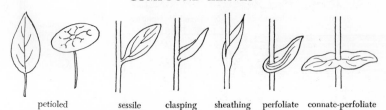

petioled   sessile   clasping   sheathing   perfoliate   connate-perfoliate
from base from center

LEAF ATTACHMENTS

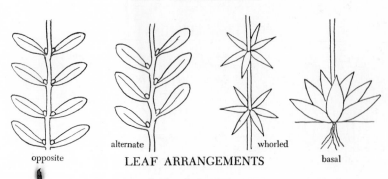

opposite   alternate   whorled   basal

LEAF ARRANGEMENTS

21

Figure 5

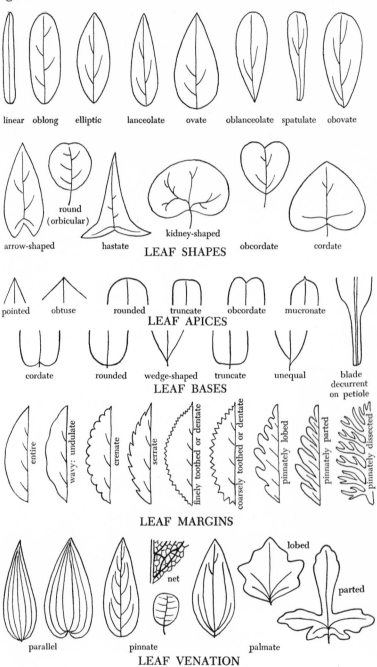

linear oblong elliptic lanceolate ovate oblanceolate spatulate obovate

round
(orbicular)

kidney-shaped

arrow-shaped   hastate   **LEAF SHAPES**   obcordate   cordate

obcordate   cordate

pointed obtuse rounded truncate obcordate mucronate
LEAF APICES

cordate   rounded   wedge-shaped   truncate   unequal   blade decurrent on petiole
LEAF BASES

entire wavy: undulate crenate serrate finely toothed or dentate coarsely toothed or dentate pinnately lobed pinnately parted pinnately dissected

LEAF MARGINS

net

parallel   pinnate   palmate

lobed

parted

LEAF VENATION

22

MONOCOTYLEDONS

CAT-TAIL FAMILY. TYPHACEAE

This cosmopolitan family includes a single genus, *Typha*, with 18 species, 2 of which occur in Michigan. Cat-tails are sometimes used in matting and chair bottoms. Rootstalks, young shoots, and young inflorescences are edible. Cat-tail marshes are frequented by musk-rats, and also provide shelter and nesting cover for blackbirds, marsh wrens, etc. Geese eat the rootstalks.

Cat-tails are characterized by erect, swordlike leaves with parallel veins; brown sausagelike terminal spikes of very densely compacted flowers; and by their habitat in water or wet places.

COMMON CAT-TAIL

Typha latifolia L.   Plate 1

Stout, stiff, erect perennial 1–3 m. tall. Flowers tiny, unisexual, borne in a tall, very dense, cylindrical terminal spike, the staminate flowers on the upper 6–11 cm., the pistillate flowers on the lower 3–20 cm. (where the spike is considerably thicker), the spike in fruit 1–3 cm. thick, dark brown, with a pebbly appearance under a lens. Perianth of bristles in flowers of both sexes, the staminate flowers with 2–7 stamens, the pistil-late with a single, small, short-stalked ovary which develops into a nutlet with copious soft down. Stem round, very stout. Leaves stiffly ascending, linear, fleshy, grayish-green or pale green, sheathing at the base, 6–23 mm. wide, the lower leaves reduced to sheaths.

In shallow water in marshes, swamps, and edges of rivers, streams, or lakes, and in roadside ditches. Flowering May to August.

Indians used the leaves in basketry and for making waterproof mattings to cover their wigwams (overlapping them and stitching them together with fibers of Swamp Milkweed and Indian Hemp). The down was used for dressing burns and wounds, and in cradles. Indians and early settlers ate the young shoots, ground the roots into meal, and used the rootstalks medicinally.

NARROW-LEAVED CAT-TAIL

Typha angustifolia L.   Plate 1

Distinguished from the preceding species by the typically longer, more slender spikes, in which the staminate portion is usually distinctly separated from the pistillate; and by the narrower (usually 5–7 mm.) leaves.

Less common than *T. latifolia* but growing in similar habitats. Flowering late May through July.

BUR-REED FAMILY. SPARGANIACEAE

A single genus and about 20 species comprise this cosmopolitan family. Several of our 12 native species occur in Michigan.

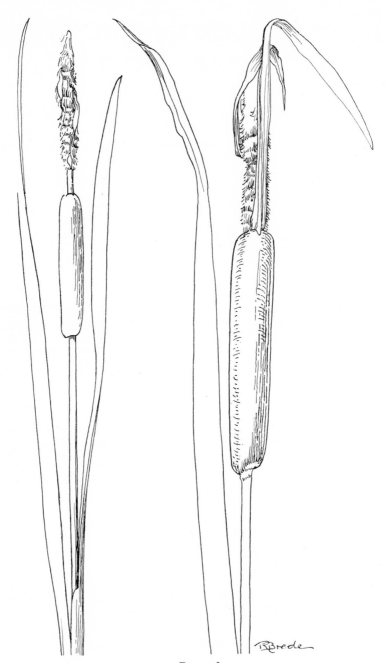

PLATE 1

Narrow-leaved Cat-tail (*Typha angustifolia*)

Common Cat-tail (*Typha latifolia*)

These marsh or aquatic perennials have unisexual flowers in compact heads scattered along the upper part of the leafy stems. The hard, burlike pistillate heads decay slowly and are sometimes found as fossils.

BUR-REED

Sparganium eurycarpum Englm.   Plate 2

Stout, erect, simple or branched perennial up to 1.5 m. tall. Flowers greenish or yellowish, densely crowded into globose heads. Staminate heads numerous, uppermost, the flowers sessile, consisting of 3 stamens and numerous scales; pistillate heads fewer, larger, the perianth of 3–6 scales, the ovary 1-celled and topped by 2 threadlike stigmas; fruits sessile, crowded into burlike heads 1.5–2.5 cm. in diameter with prominent pointed beaks. Stems stout, erect or floating, simple or branched. Leaves alternate, nearly erect, linear, almost flat, sheathing at their base.

In shallow water in sloughs and ponds, in marshes and other very wet ground, chiefly in alkaline or clay soils. Flowering May to August.

The seeds are eaten by waterfowl and marshbirds. Muskrats eat the entire plant.

ARROW-GRASS FAMILY. JUNCAGINACEAE

This family is widely distributed. Two of the three genera occur in Michigan, and both inhabit marshes or bogs.

SEASIDE ARROW-GRASS

Triglochin maritima L.   Plate 3

Rushlike perennial with several flowering stems up to 8 dm. tall. Flowers small, greenish, in a very slender, spikelike terminal raceme up to 1.3 dm. long; perianth of 3 concave greenish sepals and 3 similar petals; stamens 6; pistils usually 6, sometimes 3; fruit ovoid, about 5 mm. long, beaked at apex, rounded at the base. Leaves all basal, fleshy, roundish in cross section, 4–15 cm. long and 1–4 mm. thick above the sheathing base.

In mud flats, near sand dunes, in beach pools, and on wet shores; in swamps, bogs, and marshes. Flowering May to August.

Indians parched and ground the seeds for food and also roasted them in the manner of coffee. The leaves, fresh or dried, of both our species of Arrow-grass are poisonous, producing hydrocyanic acid, and the plants should not be allowed in pastures or included in hay.

MARSH ARROW-GRASS

Triglochin palustris L.   Plate 3

Similar to the preceding species but smaller, more slender, and usually having only 1–2 flowering stems 2–4 dm. tall; the fruit 3-celled, thinner and longer (7 mm.), linear or clavate, tapering to a slender, pointed base, blunt at the apex, separating from below upward when ripe.

Habitat and flowering time similar to those of the preceding.

25

PLATE 2

Flowering   Fruiting

Bur-reed (*Sparganium eurycarpum*)

WATER-PLANTAIN FAMILY. ALISMATACEAE

This family includes about 14 genera; 4 occur in Michigan, 2 being common. The nearly 60 species of the family are widely distributed in fresh-water swamps and marshes in the northern hemisphere. The arrowheads (*Sagittaria*) are primarily American plants. At least 5 of the 40 species grow in Michigan. Water-plantain (*Alisma*) is a small genus comprising about 8 species, 2 of which may be found in Michigan. The family is of limited economic importance, but some species of *Sagittaria* are cultivated for food by the Chinese, and several species are grown as ornamentals.

WATER-PLANTAIN, MUD-PLANTAIN

Alisma subcordatum Raf.   Plate 4

Aquatic perennial with scapelike stems and long-petioled leaves rising above the water. Flowers white or rarely rose, small (up to 1.3 cm. wide), numerous, borne on threadlike pedicels in many-branched panicles, which rise in whorls from the stiff scape; petals 3, soon falling; sepals 3, green, persistent; stamens 6; pistils numerous, borne in a circle on the flattened receptacle; achenes leathery. Leaves basal, ascending or erect on long petioles, the blades ovate-elliptic, rounded to subcordate at base, up to 2.5 dm. long and 1.5 dm. broad, the principal veins few, the cross veins strong, parallel.

In shallow water in low fields, mud flats, and ditches, and along stream banks. Flowering late June to September.

This plant can be grown in a wet-soil garden, where it gives an attractive lacy effect.

COMMON ARROWHEAD, WAPATO, DUCK-POTATO

Sagittaria latifolia Willd.   Plate 5

Plants up to 1 m. tall from a tuber embedded in mud. Flowers white, 1.5–3 cm. broad, in whorls of 3 on erect or ascending pedicels, each whorl subtended by a pair of somewhat papery bracts, the flowers usually unisexual (rarely bisexual), the lowest whorls pistillate and the upper staminate (but some plants are unisexual). Petals 3, separate; sepals 3, thin, pale green, separate; stamens numerous, the filaments slender, usually longer than the anthers; pistils numerous, distinct, borne on a globular receptacle; achenes borne in a globose head, flat, with membranous wing and incurved or horizontal beak. Flowering stem leafless, hollow, ridged, smooth or nearly so. Leaves basal, extremely variable but usually arrow-shaped (sagittate), the upper part of the blade ovate to linear and usually more than half as long as the body, but sometimes the blade merely ovate or linear-lanceolate and tapering to the base; veins few, strong, parallel, the cross veins conspicuous; petiole long, strongly ribbed, hollow, sheathing the stem at base.

In ditches, along creeks and lakes, in marshy fields and forest openings, on mud flats and beaches. Flowering July to September.

This extremely variable species has several well-defined forms and varieties which are distinguished chiefly by leaf characters. A narrow-leaved form, *Sagittaria latifolia* Willd. forma *gracilis* (Pursh) Robins., is shown (right) on Plate 5.

PLATE 3

Seaside Arrow-grass (*Triglochin maritima*)

Marsh Arrow-grass (*Triglochin palustris*)

Flowering Rush (*Butomus umbellatus*)

The tuberous roots of this and other species of *Sagittaria* were called Wapato by the Indians, for whom they formed an important food staple, as well as a medicine for indigestion and a poultice for wounds. The tubers have a bitter milky juice when fresh, but are rendered sweet and palatable by cooking or drying, and Lewis and Clark virtually subsisted on them during a winter spent at the mouth of the Columbia River. The plants were harvested by the Indian women, who waded waist-deep into the water, using their toes to loosen the tubers, which then rose to the surface of the water and could be gathered into canoes.

These attractive plants can be easily cultivated in pools, but they spread rapidly by underground stems and hence are not suitable for small pools.

FLOWERING RUSH FAMILY.   BUTOMACEAE

This small aquatic or marsh-inhabiting family includes 6 genera, but the introduced species described below is the only one found in this country. It is rare in Michigan. The plants are sometimes cultivated in water gardens.

FLOWERING RUSH

Butomus umbellatus L.   Plate 3

Marsh or aquatic perennial, up to 1 m. or more tall from a thick, fleshy rootstock in the mud, which late in the season produces many easily detached grainlike tubers. Flowers showy, roseate tinged with green, up to 2.5 cm. wide, numerous, in terminal umbels which are at first enclosed by 3 large, purple-tinged, papery bracts. Petals and sepals 3 each, the sepals petallike but slightly tinged with green; stamens 9, the anthers red; pistils 6; barely united at base; follicle inflated, long-beaked, 5–10 mm. long. Leaves basal, sword-shaped, 3-angled at base.

In shallow water, marshes, river margins. Introduced from Europe. Flowering June to September.

ARUM FAMILY.   ARACEAE

This predominantly tropical family, comprising about 1500 species, is represented in Michigan by 5 genera and 6 species. The chief value of the family in North America is for ornamentals, about three dozen species being cultivated. The florist's calla (*Zantedeschia*) is perhaps the best-known example. *Philodendron, Caladium* (Elephant's-ear), and *Monstera* (which has edible fruits) are common house plants. In other parts of the world, arums are used for food, taro being quite important.

Michigan representatives of this family are readily recognized by the minute flowers borne on a cylindric or globose spadix which is subtended, and often enveloped, by a single spathe.

29

PLATE 4
Water-plantain (*Alisma subcordatum*)

PLATE 5
Common Arrowhead (*Sagittaria latifolia*)

31

$\frac{3}{8}$

PLATE 6

Green Dragon (*Arisaema dracontium*)

Jack-in-the-pulpit (*Arisaema atrorubens*)

Sweetflag (*Acorus calamus*)

32

ARACEAE

JACK-IN-THE-PULPIT

Arisaema atrorubens (Ait.) Blume
Plate 6

Erect, unbranching, smooth perennial up to nearly 1 m. tall. Flowers tiny, unisexual, borne on the base of the pale-green or purple, mottled, slenderly club-shaped spadix (the "jack"); spathe (the "pulpit and canopy") tubular below, the tube shallowly corrugated and with a narrow flange above, becoming expanded and arching over the spadix, all green or purple to bronze with pale greenish stripes (quite variable in coloration and markings); the staminate flowers a cluster of lavender anthers, the pistillate consisting of a bright-green, 1-celled, ovoid pistil; fruiting heads ovoid to globose, the berries shiny and bright scarlet. Stems stout, sheathed at base, whitish below, green above, often mottled with purple. Leaves 1–3 (usually 2), expanding at flowering time, trifoliate, the lateral leaflets strongly unsymmetrical; venation pinnate. Tuber brown, globose, rooting and producing basal offsets. (Called *A. triphyllum* in many books.)

In rich woods and thickets, usually in rather moist locations. Flowering late April and May.

This highly variable species is one of our most interesting wildflowers. Children often call it Indian Turnip and entice others to eat the tuber, which has a very sharp taste due to crystals of calcium oxalate. It is said that even after being boiled in several changes of water these tubers are too pungent to eat, but if thoroughly dried for several weeks they become edible. Even though the fresh plants are poisonous, they have medicinal qualities and were often collected for drug use. The Indians used them for treating sore eyes and ulcers. The pungent taste makes them unacceptable to most wildlife.

Jack-in-the-pulpit is very easy to grow in the wildflower garden; it flourishes without special attention.

GREEN DRAGON, DRAGON-ROOT

Arisaema dracontium (L.) Schott
Plate 6

Perennial, 6–10 dm. tall. Flowers tiny, similar to those of Jack-in-the-pulpit, but the spadix slender and tapering to a long slender point that extends far beyond the spathe; the mature fruiting head slenderly conical, the berries reddish-orange. Leaf solitary, compound, the leaflets 5–15, unequal in size.

In rich woods, in thickets, and in swales. Flowering May and June.

This plant can be readily grown in the woodland garden, but is neither so attractive nor so common as Jack-in-the-pulpit.

Fruiting   Flowering

Plate 7

Tuckahoe (*Peltandra virginica*)

Wild Calla (*Calla palustris*)

34

PLATE 8

Skunk-cabbage (*Symplocarpus foetidus*)

35

TUCKAHOE, ARROW-ARUM

Peltandra virginica (L.) Schott & Endl.   Plate 7

Perennial 2–3.5 dm. tall from thick subtuberous roots. Flowers minute, borne on a slender, tapering, whitish spadix, the staminate flowers above, covering a much larger portion than the pistillate; anther masses 4–6-celled, embedded in the margin of a shield-shaped connective; ovaries 1-celled, surrounded by 4–5 distinct, scalelike staminodes; berries green or amber, in an ovoid, fleshy head enveloped by the base of the spathe. Leaves basal, arrow-shaped, the basal lobes usually well developed and spreading, the margin entire; blade 1–3.5 dm. long, the principal veins 3, one to each of the basal lobes, the secondary veins pinnate, fine, very numerous, arching within the margin and forming a fine network; petioles long, sheathing.

In marly lake margins, muddy shores, bogs, mud flats, and shallow water. Flowering June and July.

This was the "breadroot" of the eastern Indians. The large bitter roots were roasted in pits for a day or so, then dried and ground into meal. The boiled spadix and berries were considered luxuries. The berries are eaten by wood ducks and, infrequently, by other birds.

WILD CALLA

Calla palustris L.   Plate 7

Low-growing, smooth perennial 1.5–4 dm. tall, the solitary flowering stalk and long-petioled leaves rising from thick, often green, creeping rootstocks. Inflorescence showy, the spathe large, white, petallike but thick, ovate, abruptly pointed, up to 3.5 cm. wide and 1.5–7.5 cm. long; flowers small, borne on the knoblike spadix, perfect or the upper ones staminate, the perianth lacking; stamens 6; ovary 1-celled, forming in fruit a head of large red berries. Leaves numerous, thick, broadly ovate, heart-shaped or rounded at the base and tapering abruptly to a pointed apex, bright green, glossy, 5–10 cm. in width and length, the parallel veins numerous.

In low wet places, particularly swamps and bogs, pond margins, quagmires. Flowering May to July.

The Indians used the underground parts of Wild Calla for poultices and also for food. The plant may be grown in the cool bog garden. The florist's calla is somewhat similar in appearance to this plant but belongs to the genus *Zantedeschia*.

SKUNK-CABBAGE

Symplocarpus foetidus (L.) Nutt.   Plate 8

Stemless perennial with a skunklike odor. Flowers tiny, inconspicuous, covering a fleshy, globose, yellowish, stalked spadix which is partially enclosed by the fleshy, nearly sessile, ovoid spathe; spathe protruding only a little way from the ground, green, spotted and streaked with purple and yellowish-green, the margins inrolled; at least some flowers perfect; stamens 4, sepals 4; fruit a globular to ovoid mass consisting of the enlarged spongy spadix with the spherical seeds just under the surface. Leaves appearing after the spathes, all basal and becoming large (3–6 dm. long), smooth, entire, the midrib fleshy, the veins pinnate, the petiole short and fleshy.

In low wet woods, flood plains, open or shady stream banks, swampy forests, or wet thickets. Most common in southern Michigan. Flowering mid-March to mid-May.

Michigan Lily

Yellow Beadlily

The tender leaves while still folded and just pushing through the ground are said to be edible if cooked in 2 or 3 changes of water. A number of game birds, including the ring-necked pheasant, grouse, and quail, eat the seeds. This species may be grown in a moist shady garden, but requires considerable space.

SWEETFLAG, FLAG-ROOT, CALAMUS

Acorus calamus L. Plate 6

Aromatic perennial up to 1 m. tall from a thick, creeping, aromatic rootstock. Flowers tiny, yellowish-green, borne on a spikelike spadix which extends obliquely outward from a long leaflike spathe; sepals 6; stamens 6, with kidney-shaped anthers; ovary solitary; fruit dry, but gelatinous inside, with 1 or more seeds. Flowering stalk 3-angled, having a sweet odor when broken. Leaves flattish, swordlike, thicker at the middle, the edges sharp, up to 1 m. or more long and 0.6–2 cm. wide.

In clumps and large masses in wet places along the borders of quiet water and in small woodland pools. Flowering May to August.

When not in flower these plants could be mistaken for Iris, but are readily distinguished by their aromatic odor when crushed or broken, and by the flat leaves, which are a yellowish-green and are not folded at the base, in contrast to the blue-green folded leaves of the Iris.

In the past, the roots were boiled in water to remove the bitterness, then sliced thin and boiled in a heavy syrup to make a confection.

YELLOW-EYED GRASS FAMILY. XYRIDACEAE

A small family of 2 genera and about 200 species, most of which grow in the tropics. Three species occur in Michigan.

YELLOW-EYED GRASS

Xyris montana Ries Plate 9

Tufted or densely matted, rushlike plants up to 4.5 dm. tall from forking rootstocks. Flowers yellow, solitary in the axils of leathery, scalelike, tightly overlapping bracts which form brown, conelike, terminal spikes or heads on naked wiry flowering stems, the spikes 4–10 mm. long and 2–7 mm. in diameter; petals 3, yellow, soon falling; sepals 3, the lateral ones with brown or purplish tips extending beyond the bracts, the third sepal keeled, enclosing the corolla in bud and falling off with it; fertile stamens 3, inserted on the claws of the petal and alternating with the 3 sterile, bearded filaments; fruit a many-seeded capsule. Leaves sheathing the base of the stem, grasslike, less than half as long as the stem and up to 2.5 mm. broad.

In wet peat and sand. Flowering July to early September.

SPIDERWORT FAMILY. COMMELINACEAE

A large tropical family of about 37 genera and 600 species; 3 or 4

PLATE 9
Pickerelweed (*Pontederia cordata*)
Spiderwort (*Tradescantia ohiensis*)
Yellow-eyed Grass (*Xyris montana*)

38

species (2 genera) are found in Michigan. Both genera, Spiderwort (*Tradescantia*) and Dayflower (*Commelina*), are grown in gardens.

Tradescantia ohiensis Raf.   Plate 9

Erect glaucous and glabrous perennial with mucilaginous juice, the stem fleshy, often branching, up to 7 dm. tall. Flowers lasting a very short time, violet, blue, rose, or rarely white, up to 3.5 cm. wide, borne on purplish to pale-yellow pedicels which droop in the bud and after flowering, the cymes solitary and terminal and having 2 leaflike reflexed bracts at the base which are nearly as long as the leaves. Petals 3, nearly round, narrowed to a short claw; sepals 3, green or tinged with rose-purple, smooth or with short hairs at the tip; stamens 6, all alike, the filaments colored like the petals and densely bearded with long jointed hairs; ovary superior, the fruit a capsule. Leaves linear-lanceolate, sheathing at their base, up to 5 dm. long.

On banks, in thickets, meadows, and woodlands. Flowering April to June.

Spiderworts were formerly very common garden plants. They are easily grown. Another roadside species, *T. virginiana* L., has pubescent pedicels and sepals and thin, dull-green leaves.

PICKERELWEED FAMILY. PONTEDERIACEAE

A small family of aquatic or marsh perennials. There are 6 or 7 genera and about 28 species, of which Michigan has only two. The members of this family are of some importance as ornamentals. Like the well-known introduced Water Hyacinth, *Eichornia crassipes* (Mart.) Solms, Pickerelweed is often grown in pools. The Water Hyacinth becomes a pest in the southeast, where it grows so profusely that it often clogs waterways.

Pontederia cordata L.   Plate 9

Creeping perennial with stout, erect flowering stems having a single well-developed leaf and several sheathing bractlike basal leaves; the rootstock thick. Flowers lasting a very short time, intensely blue, rarely white, about 5 mm. long, borne in an erect, dense, terminal spike which has a sheathing bract at the base; perianth irregular, funnel-shaped, 2-lipped, the 3-lobed upper lip with a pair of yellow spots, the 3 divisions of the lower lip spreading, their claws forming the lower part of the curving tube and more or less separate to the base, the tube withering above and becoming coiled, the base hardening around the fruit; stamens 6, some of them often sterile or imperfect, blue to purple; ovary superior, 3-celled, the mature fruit 1-seeded, with 6 toothed ridges. Leaves heart-shaped-ovate, the veins parallel, the sheath longer than the petiole and completely enclosing the stem, the margin wavy or with small rounded teeth.

In shallow water or on muddy shores. Flowering June to September.

LILY FAMILY. LILIACEAE

This large, widely distributed family includes about 240 genera and 4000 species. It is especially abundant in warm-temperate and

PLATE 10

Glutinous False Asphodel (*Tofieldia glutinosa*)
Wild Leek (*Allium tricoccum*)
White Camas (*Zigadenus glaucus*)

40

tropical regions. About 28 genera and some 60 species occur in Michigan. Over 160 species of the family are listed for horticultural purposes, including a large number of our most attractive ornamentals. Tulips, lilies, fritillarias, yuccas, lily-of-the-valley, hyacinths, and many others are extensively cultivated. Such foods as asparagus, onion, garlic, and leek are members of this family.

The flowers are usually regular, with a perianth of 6 petallike parts, 6 stamens, and a 3-celled ovary with 3 stigmas or one 3-lobed stigma. The fruit is a capsule or berry. The leaves are basal or on the stem, and the blade may be expanded or linear. Two of our common genera do not conform: in *Trillium* the 3 sepals are green; in *Maianthemum* there are 4 perianth parts and 4 stamens.

LILIACEAE

1. Flowers or flower clusters rising from axils of stem leaves 2
1. Flowers or flower clusters at end of stem or scape 5
  2. Sepals and petals united into a tube nearly to tip
    of corolla . . *Polygonatum pubescens* or *canaliculatum*, Plate 16
  2. Sepals and petals separate to base 3
3. Flowers borne in globose clusters . . . *Smilax lasioneura*, Plate 19
3. Flowers solitary or in pairs, hanging from axils 4
  4. Flowers yellow;
    fruit a capsule . . . *Uvularia grandiflora* or *sessilifolia*, Plate 11
  4. Flowers not yellow;
    fruit a berry . . . *Streptopus roseus* or *amplexifolius*, Plate 15
5. Leaves borne in 2 distinct whorls, one at summit,
    the other about middle of stem . . . *Medeola virginiana*, Plate 17
5. Not as in alternate choice 6
  6. Flowers solitary or 1–3 (4) and showy 7
  6. Flowers borne in clusters 10
7. Plants having only 2 or 3 leaves 8
7. Plants normally with numerous leaves 9
  8. Leaves 2, basal . . *Erythronium americanum* or *albidum*, Plate 13
  8. Leaves 3, at top of stem . . . . *Trillium*, p. 55
9. Leaves narrow, elongate; stem unbranched below; flowers large and
    showy . *Lilium philadelphicum* or *michiganense*, Plate 12; Color Plate 1
9. Leaves oblong or ovate; stem usually forked;
    flowers not very showy . . *Uvularia grandiflora* or *sessifolia*, Plate 11
  10. Flowers large and showy, funnelform and lilylike 11
  10. Flowers typically smaller (usually less than 3 cm.) . . . 12
11. Stem leafless or nearly so; leaves long and slender;
    sepals and petals united at base . . . . *Hemerocallis fulva*, Plate 12
11. Stem bearing whorled or scattered leaves; sepals and petals entirely
    separate . *Lilium philadelphicum* or *michiganense*, Plate 12; Color Plate 1
  12. Flowers borne in umbels (all rising from same place) . . . 13
  12. Flowers in racemes or panicles 14
13. Flowers white; plants strongly onion-scented . . *Allium tricoccum*, Plate 10
13. Flowers yellow, plant not strongly scented . *Clintonia borealis*, Color Plate 2

41

PLATE 11
Large-flowered Bellwort (*Uvularia grandiflora*)
Sessile Bellwort (*Uvularia sessilifolia*)

42

GLUTINOUS FALSE ASPHODEL

Tofieldia glutinosa (Michx.) Pers.   Plate 10

Simple, erect, sticky perennial up to 5 dm. tall, the stem somewhat bulbous at base, covered (as are also the pedicels) with red to black glands. Flowers white, 5–15 mm. wide, borne in a terminal spikelike compound raceme, the short pedicels mostly in groups of 3, the flowers having a calyxlike, rather close fitting involucre, the raceme compact at first, becoming 1–9 cm. long and 2.5 cm. thick. Perianth segments 6, petallike, spreading, the outer ones broader; stamens 6, the anthers pink; styles 3, short, persistent; capsule oblong, the seeds numerous and bearing small taillike appendages at each end. Leaves few, sheathing, mostly at or near the base, in 2 rows, grasslike, 5–17 cm. long.

In sphagnum or marly bogs, calcareous marshes, and on damp ledges and shores. Often abundant along the shores of the Great Lakes. Flowering June to August.

The Small False Asphodel, *T. pusilla* (Michx.) Pers., also grows in northern Michigan. It has smaller flowers, the seeds are without appendages, and the stem is not sticky.

LARGE-FLOWERED BELLWORT

Uvularia grandiflora Sm.   Plate 11

Slender perennial, simple below, forking above, up to 8 dm. tall, the stem zigzag and leafy above, sheathed below, from a short rootstock with fleshy root fibers. Flowers straw-colored to orange-yellow, narrowly bell-shaped, 2–5 cm. long, drooping, solitary on peduncles, terminal at first but appearing axillary in fruit. Perianth parts separate, 6, similar, long and narrow, often twisted longitudinally, green at the swollen base, glabrous inside; stamens 6, the filaments short, closely appressed to the ovary, the anthers 1–1.5 cm. long; pistil solitary, superior, the ovary ovoid, green, the style 3-cleft; capsule truncate, 3-lobed. Leaves alternate, perfoliate, 1 or 2 below the fork of the stem, several above, lance-oblong, bright green on upper surface, pubescent and grayish beneath, the veins few.

In rich woods and thickets; often abundant. Flowering April to early June.

Indians made an infusion from the roots to treat backache and also used this species with lard in massaging sore muscles.

This plant grows readily in a woodland garden and will sometimes grow in borders.

43

PLATE 12

Wood Lily (*Lilium philadelphicum*)

Common Orange Day Lily (*Hemerocallis fulva*)

44

SESSILE BELLWORT, WILD-OATS

Uvularia sessilifolia L. Plate 11

Similar to *U. grandifolia,* but shorter (up to 4.5 dm. tall); rootstock elongate; leaves sessile, not perfoliate, whitish and glabrous beneath; capsule distinctly stalked, ellipsoid.

In woods, thickets, clearings. Flowering April to mid-June.

WHITE CAMAS, DEATH CAMAS

Zigadenus glaucus Nutt. Plate 10

Stiffly erect, slender, glaucous, rarely branched perennial 2.5 dm.–1 m. tall. Flowers greenish-white, 1.2–2 cm. in diameter, borne in a terminal raceme or panicle, each on a long pedicel which has a linear bract at the base. Perianth parts 6, pale green to whitish, sometimes bronze or purple on the back, each with a conspicuous, inverted heart-shaped, greenish gland at the base; stamens 6; ovary superior, forming a 3-lobed capsule with 3 recurving beaks. Leaves mostly crowded at the base of the plant, linear, leathery, up to 5 dm. long, the stem leaves similar but smaller.

In calcareous gravel and sand along shores, on cliffs, and in bogs. Common in the northern part of the Lower Peninsula, especially along the shores of Lakes Huron and Michigan. Flowering mid-July to September.

These plants are poisonous; all parts contain poison. They retain their toxic properties even after drying. Milk from cows that have eaten this species can cause a mild to fatal sickness.

WILD LEEK, RAMP

Allium tricoccum Ait. Plate 10

Onion-scented perennial, leafless at flowering time, the erect flowering stems 1.5–3 dm. tall. Flowers white, small, borne on stout pedicels in a hemispherical terminal umbel on the glabrous flowering stem; umbel bracts usually 2, enclosing the flowers, soon falling. Sepals and petals each 3, similar, separate, white, rather dry, 1-nerved; stamens 6, about the same length as the perianth, the filaments about as broad as the sepals and petals at the base, tapering above; ovary superior, deeply 3-lobed; style 1, rather slender; seeds globose, black, 1 in each cell. Leaves present in early spring, flat, fleshy, elliptic-lanceolate, tapering to a long slender petiole, 1–3 dm. long, 2–5.5 cm. wide, the veins fine. Bulbs slender, long-ovoid, white, very strongly onion-flavored, clustered.

In deep rich woods and bottom land, often forming large beds. Flowering in June and July.

Very common in the deciduous woods in the northern part of the Lower Peninsula. The clumps of leaves form the most conspicuous ground-cover in some woods in late April, but not a vestige of the leaves can be found by flowering time. The bulbs taste strongly of onion—almost burning. However, the bulbs, both raw and dried, were used by Indians for food, and an emetic was also derived from them.

These plants will grow in a wild garden, but are not especially attractive.

COMMON ORANGE DAY LILY

Hemerocallis fulva L.

Plate 12

Showy perennial 1–2 m. tall above clustered basal leaves. Flowers large, showy, tawny-orange, deeper-colored toward the center, up to 10 cm. long, 3–15 borne at the top of the naked flowering stem, produced in succession through a long period, but each flower lasting but a single day. Perianth funnel-shaped, the tube narrow below, the 6 segments abruptly flaring above, the 3 inner segments wider than the outer ones, obtuse, with wavy margins; stamens inserted in the throat of the tube, the filaments colored like the corolla and directed slightly downward, the tips curving upward and on casual inspection giving the impression that the flower is unsymmetrical; ovary superior, the style slender, curving, longer than the perianth. Leaves basal, very long and narrow (3–6 dm. long, 1–1.5 cm. wide), tapering to both ends and sheathing at the base, usually curved downward.

Along roadsides, borders of thickets, in fields, meadows, along streams. Introduced from Europe. Flowering May to July.

The Yellow Day Lily, *H. flava* L., is often found in the vicinity of abandoned houses, around cemeteries, and sometimes along roads. It has similar but smaller and yellow flowers, with a pleasing fragrance. Day Lilies are very popular garden flowers, and many beautiful hybrids have been developed in recent years. Orange Day Lily has lost the ability to produce fertile seeds.

WOOD LILY

Lilium philadelphicum L.

Plate 12

Stiffly erect perennial up to 1 m. tall, branching only at the top. Flowers erect, showy, faded-orange to deep orange-red, spotted, open bell-shaped, 1–5 at the top of the plant, 5.5–7.5 cm. long and 10–12 cm. wide. Perianth segments alike, lanceolate, obtuse at apex, tapering to a long claw at base, spotted with conspicuous red or purple oblong dots near the base, somewhat spreading; stamens 6, the filaments the same color as the perianth, the anthers dark purple, about 1 cm. long, attached near the middle, free-swinging; ovary green, 3-celled, superior; style long, orange to orange-red, the stigma blackish, 3-lobed; capsule rounded at summit, tapering at base, 3–5 cm. long. Leaves in whorls or scattered along the stem, lanceolate or linear-lanceolate, 5–10 cm. long, sessile.

In open woods and clearings, along roadsides, and in bogs. Flowering mid-June to mid-August.

This beautiful species is very common along highways at the northern tip of the Lower Peninsula. The Indians used the bulbs like potatoes. They made a medicinal charm from the plants.

Wood Lily can be cultivated in an acid garden if rodents are controlled.

MICHIGAN LILY

Lilium michiganense Farw.

Color Plate 1

Erect perennial, up to 2 m. or more tall, from yellowish bulbs. Flowers 1 to several, chiefly in 1–3 umbels, nodding, orange to orange-red, the sepals and petals alike and strongly recurved, their tips extending back to or beyond

PLATE 13
Yellow Adder's-tongue (*Erythronium americanum*)
White-Fawn Lily (*Erythronium albidum*)

47

the base of the perianth tube; stamens 6, the filaments curving strongly outward; stigma broadly 3-lobed. Leaves whorled, lanceolate, tapering toward both base and apex, the margins and veins beneath usually with minute spicules (points).

In meadows, low woods, thickets, or bogs. Flowering late June to August.

This attractive plant can be grown in the garden if the bulbs are protected from rodents.

YELLOW ADDER'S-TONGUE, YELLOW FAWN LILY, YELLOW DOG'S-TOOTH VIOLET, TROUT LILY

Erythronium americanum Ker   Plate 13

Nearly stemless perennial up to 3 dm. tall from a deep-seated scaly bulb which sends out numerous elongate underground shoots. Flower lilylike, yellow, 1.8–4 cm. long, solitary and nodding at the end of the flowering stem. Perianth of 6 spreading separate divisions in 2 rows, the 3 inner divisions with small projections at the base, pale yellow within and often spotted near the base; stamens 6, the filaments tapering to apex, the anthers linear, yellow or red; ovary 1, the style elongate, the stigmas 3, erect. Leaves of mature plant 2, opposite, fleshy, mottled or plain, elongate-elliptic, tapering to the petiole, which sheathes the flowering stem; leaves of young plants solitary, elliptic, usually mottled.

In rich woods, thickets, bottomlands, and meadows; usually in extensive colonies. Flowering late March to June.

This attractive woodland flower often carpets open woods in early spring. Because the underground shoots produce numerous new bulbs, extensive colonies are formed. The flowers are short-lived. Several years, usually 6 or more, are required to produce flowering plants from seed.

The Indians steeped the leaves to make an infusion used for stomach distress.

The species is popular in the garden but tends to die out. Many beautiful kinds are offered for sale by nurserymen.

WHITE FAWN LILY, WHITE DOG'S-TOOTH VIOLET, TROUT LILY

Erythronium albidum Nutt.   Plate 13

Quite similar to the preceding species, but the flowers pinkish- or bluish-white, the stigmas spreading or drooping, the leaves only rarely mottled.

In woods and thickets. Flowering April to June.

In southern Michigan this species is usually through blooming at about the time the yellow species begins to flower.

YELLOW BEADLILY, BLUEBEAD LILY, CORN LILY

Clintonia borealis (Ait.) Raf.   Color Plate 2

Perennial, 1.5–4 dm. tall from a slender creeping rootstock. Flowers yellow or greenish-yellow, 2–2.5 cm. long, bell-shaped, usually drooping, 2–8 in a loose terminal umbel on a pubescent, leafless or bracted flowering stem, sometimes with a small secondary umbel of 2–3 flowers below the terminal one. Perianth of 6 separate, spreading, similar segments in 2 rows, the segments linear, hairy outside; stamens 6, the filaments long, pale greenish-yellow, the anthers hanging below the corolla; pistil ovoid, style long; berry shining blue (white in one form), 5–6 mm. long. Leaves basal, 3–5, elliptic, oblong, or oval, 1–3 dm. long, very thick, finely hairy on margins, the veins fine, the petioles sheathing the flowering stem at base.

In woods and thickets, usually in moist rich soil. Flowering late May to late June. Berries ripe August, September.

The beautiful, shiny blue berries are both more striking and more attractive than the pale flowers. The Chippewa Indians believed that dogs could use the roots of Beadlily to poison their teeth in order more easily to overcome their prey. If a person was bitten by a dog with teeth so poisoned, it was thought necessary to get a root of the same species and put it on the wound to draw the poison out.

Beadlily is a difficult species to grow. It requires a cool, strongly acid, peaty soil.

Smilacina

1. Flowers borne in branched racemes (panicles) . . S. *racemosa*, Plate 14
1. Flowers borne in unbranched racemes 2

   2. Leaves 1–4, glabrous beneath . . . . . . S. *trifolia*, Plate 14
   2. Leaves 6–14, finely pubescent beneath . . . . S. *stellata*, Plate 14

False Solomon's-seal, Solomon's Zigzag, False Spikenard

Smilacina racemosa (L.) Desf.   Plate 14

Coarse, unbranched, arched or ascending perennial up to 1 m. tall from a rootstock that is knotty and jointed in appearance, fleshy, brown, 9–12 mm. thick. Flowers white, up to 6 mm. in diameter, in terminal stalked or nearly sessile panicles 5–14 cm. long, the branches of panicle and the pedicels white and hairy. Perianth segments 6, alike, separate, narrower and shorter than the filaments, spreading and often drooping slightly; stamens 6, the filaments white; pistil white, ovary 3-celled, stigma obscurely 3-lobed; berries red, often speckled with purple, about 6 mm. in diameter, aromatic. Leaves alternate, 5–13, elliptic, tapering to a blunt apex and rounded to the short petiole, 10–18 cm. or more long, 3–8 cm. wide, lighter beneath, the margin entire; veins parallel, numerous, 3 quite distinct, the others smaller.

In dry or moist open woods or thickets; often growing on hillsides or shady river banks. Flowering May to July. Berries ripe July to September.

This is a satisfactory garden plant and easy to cultivate. The berries have a strong, pleasant odor and seem to be liked by birds. They are also sometimes eaten by people.

PLATE 14

False Solomon's-seal (*Smilacina racemosa*)

Three-leaved False Solomon's-seal (*Smilacina trifolia*)

Starry False Solomon's-seal (*Smilacina stellata*)

50

PLATE 15

Rosy Twisted-stalk (*Streptopus roseus*)
White Twisted-stalk (*Streptopus amplexifolius*)
Wild Lily-of-the-valley (*Maianthemum canadense*)

51

THREE-LEAVED FALSE SOLOMON'S-SEAL
Smilacina stellata (L.) Desf.

Smaller and weaker than the preceding two species, usually erect, up to 2.4 dm. tall from a slender, whitish, extensively creeping rootstock. Flowers white, in a stalked, few-flowered terminal raceme, the pedicels longer and more nearly erect than in the preceding species. Perianth segments longer than the stamens, remaining attached and withering and drooping as the fruit matures; berry dark red. Leaves 2–4, usually 3, alternate, elliptic or ovate, somewhat clasping at the base, 3–10 cm. long, glabrous.

In bogs, wet places in the forest, clearings, and swamps. More common in the northern part of the state. Flowering mid-May to July (occasionally September). Berries ripe late July to September.

Difficult to grow in the garden because it requires cool, acid soil.

STARRY FALSE SOLOMON'S-SEAL
Smilacina trifolia (L.) Desf.
Plate 14

Arching or inclined unbranched perennial up to 1 m. tall from a slender, freely forking rootstock. Flowers white, small, 6–8 mm. in diameter, borne on short pedicels in a few-flowered terminal raceme; raceme sessile or nearly so, sometimes zigzag, 2–6 cm. long. Perianth parts 6, white, alike, slightly longer than the stamens; stamens 6; berry green, with black stripes or sometimes all black, usually turning bronzy at maturity and usually 6-seeded. Leaves alternate, 7–14, lanceolate or narrowly elliptic, sessile or slightly clasping at base, 4–14 cm. long, 1.5–2.3 cm. wide, downy beneath.

In rich sandy or gravelly soil in open woods or thickets, on sandy lake shores, between dune ridges, and along margins of bogs. Flowering mid-May to mid-July. Berries ripe July to September.

Easily grown in the garden, this species spreads rapidly by means of the rootstock.

WILD or FALSE LILY-OF-THE-VALLEY
Maianthemum canadense Desf.
Plate 15

Perennial with erect zigzag stem up to 2.5 dm. tall from a horizontal, threadlike rootstock which bears stalked tuberous enlargements. Flowers white, often fragrant, about 4 mm. wide, on short pedicels, usually rising in pairs in a terminal raceme which is 1–4 cm. long. Perianth of 4 similar, separate, lanceolate segments; stamens 4; pistil 1, 2-celled, the stigma 2-lobed; berries pale red, speckled, about 5 mm. in diameter, with 1 or 2 seeds. Leaves usually 2 or 3 (one on stemless plants, in which the petiole comes directly from the rootstock), ovate or lanceolate, heart-shaped at base, 2.5–10 cm. long, sessile or nearly so.

In moist woods, thickets, and recent clearings; also in rather dry sandy soil under aspens and in cedar bogs. Flowering May to June.

This species is not like the cultivated Lily-of-the-valley, which has a bell-shaped 6-lobed corolla and belongs to the genus *Convallaria*. The Indians used the rootstock of Wild Lily-of-the-valley for medicinal purposes and the berries for food. Grouse and small mammals, such as chipmunks and mice, also eat the berries.

Large-flowered Trillium

Color plate 4

Small Purple Fringed Orchid

White Twisted-stalk, White Mandarin

Streptopus amplexifolius (L.) DC.   Plate 15

Quite similar to the preceding species, but up to 9 dm. tall, the flowers greenish-white to deep purple, the perianth segments spreading from near the middle, the anthers much longer than the filaments, the stigma nearly entire or lobed, the berries usually longer than broad, and the leaves clasping the stem.

In moist woods and thickets. Flowering May to July.

Rosy Twisted-stalk, Rose Mandarin

Streptopus roseus Michx.   Plate 15

Rather stout perennial, 2.5–6 dm. tall, with forking and diverging branches usually covered above with stiff, many-celled hairs. Flowers pink to rose-purple, spreading bell-shaped, drooping singly or in pairs on bent or twisted threadlike peduncles from the leaf axils. Perianth parts 6, alike, 6–12 mm. long, the tips curving back in age; stamens 6, the anthers arrow-shaped, equal to or shorter than the flattened filaments; pistil 1, the stigma 3-cleft; fruit a nearly globose or obscurely 3-lobed cherry-red berry 5–10 mm. in diameter. Leaves alternate, sessile but not clasping, the margin finely hairy, the veins parallel.

In moist woods and thickets. Flowering April to July.

Hairy Solomon's-seal

Polygonatum pubescens (Willd.) Pursh   Plate 16

Unbranched and erect, inclined or arched perennial 3–6 dm. tall from a knotty, jointed rootstock near the surface. Flowers greenish or greenish-white, 8–12 mm. long, 1–2 drooping on smooth, slender peduncles from the leaf axils. Sepals and petals united into a slender tube which has 6 rounded lobes; stamens 6, shorter than the perianth tube and inserted on it; pistil 1, the style long, the stigma of 3 tufts of fine hairs; berry globose, bluish, about 5 mm. in diameter. Leaves narrowly elliptic to broadly oval, 5–10 cm. long, 1–5 cm. wide, sessile or on very short petioles, green and glabrous above, grayish-green and stiff-hairy along the veins beneath.

In rich woods and thickets. Flowering May and June.

This and other species of Solomon's-seal are readily grown in the woodland garden. The common name refers to the large seallike scars on the rootstock.

Large Solomon's-seal

Polygonatum canaliculatum (Muhl.) Pursh   Plate 16

Generally larger and coarser than the preceding species, the stem stout and up to 2 m. tall from a thick, deeply buried, scarcely constricted rootstock. Flowers 2–10 from an axil 1.7–2 cm. long.Leaves not quite flat, somewhat corrugated and puckered at the margins, glabrous on both sides, narrowed to a slightly sheathing base.

In rich woods and alluvial thickets, along roadsides. Flowering in May and June.

This large species is quite conspicuous along roadsides in southeastern Michigan.

PLATE 16

Hairy Solomon's-seal (*Polygonatum pubescens*)

Large Solomon's-seal (*Polygonatum canaliculatum*)

54

INDIAN CUCUMBER-ROOT

Medeola virginiana L.   Plate 17

Simple, erect perennial, 2–9 dm. tall from a thick white rootstock which somewhat resembles the cucumber in taste and smell. Flowers pale yellow to greenish-yellow, usually drooping, borne in a loose, few-flowered terminal umbel above a whorl of leaves. Perianth parts 6, alike, oblong, recurved; stamens 6; styles 3, long and threadlike, spreading and recurved; berry dark purple, globose, 3-celled. Leaves in 2 whorls, those of lower whorl 5–9, obovate to lanceolate; those of upper whorl 3 (rarely 4 or 5), smaller.

In rich woods, sandy soil under hardwoods, and in cedar bogs. Flowering May and June.

The rootstock of this species is edible and tastes like cucumber.

Trillium

1. Flowers normally white when fresh 2
1. Flowers normally brown-purple to purple;
 strongly ill-scented . . . . *T. erectum,* Plate 18
  2. Flowering stem usually straight and holding flower well above
   leaves; petals more than 3.5 cm. long . *T. grandiflorum,* Color Plate 3
  2. Flowering stem usually curving so that flower hangs below
   leaves; petals less than 3 cm. long . . . . *T. cernuum,* Plate 18

STINKING BENJAMIN, PURPLE TRILLIUM (Protected)

Trillium erectum L.   Plate 18

Stout, erect plants 1.5–6 dm. tall. Flowers ill-scented, variable in color, crimson, purple, or purple-brown at base fading into whitish above, or greenish, clear yellow, or white, 3–7 cm. wide; peduncle straight, erect, divergent or rarely bending down from the whorl of leaves. Petals 2.5–5.5 cm. long and 1–3 cm. broad, spreading from the base; sepals about the same length as the petals but narrower; stamens protruding beyond the spreading stigmas; ovary usually purple but pale in the pale flowers; berry dark red, 6-angled. Stems 1 to several. Leaves 3, whorled, broadly rhombic-ovate, sessile, the veins netted. Rootstock stout, up to 3 cm. thick, brown.

In rich woods. Flowering April to early June.

LARGE-FLOWERED TRILLIUM, WAKEROBIN,
WHITE LILY (Protected)

Trillium grandiflorum (Michx.) Salisb.   Color Plate 3

Erect, unbranched perennial 1.5–4.5 dm. tall. Flowers white, often fading to pink or rose, showy, 5–7.5 cm. broad, solitary and erect, or nearly so, at the end of the 5–15-cm.-long peduncle. Petals oblong, 4–7.5 cm. long, 1–3.5 cm. wide, erect at base, spreading toward tip; sepals 3, green, lanceolate, spreading, shorter than the petals; stamens 6, the anthers pale yellow, the filaments stout, shorter than the anthers; pistil solitary, the ovary 6-angled, pale, the stigmas 3, not tapering to the tip, spreading or erect; berry black, globose but slightly lobed, 2–2.5 cm. in diameter. Leaves a single whorl of 3 at top of stem, broadly rhombic-ovate, pointed at ends, 5–15 cm. long, sessile, the veins very prominent, netted. Rootstock coarse, brown, scaly, 1–3 cm. thick.

In rich woods and thickets, especially in ravines and on upland slopes. Flowering April to June.

PLATE 17
Indian Cucumber-root (*Medeola virginiana*)

PLATE 18
Stinking Benjamin (*Trillium erectum*)
Nodding Trillium (*Trillium cernuum*)

PLATE 19

Colic-root (*Aletris farinosa*)

Carrion Flower (*Smilax lasioneura*)

This is one of our best wildflowers for the garden. It can be obtained from several nurseries. All parts of the plant are subject to considerable modification, and one can find specimens with a whorl of many leaves or with many petals.

Indians used the roots of this and other species of *Trillium* in decoctions for treating stomach disorders, rheumatism, and sore ears.

NODDING TRILLIUM (Protected)
Trillium cernuum L.
Plate 18

Erect, unbranched perennial with 1 to several stems. Flowers white, solitary, sweet-scented, nodding and nearly hidden under the leaves, 2.3–3 cm. broad, with peduncles 0.5–4 cm. long, coming from the whorl of leaves and recurved beneath them. Petals 3, oblong-lanceolate with recurving tips, 1.5–2.5 cm. long and 0.5–1.7 cm. broad, longer than the sepals; sepals 3, green, 1.7–2.5 cm. long; stamens 6, the anthers slightly longer than the filaments, pink or pale pinkish-purple, overtopping the styles; styles 3, stout, recurved; ovary white or tinged with pink or pinkish-purple, 6-angled, berry broadly ovoid, reddish-purple. Leaves 3, whorled at top of stem, broadly rhombic, narrowed at base and sessile or nearly so, pale green, the veins netted. Rootstock thick (often over 2 cm.), brown or grayish-brown, ascending.

In damp or peaty woods or thickets and in low woodlands, usually in acid soil. Flowering May to late June.

Large-flowering Nodding Trillium, *Trillium flexipes* Raf., is similar but coarser, the flowers about twice as large; petals white, maroon, or purple, 2–5 cm. long, not recurved; ovary usually pale or white, but, with the filaments, sometimes purple; anthers creamy white, at least twice as long as the filaments. Peduncles straight, divergent or reflexed. Leaves sessile.

COLIC-ROOT, STARGRASS
Aletris farinosa L.
Plate 19

Very bitter, rosette-forming plants with flowering stems 3–9 dm. tall from a short thick rootstock. Flowers white, 5–8 mm. long, borne in a terminal spiral spike 0.8–2.5 dm. long on an unbranched stem which is clothed with a few small bracts. Sepals and petals united into a tube, the tube glandular outside, 6-lobed at the end, adherent to the base of the ovary; stamens 6, attached at the base of the lobes and enclosed in the perianth; style 3-lobed; capsule ovoid, beaked, partially enclosed by the dry, roughened perianth. Leaves in a basal rosette, linear to narrowly lanceolate or oblanceolate, up to 2 dm. long.

In dry or moist peat, sand, and gravels. Flowering late May to August.

CARRION FLOWER, GREENBRIAR
Smilax lasioneura Hook.
Plate 19

Stems elongate, climbing by tendrils which arise from the axils of the middle and upper leaves. Flowers unisexual, small, greenish, strongly carrion-scented, borne in globose 20–100-flowered umbels rising from the leaf axils, the staminate flowers often the larger; peduncles up to twice as long as the petioles which subtend them; pedicels 5–20 mm. long. Perianth seg-

PLATE 20

Yellow Stargrass (*Hypoxis hirsuta*)

Blue-eyed Grass (*Sisyrinchium albidum*)

Blue-eyed Grass (*Sisyrinchium angustifolium*)

ments 6, soon falling, those of the staminate flowers 3.5–6 mm. long, the stamens 6, inserted on the base of perianth; stamens of pistillate flowers greatly reduced and threadlike, or lacking, the ovary 3-celled, the stigmas thick and spreading; berry black, with a bloom. Leaves oblong-ovate to rounded, truncate or heart-shaped at base, glaucous or pale and hairy beneath, strongly parallel-ribbed, net-veined, the petioles 2.5–9 cm. long, the leaves at base of stem reduced to bracts.

In rich low woods, thickets, meadows, and along stream banks. Flowering May and June.

Another herbaceous species, S. *ecirrhata* (Engelm.) S. Wats., has erect or leaning stems up to 1 m. tall, which lack tendrils or have only a few weak terminal ones. The umbels are few-flowered, and the peduncles arise from the bracts below the foliage leaves.

Several woody species of *Smilax* also grow in Michigan. The medicinal qualities of the several kinds were known to the Indians, who made decoctions of the stalks for various ailments and chewed the berries to relieve hoarseness. The berries are eaten extensively by birds, and the plants provide cover for rabbits and other small mammals.

AMARYLLIS FAMILY. AMARYLLIDACEAE

The members of this family of 86 genera and 1300 species are widely distributed, but are most numerous in the tropics and subtropics. Only the species described below is native to Michigan. The family has considerable economic importance in some parts of the world. Sisal for cordage is obtained from agaves; other plants of the family also have good cordage fibers, and some are among our most attractive ornamentals—narcissus, daffodils, agave, for example.

YELLOW STARGRASS
Hypoxis hirsuta (L.) Coville

Plate 20

Stiff, tufted, grasslike perennial 1–6 dm. tall. Flowers yellow, 7–18 mm. wide, 2–7 in a small umbel on a hairy, threadlike, ascending or somewhat reclining scape which is usually shorter than the leaves. Perianth 6-parted, the divisions alike, spreading, narrowly oblong, coherent with the ovary at the base; stamens 6, attached to the perianth segments, the filaments yellow, the anthers slender, arrow-shaped, yellow, becoming brownish; pistil 1, the ovary inferior, 3-celled; capsule not opening, the seeds black, lustrous. Leaves all basal, linear, 1–8 dm. long, 3–6 mm. wide, long-hairy or nearly smooth.

In open woods and meadows or wet marshy places around lakes. Flowering late April to June, but some flowers may be produced in August and September.

IRIS FAMILY. IRIDACEAE

This family of perennial herbs includes about 58 genera and 1500 species distributed over much of the earth except for the colder regions. Two genera, comprising about 9 species, are native to Michigan. The family is of considerable economic importance. Ornamentals include *Crocus, Iris, Gladiolus, Belamcanda, Sisyrinchium, Freesia,* and *Tigridia.* Orris-root powder, to which many people are allergic, is from a species of *Iris;* it was formerly much used in flavoring dentrifices and scenting face powder. The stigmas of a species of *Crocus* are used in making saffron dyes.

The members of this family are low-growing. The leaves are parallel-veined, mostly basal and folded forward and clasping below. The flowers are usually showy and subtended by a spathe of 2 or more bracts. The flower parts are in 3's, and the ovary is inferior.

The flowers of *Iris* are large and conspicuous; the sepals and petals are unlike; and the stamens are hidden by the petallike styles. *Sisyrinchium* has much smaller flowers; the sepals and petals are similar; and the stamens are clearly visible.

BLUE-EYED GRASS
Sisyrinchium albidum Raf.

Plate 20

Tufted, stiffly erect, pale-green perennial 1.5–4.5 dm. tall. Flowers pale violet or white, about 1 cm. wide, borne in few-flowered umbels in a spathe of 2 leaflike bracts; spathes generally 2, terminal on the simple stems, subtended by an erect leaflike bract and each enclosing several smaller, dry, often purple-tinged inner bracts, the margin of the outer bract free to the base. Perianth nearly wheel-shaped; sepals and petals 3 each, alike, yellow inside at the base, giving the flowers a yellow eye-spot, separate, obovate, attached above the ovary; stamens 3, attached to the top of the ovary, the white filaments united into a tube to the summit and enclosing the style, the anthers yellow, forming a cluster just below the stigmas; pistil 1, the ovary inferior, the style branches threadlike, the stigmas 3; capsule pale straw-color, obscurely 3-angled, about 4 mm. in diameter, the seeds numerous, globular. Stems stiff, flattened, and distinctly 2-winged, less than 4 mm. wide. Leaves mostly basal, flat, linear, clasping and distinctly folded at base, 1–3 mm. wide, pointed at tip, usually less than half as long as the stems.

On prairies, in thin woodlands and open grassy places around lakes and ponds, often in sandy soil. Flowering May and June.

BLUE-EYED GRASS
Sisyrinchium angustifolium Mill.

Plate 20

Deep green plants up to 4.5 dm. tall. Flowers pale blue to dark violet. Spathes borne on peduncles from the axils of the leaflike bracts; peduncles 2–5, ascending, winged, 2–15 cm. long, the bracts of the spathe subequal, the outer bract with its margins united above the base; pedicels 1–5, thread-like, long and slender in fruit, arching or recurving, much longer than the spathe. Stems usually forked, broadly winged, flexuous or abruptly bent. Leaves 1.5–6 mm. wide.

On low ground in meadows, along damp shores and ridges, and in thickets. Flowering June and July.

WILD IRIS, BLUE FLAG
Iris versicolor L.

Plate 21

Stiff, erect perennial up to 1 m. tall. Flowers several, bluish-violet, rarely white, very showy, 10–12 cm. wide, each rising from a 2-bracted spathe,

the bracts subherbaceous or papery. Perianth tubular at base, constricted above the ovary and fairly long; petals 3, erect, 1/2 to 2/3 as long as the sepals, the blade round to obovate, the claw long; sepals 3, petallike, spreading, the blade nearly round and deep blue-violet, the claw long, narrow, variegated at base, and greenish-yellow or yellow and white with deep-purple veins at center; stamens arching, attached to the perianth tube opposite the sepals; ovary inferior, the style with 3 long, petallike branches which arch over to the sepals and completely hide the stamens, the stigmas (just below the apex of the branches) white, platelike, covered with fine white hairs and a sticky secretion; capsule ellipsoid to thick-cylindric, obtusely 3-angled, 3-celled, beaked, opening slowly, often persisting over winter, the inner surface lustrous as though varnished. Stems round, simple or with 1 or 2 branches above. Leaves mostly from the lower part of the stem and shorter than the stem, folded and clasping at the base, ascending, firm, the fresh tufts purplish at base. Rootstock irregularly branched, thick and fleshy.

In sunny or sometimes partially shady wet places such as meadows, marshes, and edges of streams or swamps. Flowering late May to July.

Southern Blue Flag, *I. virginica* L. var. *shrevei* (Small) E. Anders., resembles *I. versicolor* in general appearance and habitat but differs from it in several respects: petals nearly as long as the sepals, the blades oblong to ovate; a downy bright yellow spot at the base of the sepal; the capsule long and narrow, often unsymmetrical, soon disintegrating, the inner surface dull; leaves quite broad, and the leaf tufts buff or pale brown at the base when young. Both of these Blue Flags are quite variable through hybridization, and intermediate forms are common in Michigan, especially near the Straits of Mackinac, where the northern *I. versicolor* and southern *I. virginica* meet.

Yellow Iris, *I. pseudacorus* L., a European species which is common along streams in the east, is now found in a few localities in Michigan. This is a somewhat larger plant with very showy yellow flowers. Other cultivated species, including the common Bearded Iris, sometimes appear to grow wild.

The Indians used the rootstocks of Wild Iris medicinally, some tribes cultivating it in ponds.

DWARF LAKE IRIS

Iris lacustris Nutt.   Frontispiece

Simple dwarf plants, the flowering stems up to 1.5 dm. tall. Flowers blue, showy, with typical iris structure; perianth tube very slender, 1.3–1.8 cm. long, nearly equaling or exceeding the wedge-shaped, petallike sepals in length; petals smaller than the sepals; capsules 1–1.7 cm. long. Leaves arching, broadly linear, 4–6 cm. long at flowering time, later up to 18 cm. long, 5–15 mm. wide.

On beaches and cliffs, in sandy woods and bogs. Flowering late May to early July.

This attractive little species is found only in the upper Great

PLATE 21
Wild Iris (*Iris versicolor*)

64

Lakes region. It forms large patches and is abundant in certain localities on the shores of Lakes Huron and Michigan at the tip of the Lower Peninsula.

ORCHID FAMILY. ORCHIDACEAE

This family, which includes several hundred genera and approximately 15,000 species and varieties, is second in number of species only to the family Compositae. The family is cosmopolitan but is most highly developed in the tropics and subtropics. About 50 species grow in Michigan.

Orchids are of value chiefly for ornamental purposes and are the basis of a multimillion-dollar floral business in the United States alone. They are prized both for their exotic beauty and for the long life of most of their flowers. Vanilla is extracted from the unripened pods of various species of tropical orchids.

The irregular, 3-petaled flowers are frequently showy and strikingly beautiful. They are solitary or borne in spikes or racemes and are always subtended by leafy bracts. The lower petal, known as the lip, is usually different from the lateral ones and larger; in the Lady's-slippers it is greatly inflated. The 3 sepals may be green or colored and petallike, alike or the middle one different, separate or united to each other or to the petals. The stamens and pistil are united in a complex structure known as the column. The Lady's-slippers have a stamen on each side of the column and bear a thick fleshy petallike staminode (sterile stamen). In all other genera there is a single 2-celled anther borne at or near the top of the column. The pollen is granular in some species, but in most species the grains are waxy and stick together in masses (pollinia). The stigma is below the anther on the column and is sticky or rough, depending on the species. The ovary is inferior, long and cylindric, often so slightly swollen at flowering time that it is mistaken for the pedicel. The 1-celled, 3-valved capsule contains an incredible number of minute seeds, but these have no stored food, and the great majority do not produce new plants. The leaves of orchids are alternate or basal, simple, entire, and parallel-veined; in a few species no leaf is present at flowering time. The plants are perennial from fibrous or tuberously-thickened corms or bulbs.

These flowers are completely dependent on insects for pollination. Many species can be pollinated only by a specific kind of insect. The flower parts are arranged in such a manner that the visiting insect while trying to reach the nectary touches the stigma and deposits pollen upon it. In leaving, the insect touches the anther, thus picking up more pollen, which is deposited on the next flower. The flowers have many interesting devices that insure cross pollination, but they cannot be dealt with here.

Since all native species of orchids are protected in Michigan, they should not be picked or transplanted. The more striking ones are offered for sale by nurseries, and people interested in growing orchids can obtain them from that source. However, these plants are exacting in their requirements, and few people have the patience to work with them.

ORCHIDACEAE

1. Flowers usually solitary (sometimes 2 or 3), rather large
   and showy, lip large and conspicuous 2
1. Flowers typically numerous, lip not greatly enlarged 5

  2. Lip having a prominent beard; leaf lacking
     or solitary at flowering time 3
  2. Lip lacking a beard, inflated, margin smooth and inrolled;
     several leaves present . . . . . . *Cypripedium*, p. 69

3. Lip inflated, slipperlike or pouchlike;
   leaf round, definitely petioled . . . . *Calypso bulbosa*, Plate 35
3. Lip broad but not inflated; leaf longer than broad 4

  4. Leaf flat, well developed at
     flowering time . . . . . *Pogonia ophioglossoides*, Plate 29
  4. Leaf somewhat folded lengthwise, immature or
     absent at flowering time . . . . *Arethusa bulbosa*, Plate 29

5. Flowers having a spur at base 6
5. Flowers lacking a spur at base 7

  6. Lip white, sepals and petals pink
     to purplish . . . . *Orchis spectabilis*, Plate 24
  6. Lip, sepals, and petals colored alike . . . . *Habenaria*, p. 71

7. Flowers bright rose pink, lip at top of flower;
   leaf grasslike . . . . . . *Calopogon pulchellus*, Plate 29
7. Not as in alternate choice 8

  8. Flowering stalk spirally twisted 9
  8. Flowering stalk not spirally twisted 10

9. Leaves mottled or variegated with white;
   leaves broad and flat . . . . *Goodyera*, p. 85
9. Leaves neither mottled nor variegated with white;
   often grasslike . . . . *Spiranthes*, p. 83

  10. Leaves borne on stem 11
  10. Leaves basal or none at flowering time 12

11. Stem leaves 2 . . . . *Listera convallarioides* or *cordata*, Plate 32
11. Stem leaf solitary . . . . . . *Malaxis brachypoda*, Plate 34

  12. Leaves several in a rosette, usually mottled
     or variegated with white . . . . . . *Goodyera*, p. 85
  12. Leaves 2 or fewer 13

13. Leaves 2 . . . . *Liparis loeselii*, Plate 34
13. Leaf solitary or none 14

  14. Plant typically green, one leaf produced (may be lacking at
     flowering time); stem rising from a tuber . *Aplectrum hyemale*, Plate 35
  14. Plant lacking chlorophyll, not green, no true leaf produced;
     stem rising from a corallike mass . . . . *Corallorhiza*, p. 89

PLATE 22

Yellow Lady's-slipper (*Cypripedium calceolus*)

Showy *or* Queen Lady's-slipper (*Cypripedium reginae*)

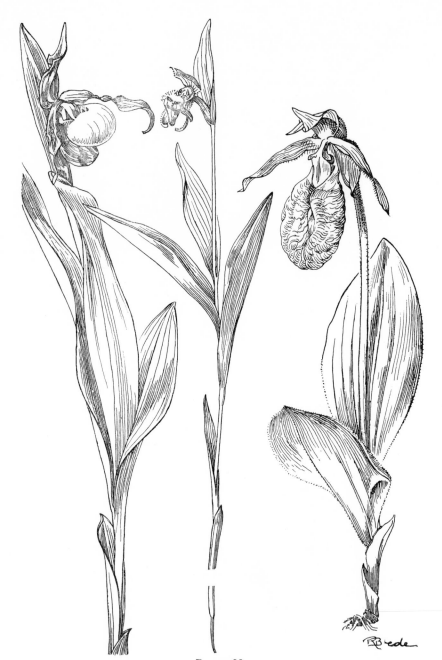

PLATE 23
Small White Lady's-slipper (*Cypripedium candidum*)
Ram's-head Lady's-slipper (*Cypripedium arietinum*)
Stemless Lady's-slipper (*Cypripedium acaule*)

68

Cypripedium

1. Lip (pouch) yellow . . . . *C. calceolus*, Plate 22
1. Lip not yellow 2
  2. Leaves only 2, borne at base of stem . . . . . *C. acaule*, Plate 23
  2. Leaves more than 2, borne on stem 3
3. Lip a moccasinlike inflated pouch, 2 sepals united to, or
  almost to, the tip 4
3. Lip a cone-shaped pouch; sepals separate nearly
  to base . . . . *C. arietinum*, Plate 23
    4. Lip magenta, rose, or white, 2.5–5 cm. long;
    petals wide-spreading . . . . *C. reginae*, Plate 22
    4. Lip waxy-white, veined with purple inside only at base,
    up to 2.5 cm. long; petals twisted. . . . . *C. candidum*, Plate 23

YELLOW LADY'S-SLIPPER, YELLOW MOCCASIN FLOWER (Protected)

Cypripedium calceolus L. var.
pubescens (Willd.) Correll   Plate 22

Downy, erect perennial with unbranched, often clustered, stems, 1.5–7 dm. tall. Flowers solitary or sometimes 2, nodding at the top of the stem, golden-yellow and greenish, or brownish-yellow to madder-purple, sometimes fragrant. Petals striped or mottled with purple or brown, linear, spirally twisted, spreading and drooping, 5–9 cm. long and about 8 mm. wide; lip sacklike, yellow with dots and stripes of maroon, about 3 cm. long; sepals colored like the petals, the upper one erect, ovate to lanceolate, 5–6 cm. long and up to 2.5 cm. wide, the lower ones partially united and appearing as one except for the forked tip; staminode large, thick and petallike, yellow, often spotted, the stigma moist, roughened, obscurely 3-lobed. Leaves 3–6, alternate, broadly ovate or elliptic, narrowed and clasping at base, strongly ribbed, parallel-veined, downy, 7–20 cm. long, and about half as wide, the upper floral one erect behind the flower, "framing" it, the margin entire or somewhat undulate, the blade somewhat plaited.

In swampy, open or shaded ground, in bogs, on wet wooded beaches, and in rich woods. Flowering mid-April to late June.

Another variety of Yellow Lady's-slipper grows in Michigan, but the two so intergrade that it is frequently difficult or impossible to distinguish them. Small Yellow Lady's-slipper, *C. calceolus* var. *parviflorum* (Salisb.) Fern., is a generally smaller plant, 1.5–5.5 dm. tall, with 3–4 leaves, the largest being 2–9 cm. broad; the sepals and petals are usually madder-purple, the upper sepal 2.5–5 cm. long; the flowers are strongly fragrant. This variety tends to bloom just as the other fades. Generally it grows in wetter places, but the two may grow together.

STEMLESS LADY'S-SLIPPER, TWO-LEAVED LADY'S-SLIPPER (Protected)

Cypripedium acaule Ait.   Plate 23

Downy perennial with 2 basal leaves and flowering stem 2–4.5 dm. tall. Flowers showy, pink to deep rose, solitary, nodding, 5–6 cm. long. Sepals and petals yellowish-green to greenish-brown, often striped with purple or brown; lower sepals entirely united; petals somewhat spirally twisted, up to 5.5 cm. long; lip a greatly inflated pouch, pink to deep rose, occasionally pure white, veined on the outer surface with rose, having a long fissure with infolded edges extending down the front. Leaves 2 (rarely 3), opposite or nearly so, broadly elliptic, strongly ribbed, 1–2.3 dm. long and 4–14 cm. wide.

In moist or dry woods, on wooded dune ridges, in and near tamarack, spruce, or cedar swamps, or in bogs. Flowering May to mid-July.

One of the most widely distributed orchids in Michigan, this species has been reported from most counties. It frequently grows in large patches but is one of the most difficult of our native plants to cultivate.

Ram's-head Lady's-slipper (Protected)
Cypripedium arietinum R. Br. Plate 23

Slender, somewhat glandular-pubescent, erect, unbranched perennial 0.7–3.4 dm. tall. Flowers white and purplish-brown or madder-purple, about 2.5 cm. long, solitary and nodding at the top of the stem. Petals resembling the lower sepals, linear, sometimes twisted; lip enlarged, prolonged downward into a blunt conical pouch, white or pinkish, strongly netted with crimson or purple, 1.2–2.5 cm. long; sepals entirely separate, the upper one the largest, dark purplish-brown to madder-purple. Stems often somewhat twisted, covered with brown tubular sheaths below, becoming leafy at about the middle. Leaves 3–4, narrowly elliptic to elliptic-lanceolate, 5–10 cm. long and 2–3 cm. wide.

In sphagnum, cedar, or tamarack swamps and bogs, in coniferous forests, and on wooded rocky slopes or wooded dunes. Flowering mid-May to early June.

This little species is rare, but it is sometimes locally abundant in the northern and eastern part of the state. In contrast to most orchids, this species has short-lived fragrant flowers—they remain in their prime but a single day. An even more rare, all white, form is known.

Showy *or* Queen Lady's-slipper,
Showy *or* Queen Moccasin Flower (Protected)
Cypripedium reginae Walt. Plate 22

Glandular-hairy, usually erect, unbranched perennial 3–9 dm. tall. Flowers showy, white and magenta or rose, usually 1 to 2 but sometimes 3 at the top of the plant, the larger ones about 8.8 cm. wide (somewhat wider than high). Petals wide-spreading, white, narrower than the sepals; lip white, striped and dotted with magenta or rose, greatly inflated, 2.5–5 cm. long, the opening at the top nearly circular and covered with long, fine, upward-pointing hairs; sepals white, the upper one large and erect, the lower pair appearing as one. Leaves alternate, broadly elliptic, strongly ridged.

In mossy swamps, bogs, cedar swamps, or in woodland glades, usually in neutral or slightly alkaline soil. Flowering June and early July.

This beautiful species is worthy of its name and has been adopted as the state flower of Minnesota. It frequently grows in colonies of dozens, hundreds, or—according to some authorities—even thousands. In northern Michigan it is often found in cedar bogs, flowering at the same time as the Wood Lily. Some people get a severe dermatitis similar to that of poison ivy from touching this plant. Many of the cells contain a large number of needlelike crystals which make it unattractive to grazing animals. The species is susceptible to parasitic fungi and is difficult to maintain in cultivation.

SMALL WHITE LADY'S-SLIPPER (Protected)

Cypripedium candidum Muhl.   Plate 23

Generally similar to the preceding species but smaller throughout, up to 4 dm. tall; the flowers white, usually solitary, slightly fragrant, the lip 2–3 cm. long, white, with rose-purple veins inside, the petals greenish-yellow, veined with purple or maroon, the two lower sepals united to the tip; leaves 3–6, nearly erect, narrowly elliptic to lanceolate.

In marly bogs, open marshes, mossy glades, sphagnum bogs, and sometimes on dry rocky hills and in woods. Rather rare in Michigan. Flowering May and June.

This is the only species of Lady's-slipper that grows in open prairies in Michigan. It is often associated with the Prairie White Fringed Orchis, *Habenaria leucophaea* (Nutt.) Gray, in the southwestern part of the state.

SHOWY ORCHIS (Protected)

Orchis spectabilis L.   Plate 24

Low-growing, smooth, succulent perennial 1–4.5 dm. tall, with basal leaves. Flowers showy, pink to mauve and white, about 2 cm. long, borne in lax 2–5-flowered racemes up to 10 cm. long, the leaflike bracts equaling or slightly exceeding the flowers in length. Petals and sepals all free, erect or nearly so and forming a hood over the column, pink to mauve, rarely white; lip white, rarely pink, spurred below; column stout, the anther cells parallel, the 2 pollen masses borne on slender stalks attached to the viscid stigmatic disks, which are contained in a pouch (bursicle) just above the opening of the spur; capsule ellipsoid, up to 2.5 cm. long. Flowering stalk stout, 4–5-angled. Leaves 2, basal, suborbicular to oblong-obovate or broadly elliptic, narrowed to an indistinct sheathing petiole, 7–18 cm. long, 5.5–7 cm. wide.

In rich hardwood or, less frequently, coniferous forests, in wooded ravines, and on slopes. Flowering May to early July.

This is one of our earliest-flowering woodland orchids. It may form extensive colonies.

Habenaria

1. Lip fringed along margin 2
1. Lip not fringed along margin 4
   2. Lip deeply 3-parted 3
   2. Lip not parted, tongue-shaped . . . . . *H. blephariglottis*, Plate 25

PLATE 24
Showy Orchis (*Orchis spectabilis*)

WHITE FRINGED REIN-ORCHID (Protected)
Habenaria blephariglottis (Willd.) Hook   Plate 25

Slender, erect perennial up to 6 dm. tall. Flowers white, crowded in flat-topped, terminal raceme 2.5–15 cm. long and 4.5–12 cm. wide. Upper concave sepal and the 2 smaller petals form an upstanding hood, the 2 lateral sepals spreading, the lip fringed around the margin, oblong or tongue-shaped, not cleft, the spur slender, 2–3 cm. long.

In bogs, peaty soil, in spruce, tamarack, or other swamps, often in sphagnum around bog lakes. Flowering July and August.

This species is often locally abundant in sphagnum mats around bog lakes, where it may be found blooming with Rose Pogonia, Grass Pink, and Arethusa. This is not as common as our other fringed rein-orchids.

SMALL PURPLE FRINGED ORCHID (Protected)
Habenaria psycodes (L.) Spreng.   Color Plate 4

Slender, unbranched, leafy-stemmed perennial, up to 9 dm. tall. Flowers numerous (up to 80), fragrant, lilac-purple to deep rose, pink, or white, crowded in cylindrical, terminal racemes 5–20 cm. long and 2.5–5 cm. thick. Petals and upper sepal entire or finely toothed on the margin, the lip broad, usually cleft nearly to the base into 3 finely fringed, fan-shaped divisions; spur about equalling or exceeding the ovary in length; capsule long and slender. Leaves alternate, oblong-lanceolate or elliptic, 7.6–25 cm. long, 1.4–7.5 cm. wide (the upper ones smaller); margins entire, base sheathing.

In wet meadows, swamps, marshes, the margins of beach pools, along wet roadsides, at the edge of woods and thickets, and in open hardwood forests. Flowering mid-July through August.

73

PLATE 25

White Fringed Rein-orchid (*Habenaria blephariglottis*)

Ragged Fringed Orchid (*Habenaria lacera*)

RAGGED FRINGED ORCHID (Protected)

Habenaria lacera (Michx.) Lodd.   Plate 25

As in the preceding species, the lip 3-cleft nearly to the base; the 3 divisions even more deeply fringed with long, threadlike segments, the flowers fragrant, yellowish-green, sordid, or bronzy. The plants grow 2–8 dm. tall and have 4–9 leaves.

In open swamps and marshes, dry to wet meadows, wet open woods, sometimes in dryish woods and clearings. Flowering in July and early August.

BLUNT-LEAF ORCHID,
ONE-LEAF REIN-ORCHID (Protected)

Habenaria obtusata (Pursh) Richards.   Plate 26

Slender, unbranching perennial with 4-angled leafless stem, up to 3.8 dm. tall. Flowers greenish-white, about 1 cm. long, 3–15 borne on very short pedicels in a loose, slender terminal raceme. Lateral petals curving upward, the upper sepal large, forming a hood; lip entire, tapering, the spur long, curving downward, the lower sepals turned back. Leaf typically solitary, basal, obovate to oblanceolate, rounded or blunt at apex, tapering below to the sheathing base, up to 13 cm. long; occasionally one stem leaf present.

In deep shade in cold boggy or mossy forests; in cedar, tamarack, or balsam-spruce swamps. Flowering late June to mid-August.

SMALL GREEN REIN-ORCHID,
LITTLE CLUB-SPUR ORCHID (Protected)

Habenaria clavellata (Michx.) Spreng.   Plate 28

Slender perennial, up to 4.5 dm. tall with a single well-developed leaf; flowers few, greenish, greenish-yellow, or greenish-white, borne in an oblong-cylindric spike, often turned so that the lip and spur project from the side, the lip with 3 short, rounded teeth at apex, the spur slenderly club-shaped, upward-curved, equaling or exceeding the ovary in length. Well-developed leaf (rarely 2) at about the middle of the stem, narrow, oblong, tapering to the base, 5 or 10 times as long as broad; other leaves reduced to bracts.

In water and at the edge of water in swamps, woods, meadows, and bogs. Flowering June to August.

This is one of our most common and easily recognized rein-orchids. This species is unlike most orchids in being self-pollinated and able to produce more seed-filled capsules than they.

ROUND-LEAVED REIN-ORCHID (Protected)

Habenaria orbiculata (Pursh) Torr.   Plate 26

Unbranched perennial with bracted flowering stem up to 5 dm. tall above pair of basal leaves. Flowers greenish-white, borne on short, slender pedicels in a loose terminal raceme 2.5–7.5 cm. in diameter and up to 30 cm. long. Lateral petals lanceolate, the lip narrowly lanceolate with a blunt tip, bent abruptly downward, the spur about twice as long as the lip, slender or somewhat club-shaped, incurved toward the apex. Leaves growing flat

75

PLATE 26

Hooker's Rein-orchid (*Habenaria hookeri*)
Round-leaved Rein-orchid (*Habenaria orbiculata*)
Blunt-leaf Orchid (*Habenaria obtusata*)

PLATE 27

Leafy White Rein-orchid (*Habenaria dilatata*)

Leafy Northern Green Rein-orchid (*Habenaria hyperborea*)

PLATE 28
Small Green Rein-orchid (*Habenaria clavellata*)
Long-bracted Green Rein-orchid (*Habenaria viridis*)
Pale Green Rein-orchid (*Habenaria flava*)

against the ground, nearly round, 7–20 cm. in diameter, smooth and shining green above, silvery beneath, rather thick and fleshy, the veins numerous and quite conspicuous.

Under hardwoods, in mixed woods or coniferous forests, on dunes and in rich, sandy or swampy ground. Flowering July to mid-September.

A much larger plant with whiter flowers having a very long, drooping spur is called *H. macrophylla* Goldie by some authors; by others it is considered merely a large form of *H. orbiculata*.

HOOKER'S REIN-ORCHID (Protected)
Habenaria hookeri Torr.   Plate 26

Greatly resembling Round-leaved Rein-Orchid, this species may usually be distinguished by the absence of bracts on the stem, by the more yellow cast to the

flowers, and by the tapering of the spur.

In dryish woods or sometimes in swampy places. Flowering June and July.

LONG-BRACTED GREEN REIN-ORCHID (Protected)
Habenaria viridis (L.) R. Br. var.
  bracteata (Muhl.) Gray   Plate 28

Stout, erect, leafy-stemmed perennial, up to 5 or 6 dm. tall. Flowers small, green, borne on stout pedicels in a raceme up to 20 cm. long, with very conspicuous, linear or lanceolate, spreading floral bracts, the lower bracts 2–6 times as long as the flowers, upper ones shorter. Flower structure typical, the lip often tinged with bronze, 2–3-toothed at the apex, 2–4

times as long as the short, sacklike spur; capsule ellipsoid, up to 6.5 cm. long. Leaves 2–7, the lower ones oblong, the upper ones lanceolate, all sheathing at the base.

In rich woods and thickets, meadows, bogs, open grassy swamps, and beach meadows. Flowering mid-May to early August.

LEAFY WHITE REIN-ORCHID (Protected)
Habenaria dilatata (Pursh) Hook.   Plate 27

Leafy-stemmed perennial, up to 1 m. tall. Floral bracts usually incurved against the stem, giving the raceme a slender, wandlike appearance. Flowers usually milk-white but sometimes yellowish or greenish-white, the fragrance strong and spicy, somewhat like that of cloves or vanilla. Petals and sepals

soft, the lip dilated at the base and projecting outward; spur about the same length as the lip. Leaves narrow, up to 30 cm. long and 5.5 cm. wide.

In moist meadows, swamps, bogs, marshes, and wet forests; on beaches and along streams. Flowering late May to early September.

LEAFY NORTHERN GREEN REIN-ORCHID (Protected)
Habenaria hyperborea (L.) R. Br. var.
  huronensis (Nutt.) Farw.   Plate 27

Somewhat fleshy and coarse leafy-stemmed perennial, up to 1 m. tall. Flowers greenish, often faintly fragrant, about 6 mm. long, borne in a dense (rarely loose) raceme, the lower

floral bracts longer than the flowers. Perianth herbaceous, the upper sepal united to the petals to form a hood; lip not dilated at the base, upturned or projecting forward, lan-

79

PLATE 29

Rose Pogonia (*Pogonia ophioglossoides*)
Grass Pink (*Calopogon pulchellus*)
Arethusa (*Arethusa bulbosa*)

80

ceolate, blunt and entire at apex, the spur slender, usually shorter than or about equaling the lip and shorter than the plump ovary, curving outward. Leaves alternate, decreasing in size upward, the lower leaves linear-lanceolate, tapering to a point at the apex and to the sheathing base, up to 20 cm. long and 5 cm. broad, veins obscure.

In wet meadows, shady places, margins of beach pools, marshes, swamps, cedar bogs, and roadsides. Flowering late June to September.

This species grades into the Leafy White Rein-orchid (*H. dilatata*). The two plants frequently hybridize to produce forms with greenish-yellow to straw-colored flowers with herbaceous perianth and lip dilated at base. These may be called *H.* × *media* (Rydb.) Niles.

PALE GREEN REIN-ORCHID (Protected)
Habenaria flava (L.) R. Br. var.
  herbiola (R. Br.) Ames & Correll   Plate 28

Rather stout perennial with 2–5 stem leaves, distinguished from the preceding species by the yellowish-green flowers, which have a tongue-shaped lip with a small tooth on each side at the base and a central tubercle near the base.

In similar habitats and flowering at about the same time.

ROSE POGONIA (Protected)
Pogonia ophioglossoides (L.) Ker   Plate 29

Slender, erect perennial up to 6 dm. tall, usually with a single leaflike bract just below the flower, and a leaf about the middle of the stem. Flowers usually solitary but occasionally 2, showy, fragrant, pale to deep pink or rose, 1–2 cm. long (exclusive of the ovary). Petals arching over the column; lip broadly wedge-shaped or spatulate, having 3 longitudinal rows of short, fleshy, yellow- or brown-tipped hairs, the margin lacerate; sepals spreading, column club-shaped, arching forward. Stem leaf one (occasionally 2–3), narrow, lanceolate or obovate, up to 6 cm. long, ascending close to the stem, sessile and clasping, 3–5-ribbed; basal leaf (not often seen) lanceolate, oblong or narrowly obovate, long-petioled.

In open sunny bogs and peaty swales, on wet mossy shores, grassy flats, low wet open woods and old beach pools along the Great Lakes. Flowering mid-June to mid-August.

This beautiful orchid is frequently found growing abundantly with Grass Pink, Pitcher-plant (*Sarracenia*), and cranberries in open sphagnum bogs.

GRASS PINK (Protected)
Calopogon pulchellus (Salisb.) R. Br.   Plate 29

Slender perennial with solitary flowering stem up to 5 dm. tall. Flowers showy, rose-purple, magenta, lilac, rose-pink or white, 3–3.7 cm. wide, borne in a loose, zigzag, terminal raceme of 2–12 flowers. Sepals and petals nearly alike, separate, spreading, the flower inverted so that the lip is uppermost; lip broadened at the apex, flanged on each side toward the base, copiously

PLATE 30

Northern Slender Lady's-tresses (*Spiranthes lacera*)

Common Lady's-tresses (*Spiranthes cernua*)

Hooded Lady's-tresses (*Spiranthes romanzoffiana*)

82

PLATE 31
Checkered Rattlesnake Orchid (*Goodyera tesselata*)
Dwarf Rattlesnake Orchid (*Goodyera repens*)
Giant Rattlesnake Orchid (*Goodyera oblongifolia*)

bearded with 3 longitudinal rows of short, fleshy, white, yellow-tipped hairs; column colored like the perianth, bending down, then arching upward and outward, but position varying with age and weather conditions; ovary much shorter than the perianth segments. Leaf solitary, narrow, aris-ing from the upper sheath and remaining close to the stem, 10–20 cm. long and 4–20 mm. wide.

In wet, open grassy meadows, sphagnum bogs, tamarack and cedar swamps. Flowering mid-June to mid-July.

This flower blooms at the same time as Arethusa, Rose Pogonia and White Fringed Orchid, and often grows in association with them. Frequently very abundant.

ARETHUSA, SWAMP PINK (Protected)
Arethusa bulbosa L.   Plate 29

Slender perennial, usually leafless at flowering time, the sheathed flowering stalk 5–30 cm. tall. Flowers usually magenta-pink, sometimes bluish-lilac or white, 2–5.5 cm. long, solitary and slightly nodding at the tip of the unbranched stem. Sepals and petals quite similar, arching over the column; lip partly erect, the apical portion drooping and having 3–6 fringed, yellow or white crests, the margin fringed, often spotted and striped with purplish-red; column arching upward, petallike at apex; capsule erect, long-beaked. Leaf solitary, linear, usually hidden in the sheaths until after the flower opens.

In open sphagnum bogs, in tamarack, cedar, and other swamps and in peaty meadows. Flowering late May to mid-July.

This strange little flower has somewhat the appearance of a startled animal. The only other species in this genus occurs in Japan. Arethusa was formerly used as a remedy for toothache.

Spiranthes

1. Leaves linear to lanceolate, sheathing; flowers in
   several longitudinal rows 2
1. Leaves ovate to elliptic; flowers in a single,
   twisted longitudinal row . . . . *S. lacera,* Plate 30

   2. Flowers in spiral or nearly straight longitudinal
      rows; lip tongue-shaped or only slightly narrowed
      about middle; flowers nodding . . . . . . *S. cernua,* Plate 30
   2. Flowers in compact spiral rows; lip decidedly narrowed
      near the middle; flowers ascending . . . *S. romanzoffiana,* Plate 30

NORTHERN SLENDER LADY'S-TRESSES (Protected)
Spiranthes lacera Raf.   Plate 30

Stiff, erect perennial 1–5 dm. tall. Flowers white, small, borne in a single twisted row on one-sided spikes 2–5 cm. long. Sepals and petals united into a forward-pointing tube, the lip trough-like and flaring at end, green except at tip. Leaves basal, thin, ovate to el-liptic, usually withered at flowering time.

In sand under jack-pines or aspen, in dry or moist peaty meadows, dune hollows, barren fields, or thickets. Flowering mid-July to early September.

Striped Coral-root

Color plate 6

Marsh Marigold

COMMON *or* NODDING LADY'S-TRESSES, SCREW-AUGER (Protected)

Spiranthes cernua (L.) Richard   Plate 30

Perennial 1–6 dm. tall. Flowers small, creamy or white, usually with a vanilla-like odor, in 2–4 spiral or nearly vertical rows forming a rather compact spike. Perianth downy, the upper sepal and petals somewhat united at the base to form the hood, the lateral sepals free, spreading; lip tongue-shaped, with wrinkled or slightly eroded margin at the apex and 2 small basal callouses. Leaves few, mostly basal and upstanding, linear to linear-lanceolate, petioled, sheathing at the base, pale green.

In bogs, swamps, marshes, boggy edges of lakes and streams, wet fields, meadows, sand dunes and low woods. Flowering August to early October.

The Wide-leaved Lady's-tresses, *S. lucida* (H. H. Eat.) Ames, occurs rarely in Michigan. It has a yellow lip and dark-green, oblong-elliptic leaves.

HOODED *or* ROMANZOFF'S LADY'S-TRESSES (Protected)

Spiranthes romanzoffiana Cham.   Plate 30

Stiff, erect perennial, the stem up to 5 dm. tall, sometimes leafy below, bracted above. Flowers white, creamy, or straw-colored, fragrant, about 7 mm. long, ascending, borne in 3 spiral rows in a compact spike, each flower subtended by a leafy bract which may be longer than the flower. Sepals and petals joined to form an upward-arching hood; lip, when spread open, constricted below the apex and appearing fiddle-shaped. Leaves mostly basal, linear-lanceolate, pointed at apex, the lowest usually petioled, clasping at the base.

On wet marly lake shores and slopes, in rich damp meadows, sandy edges of bogs and marshes, old beach pools, swamps in dune areas, and thickets. Flowering mid-July through September.

Goodyera

1. Flowers 6–9 mm. long; leaves green over all or mottled
   with white . . . . *G. oblongifolia,* Plate 31
1. Flowers 2.5–5 mm. long; some veins and/or margin of
   leaves bordered with white or pale green 2

   2. Leaves 1–3 cm. long, veins bordered with white . . *G. repens,* Plate 31
   2. Leaves 2–7 cm. long, veins bordered with white to
      pale green . . . . *G. tesselata,* Plate 31

GIANT *or* MENZIES' RATTLESNAKE ORCHID (Protected)

Goodyera oblongifolia Raf.   Plate 31

Perennial up to 4.5 dm. tall, the racemes loosely spiral or 1-sided. Perianth 8–9 mm. long, the lip elongated, only slightly sacklike, the margin incurved. Leaves 4–10 cm. long, uniformly green or mottled or with the midrib white, without evident netted venation, often reddish at least in dried specimens.

In deep cedar woods, other coniferous forest, and in rather dry, deciduous or mixed woods. Flowering July and August.

The various species of Rattlesnake Orchid are often used in en-

PLATE 32

Broad-lipped Twayblade (*Listera convallarioides*)

Heartleaf Twayblade (*Listera cordata*)

closed "dish gardens" or terraria, where they may thrive for a considerable length of time, sometimes even blooming.

DWARF RATTLESNAKE ORCHID, LATTICE-LEAF (Protected)
Goodyera repens (L.) var. *ophioides* Fern.   Plate 31

Creeping evergreen perennial, the unbranched flowering stalk up to 27 cm. tall from an evergreen rosette; often spreading by slender runners. Flowers white or greenish-white, 10–20 in a loose 1-sided raceme, the flowering stalk, bracts, ovaries and perianth glandular-hairy. Upper sepal and petals united into a hood over the lip, the lateral sepals free; lip sacklike, inflated, with a recurved tip, spurless. Leaves all basal, thick, smooth, ovate with a blunt apex, tapering abruptly to a winged, sheathing petiole, the blade 1–3 cm. long, dark green, with about 5 parallel veins, these and the horizontal to slightly oblique cross veins bordered with white on the upper surface (sometimes the blade blotched with white), the fine veins netted.

In damp or dry cold woods, usually under conifers, sometimes in bogs or swamps. Flowering July to early September.

The name Rattlesnake Orchid is preferable to the more common name, Rattlesnake Plantain, because it expresses the true affinity of these plants and because a well-known group of dicotyledons are called plantains. Since several species of this genus hybridize freely, particularly in the Great Lakes region, it is often very difficult to identify them. None of the Michigan species of this genus is easy to cultivate, but the Downy Rattlesnake Orchid, *G. pubescens* (Willd.) R. Br., is probably the easiest. This grows up to 4.5 dm. tall and has a dense cylindric raceme of globose flowers, the perianth is 4–5 mm. long, and the lip is beaked; the 5–10 leaves are dark green above, with 5–7 white nerves and numerous white cross veins.

CHECKERED *or* LODDIGES' RATTLESNAKE ORCHID (Protected)
Goodyera tesselata Lodd.   Plate 31

Plants 1–3.5 dm. tall, the raceme loosely spiral or somewhat 1-sided. Perianth about 5 mm. long, the lip only slightly inflated, its tip slightly recurved. Leaves 2–7 cm. long, 5–6-nerved, the bordering of the veins usually a light green.

In dry to moist deciduous, coniferous, or mixed woods and cedar swamps. Flowering mid-July to September.

BROAD-LIPPED TWAYBLADE (Protected)
Listera convallarioides (Sw.) Nutt.   Plate 32

Stout, erect, glandular-pubescent perennial with solitary stem 6–30 cm. tall. Flowers pale green or yellowish green, about 1 cm. long exclusive of the ovary, borne on short, slender, glandular-hairy pedicels in rather loose terminal racemes 2–12 cm. long. Petals and sepals separate, reflexed and closely appressed against the ovary, the petals almost linear; lip long and narrow, forward pointing, dilated at apex and with 2 rounded lobes, bearing a tooth at each side of the base; column arching upward, green,

87

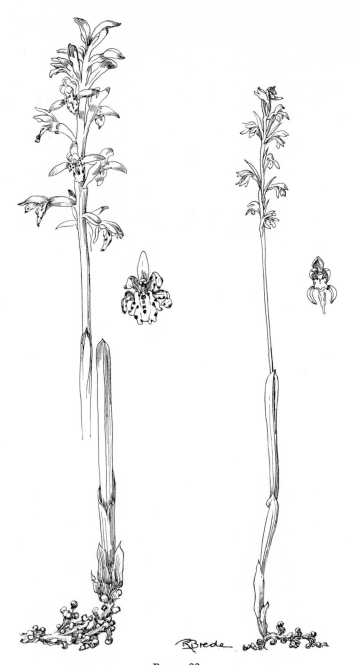

PLATE 33

Spotted Coral-root (*Corallorhiza maculata*)

Early Coral-root (*Corallorhiza trifida*)

88

thought by some to resemble the open mouth of a snake. Leaves 2, opposite, sessile, about the middle of the stem, broadly ovate to nearly round, 2.5–5 cm. long and 2–4 cm. broad, 3–9-veined.

In leaf mold in peaty or mossy glades, mixed woods, thickets, and swamps, and along shores. Flowering June and July.

Another member of this genus, the rare Auricled Twayblade, *L. auriculata* Wieg., is sometimes found in Michigan. It has pale-green or greenish-white flowers; the lip is dilated and deeply cleft above (the sinus narrow), and has 2 short incurved teeth or auricles at the base.

HEARTLEAF TWAYBLADE (Protected)
Listera cordata (L.) R. Br.

Plate 32

Delicate, erect perennial 5–24 cm. tall, glabrous except near the leaves. Flowers small, dark purplish or greenish to straw-colored, borne in a slender, terminal, long-peduncled raceme 2.5–10 cm. long on pedicels that are much longer than the subtending bracts. Petals ovate-lanceolate; lip linear-oblong, deeply cleft into 2 narrow, spreading lobes, with a pair of hornlike teeth at the base; sepals ovate. Leaves 2, opposite, sessile, about the middle of the stem, heart-shaped or rounded triangular, much shorter than the peduncle of the raceme.

In damp mossy coniferous forests, mixed woods, bogs, and evergreen swamps. Flowering June to mid-July.

Corallorhiza

1. Lip not lobed, tongue-shaped with inrolled edges;
   flowers with reddish-purple stripes . . . . *C. striata*, Color Plate 5
1. Lip with a small lobe on each side; flowers not striped 2
   2. Lip spotted with crimson or magenta; sepals
      usually having 3 veins . . . . *C. maculata*, Plate 33
   2. Lip seldom spotted; sepals usually with 1 vein . . . *C. trifida*, Plate 33

STRIPED CORAL-ROOT (Protected)
Corallorhiza striata Lindl.

Color Plate 5

Unbranched, leafless, reddish to purplish perennial up to 4 dm. tall, the stoutish, succulent stem bearing a few large, striped, sheathing bracts and rising from a cluster of many-branched, corallike roots. Flowers madder-purple or nearly ruby-red, somewhat drooping, borne in a loose terminal raceme 8–16 cm. long. Perianth 1–1.5 cm. long, the petals similar to the sepals but usually 5-veined; lip sharply turned down, unlobed, boat-shaped with an inrolled margin, deep red at apex, somewhat striped at the base; sepals sometimes yellowish or whitish, with 3 conspicuous madder-purple veins.

In rich woods, either hardwoods or mixed forest; said to do best in calcareous areas. Flowering late May to July.

Coral-roots, like other saprophytic plants, cannot be transplanted successfully. They may be grown from seeds if soil conditions are suitable. It is said to take from 5 to 10 years for them to attain blooming size. Most species in this genus have been used for medicinal purposes at one time or another.

PLATE 34

Adder's-mouth (*Malaxis brachypoda*)

Loesel's Twayblade (*Liparis loeselii*)

SPOTTED CORAL-ROOT (Protected)

Corallorhiza maculata Raf.   Plate 33

Erect, unbranching fleshy perennial, up to 6 dm. tall, the leafless stem yellow to brown, purple-brown or reddish-brown. Flowers pale yellowish to whitish with red or purple spots, few to many, in racemes 4–20 cm. long, ascending at flowering time but drooping after pollination. Petals separate; lip white, spotted, 3-lobed, the middle lobe the largest; spur small, sepals 3-veined.

In dry woods, common on slopes and frequent at the base of wooded dunes. Flowering late June to August.

This, our most common coral-root, is quite variable in color. In addition to the typical form described above, three other forms may be distinguished. In one the lip is unspotted; in another the perianth is yellowish-brown; in the third, the flower stalk, sheaths, and perianth are reddish-purple and the lip is spotted.

The Autumn or Late Coral-root, *C. odontorhiza* (Willd.) Nutt., is a frail, slender plant, light brown to madder-purple. It has a purple-spotted white lip, often wider than long, with an eroded, wavy margin, and the sepals have one vein. This is our only coral-root with a thickened, bulbous base. It flowers in late summer and fall.

EARLY *or* PALE CORAL-ROOT (Protected)

Corallorhiza trifida Chat.   Plate 33

Slender, unbranched pale yellow or yellowish-green perennial up to 4.5 dm. tall, the solitary or clustered sheathed stems rising from a whitish, intricately branched root. Flowers pale greenish-yellow, sometimes (particularly in age) tipped with brown, borne in loose terminal, 2–20-flowered racemes. Sepals and petals alike, unspotted; lip white, unspotted or sometimes with a few red spots at the base, notched on each side toward the base and blunt or bluntly rounded and notched at the apex.

In damp woods and thickets, cedar or tamarack swamps, and in bogs. Flowering May to July.

ADDER'S-MOUTH, MALAXIS (Protected)

Malaxis brachypoda (Gray) Fern.   Plate 34

Slender perennial 5–15 cm. tall. Flowers small, yellowish-green, borne in a very slender elongate terminal raceme 1.5–2 cm. long. Pedicels and ovaries about the same length at flowering time; perianth parts strongly divergent; lip drooping, entire, ovate, with a slender pointed tip. Leaf usually solitary, less than half as tall as the flowering stalk, basal or subbasal on the stem, oblong to broadly elliptic-oval, 1–9 cm. long; petioled (in one form a second, smaller, leaf may also be present).

In bogs, peaty places, swales, swamps, damp calcareous gravels, in crevices in wet shady places, and on ledges. Flowering June to mid-August.

The Green Adder's-mouth, *M. unifolia* Michx., is somewhat less common. It is quite similar in general aspect, but the raceme is oblong-cylindric and more dense at the developing tip; the leaf is a

PLATE 35

Putty-root (*Aplectrum hyemale*)

Calypso (*Calypso bulbosa*)

92

darker green and usually about midway on the scape; the lip (drooping at first) becomes erect, is 2-lobed at the summit, and may have a small central tooth.

LOESEL'S TWAYBLADE, BOG or YELLOW TWAYBLADE (Protected)
Liparis loeselii (L.) Richard

Plate 34

Small, erect, pale-green or yellowish-green perennial 6–26 cm. tall. Flowers yellowish-green or whitish, 2–25 on short ascending pedicels in a slender terminal raceme. Petals threadlike, tubular; sepals oblong-lanceolate or suborbicular, with wavy margin; column short and stout; capsule ellipsoid, erect. Leaves 2, basal, greasy-looking, sheathing the stem at base, oblong-elliptic to elliptic-lanceolate, keeled beneath, 3–19 cm. long and 1–6 cm. wide.

In bogs, in sedge mats around bogs, in peaty meadows, damp thickets, and woods, cedar or tamarack swamps, on marshy shores, or around beach pools. Flowering June to mid-July.

PUTTY-ROOT (Protected)
Aplectrum hyemale (Muhl.) Torr.

Plate 35

Smooth perennial up to 3.5 dm. tall, leafless at flowering time, the flowering stalk rising from a horizontal rootstock which typically has 2 (sometimes more) subglobose, glutinous corms connected by slender stolons. Flowers greenish, yellowish, or whitish, marked with madder-purple or unspotted; raceme 4–14 cm. long, the flowers ascending, fruit drooping. Petals long (about 1.2 cm.) and narrow; lip 3-lobed, white, spotted with magenta. Leaf solitary, basal, dark green, the veins whitish or tinged with purple, elliptic, short-petioled, appearing in autumn, decaying before the appearance of the flowering stalk in the spring.

In rich woods, wet mucky soil, low moist hardwoods, peat bogs, and tamarack swamps. Flowering May to June.

Because the 2 joined corms are common, this plant is frequently called "Adam and Eve." A sticky paste can be made by adding water to the ground corms of this species. A paste so made was formerly used to mend broken pottery.

CALYPSO, FAIRY SLIPPER (Protected)
Calypso bulbosa (L.) Oakes

Plate 35

Small, smooth perennial 6–22 cm. tall. Flowers purplish to rose-purplish, solitary, showy, nodding, about 3 cm. long. Sepals and petals separate, alike, purplish, magenta, crimson, or rarely white, linear-lanceolate, spreading; lip larger than the rest of the flower, sacklike, expanded in front, forming a spreading, whitish, purple-spotted apron over the 2-horned apex, bearded at the middle of the base with 3 rows of golden-yellow or brown-spotted (rarely white) hairs; column winged, petallike, nearly round. Leaf solitary, oval to nearly round, 2–6.5 cm. long, 1.5–5 cm. wide, plaited, petioled, the margin undulate, the veins prominent, produced from the summit of the corm in autumn, overwintering and shriveling soon after the flowering season.

In cool mossy forests, chiefly calcareous, and in tamarack and cedar swamps. Flowering mid-May to early July.

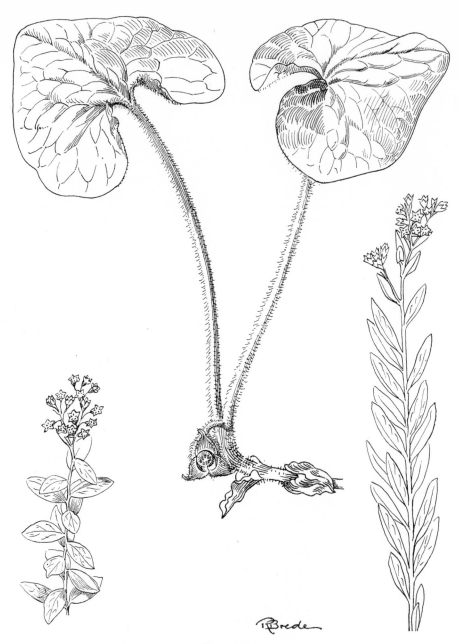

PLATE 36
Wild Ginger (*Asarum canadense*)
Bastard-toadflax (*Comandra umbellata*, left; *C. richardsiana*, right)

This beautiful little species is rather rare in Michigan. It usually grows singly, but often in association with Twin Flower and Fringed Polygala.

DICOTYLEDONS

SANDALWOOD FAMILY. SANTALACEAE

This family, of temperate and tropical regions, includes 26 genera and more than 250 species (up to 600 species, according to some authorities); only 2 genera and 3 species occur in Michigan. The family is of no economic importance here, but the sweet-scented sandalwood of the tropics is prized for cabinet-making and for use in perfumes.

BASTARD-TOADFLAX

Comandra richardsiana Fern.   Plate 36

Glabrous, erect perennial up to 30 cm. tall, from a long, freely branching rootstock on or near the surface. Flowers white, about 5 mm. wide, borne in small clusters on the strongly ascending branches of terminal corymbs. Petals lacking; calyx petallike, slender, bell-shaped, 5-lobed at the apex and having a 5-lobed disk in the center; stamens 5, opposite the sepals and inserted in the edge of the disk between the lobes; pistil solitary, the style long and slender; fruit a dry, 1-seeded, roundish nut, covered by the lower part of the leathery calyx tube. Leaves very numerous, elliptic to oblanceolate, the veins rather obscure, the upper leaves the largest, quite firm, equally green on upper and lower surfaces.

In dry sandy soil, calcareous gravels, or marly soils. Flowering May to August.

C. umbellata (L.) Nutt. is similar to this species, but its rootstocks are underground; the clusters of flowers are on strongly divergent branches; and the leaves are thin, pale beneath, with quite distinct veins.

BIRTHWORT FAMILY. ARISTOLOCHIACEAE

This primarily tropical family includes 6 genera and about 400 species, only one of which occurs in Michigan. Several species of Dutchman's-pipe (*Aristolochia*) and Wild Ginger are cultivated as ornamentals.

WILD GINGER

Asarum canadense L.   Plate 36

Low, creeping hairy perennial up to 24 cm. tall at flowering time, the rootstock thick, elongate, brown to green, on or just below the surface, and giving rise to the pairs of leaves, spicy and aromatic. Flowers solitary, borne

95

PLATE 37

Jointweed (*Polygonella articulata*)

Sheep Sorrel (*Rumex acetosella*)

96

on short stout peduncles from the leaf axils and usually hidden under the leaves. Petals lacking; calyx bell-shaped, with 3 spreading, pointed lobes, purplish-green and woolly outside, rich brownish-purple, chocolate, or dark maroon inside; stamens 12, rich purple, attached to the top of the ovary, at first curved outward and down, becoming erect; pistil solitary, the ovary inferior, the styles united into a purple column, spreading somewhat at the top. Leaves more or less in pairs, kidney-shaped, sometimes with a short point at the apex, glabrous on the upper surface, finely hairy beneath, 7–16 cm. broad, the petioles stout, densely long-woolly.

In rich woods; often abundant. Flowering late April to early June.

Several varieties of this species have been described. They are based primarily on differences in the calyx.

Recent studies have shown that this species is self-pollinated by an interesting mechanism. The stamens are at first curved downward and outward, well away from the stigmas. As the stigmas mature and become bristly and sticky, the stamens become erect and thus can drop the pollen on the sticky surface.

The rootstocks have a strong aromatic flavor and have sometimes been dried and pulverized as a substitute for ginger. A perfume was made by dampening the roasted rootstocks and roots. Medicinal uses of the plant have included treatment of whooping cough and other coughs, as well as treatment of bruises, contusions, and inflammations by application of the leaves.

BUCKWHEAT FAMILY. POLYGONACEAE

This family, which grows in the temperate regions but primarily in the northern hemisphere, includes 32 genera and more than 800 species; 5 genera grow in Michigan. The family is of limited economic importance. Buckwheat and rhubarb (*Rheum*) are used for food, and a few species, such as Silver-lace-vine, are grown as ornamentals. Several species are common troublesome weeds.

The members of this family are characterized by the stipules in the form of cylindrical sheaths (called ocreae) above the swollen joints of the stems. The regular flowers have no petals, but the 3–6 sepals may be petallike; there are 6–9 stamens, and the single pistil has a superior ovary.

POLYGONACEAE

1. Flowers greenish-yellow, often tinged with red, borne in
   terminal panicles; at least basal and lower leaves having
   spreading lobes; foliage acid to taste . . . . *Rumex acetosella*, Plate 37
1. Not as in alternate choice 2

    2. Flowers solitary from axils of scales, which give a jointed
       appearance to ends of branchlets . . . *Polygonella articulata*, Plate 37
       2. Not as in alternate choice 3

PLATE 38

Lady's-thumb (*Polygonum persicaria*)

Water Smartweed (*Polygonum amphibium*)

PLATE 39

Pinkweed (*Polygonum pensylvanicum*)
Dock-leaved Smartweed (*Polygonum lapathifolium*)
Arrow-leaved Tearthumb (*Polygonum sagittatum*)

99

3. Plants erect; leaves broadly triangular; calyx shriveling
   to expose seed . . . . *Fagopyrum sagittatum,* Plate 40
3. Plants usually partly decumbent, twining or creeping; leaves
   lanceolate, arrow-shaped, or heart-shaped;
   seeds enclosed by calyx . . . . *Polygonum,* 4
    4. Stem prickly, flowers borne in short heads . . . *P. sagittatum,* Plate 39
    4. Stem not prickly; flowers in elongate clusters 5
5. Plants having elongate creeping stems . . . *P. amphibium,* Plate 38
5. Plants lacking elongate creeping stems 6
    6. Stems twining . . . . *P. cilinode,* Plate 40
    6. Stems not twining 7
7. Summit of sheath fringed with bristles . . . . *P. persicaria,* Plate 38
7. Summit of sheath having few or no bristles 8
    8. Racemes erect . . . . *P. pensylvanicum,* Plate 39
    8. Racemes arching or nodding at tip . . . *P. lapathifolium,* Plate 39

SHEEP SORREL, SOURWEED

Rumex acetosella L.   Plate 37

Low, hairy, many-branched perennial up to 3 dm. tall. Flowers usually unisexual, tiny, reddish, yellowish, or greenish, borne in slender panicles. Petals lacking; sepals 6, united at base, the 3 outer ones spreading at least in fruit, the inner ones convergent over the ovary. Leaves mostly basal, arrow-shaped with divergent lobes, petioled, the upper stem-leaves sessile and clasping.

In poor, dry or sandy, usually acid soil, in abandoned fields, along roadsides, and in disturbed ground of all kinds, often making an extensive ground cover. Introduced from Europe. Flowering May to August.

This is a difficult weed to eradicate. The stems and leaves have a refreshing acid taste. Leaves of the larger Curled or Yellow Dock, *R. crispus* L., are frequently used for greens in the spring. Several native species also occur here.

ARROW-LEAVED TEARTHUMB, ARROW-VINE

Polygonum sagittatum L.   Plate 39

Prickly, weak, usually leaning perennial with backward-pointing barbs on the ridges of the 4-angled stems. Flowers pink to white, borne in dense heads on long, glabrous peduncles. Leaves narrowly arrow-shaped, 3–10 cm. long, barbed on the under side of the midrib.

In low ground and marshy places, and on wet sandy shores. Flowering July to October.

WATER SMARTWEED

Polygonum amphibium L.   Plate 38

Aquatic or terrestrial, smooth or hairy, creeping perennial with tough branching stems up to 7 m. long, leafy to the summit, floating, submersed, or creeping. Flowers pink, borne in 1–4 very dense, oblong or ovoid, erect spikes 1–4 cm. long and 1–2 cm. thick. Peduncles usually solitary (sometimes 2–4), holding the spike well above the water when in aquatic habitats. Leaves alternate, oblong-elliptic to narrowly lanceolate, often shining on

3. Plants erect; leaves broadly triangular; calyx shriveling
to expose seed . . . . *Fagopyrum sagittatum*, Plate 40
3. Plants usually partly decumbent, twining or creeping; leaves
lanceolate, arrow-shaped, or heart-shaped;
seeds enclosed by calyx . . . . *Polygonum*, 4
    4. Stem prickly, flowers borne in short heads . . . *P. sagittatum*, Plate 39
    4. Stem not prickly; flowers in elongate clusters 5
5. Plants having elongate creeping stems . . . *P. amphibium*, Plate 38
5. Plants lacking elongate creeping stems 6
    6. Stems twining . . . . *P. cilinode*, Plate 40
    6. Stems not twining 7
7. Summit of sheath fringed with bristles . . . . *P. persicaria*, Plate 38
7. Summit of sheath having few or no bristles 8
    8. Racemes erect . . . . *P. pensylvanicum*, Plate 39
    8. Racemes arching or nodding at tip . . . *P. lapathifolium*, Plate 39

SHEEP SORREL, SOURWEED

Rumex acetosella L.
Plate 37

Low, hairy, many-branched perennial up to 3 dm. tall. Flowers usually unisexual, tiny, reddish, yellowish, or greenish, borne in slender panicles. Petals lacking; sepals 6, united at base, the 3 outer ones spreading at least in fruit, the inner ones convergent over the ovary. Leaves mostly basal, arrow-shaped with divergent lobes, petioled, the upper stem-leaves sessile and clasping.

In poor, dry or sandy, usually acid soil, in abandoned fields, along roadsides, and in disturbed ground of all kinds, often making an extensive ground cover. Introduced from Europe. Flowering May to August.

This is a difficult weed to eradicate. The stems and leaves have a refreshing acid taste. Leaves of the larger Curled or Yellow Dock, *R. crispus* L., are frequently used for greens in the spring. Several native species also occur here.

ARROW-LEAVED TEARTHUMB, ARROW-VINE

Polygonum sagittatum L.
Plate 39

Prickly, weak, usually leaning perennial with backward-pointing barbs on the ridges of the 4-angled stems. Flowers pink to white, borne in dense heads on long, glabrous peduncles. Leaves narrowly arrow-shaped, 3–10 cm. long, barbed on the under side of the midrib.

In low ground and marshy places, and on wet sandy shores. Flowering July to October.

WATER SMARTWEED

Polygonum amphibium L.
Plate 38

Aquatic or terrestrial, smooth or hairy, creeping perennial with tough branching stems up to 7 m. long, leafy to the summit, floating, submersed, or creeping. Flowers pink, borne in 1–4 very dense, oblong or ovoid, erect spikes 1–4 cm. long and 1–2 cm. thick. Peduncles usually solitary (sometimes 2–4), holding the spike well above the water when in aquatic habitats. Leaves alternate, oblong-elliptic to narrowly lanceolate, often shining on

PLATE 39

Pinkweed (*Polygonum pensylvanicum*)
Dock-leaved Smartweed (*Polygonum lapathifolium*)
Arrow-leaved Tearthumb (*Polygonum sagittatum*)

99

Wild Columbine

Wild Lupine

upper surface and sometimes purplish or reddish beneath, the veins pinnate and prominent. The plants are nearly smooth in the aquatic forms and hairy in the terrestrial forms. Plate 38 shows the hairy, terrestrial var. *stipulaceum* Coleman on the upper right.

Along the edges of lakes, in ditches, ponds, meadows, swamps. Common. Flowering June to mid-September.

CLIMBING BUCKWHEAT

Polygonum cilinode Michx.   Plate 40

Freely-branching, twining, high-climbing perennial which often covers other plants in extensive patches. Flowers small, borne in loose, slender racemes in numerous panicles; calyx white or pink-tinged, 4–5 mm. long in fruit, not winged. Leaves heart-shaped-ovate, long-pointed at apex; sheathing stipules with a ring of deflexed bristles at base.

Along roadsides, in dry thickets and borders of woods. Flowering July and August.

Two other, quite similar, species occur in Michigan, but neither has bristles at the base of the sheath. Black Bindweed, *P. convolvulus* L., an introduced species, has the calyx greenish, 4–5 mm. long in fruit and barely or not at all winged. Climbing False Buckwheat, *P. scandens* L., a native species, has thicker racemes; the fruiting

LADY'S-THUMB, HEART'S-EASE

Polygonum persicaria L.   Plate 38

Nearly glabrous, erect or partly reclining annual with simple or branching stems up to 10 dm. tall. Flowers pink or purplish to pink and green or nearly white, borne in 1 to several dense, cylindric spikes 1.5–4.5 cm. long, the spikes usually in panicles. Petals lacking; sepals usually 5 (4–6), petallike; stamens 3–9; achenes shiny. Leaves lanceolate, the well-developed ones 3–15 cm. long, usually firm, often blotched with purple, sometimes thin in plants that are submerged part of the time; sheathing stipules fringed with bristles.

Along roadsides and railroads, in cultivated ground and waste places; usually in damp soil. Introduced from Europe; now an ever-present weed. Flowering June to October.

PINKWEED

Polygonum pensylvanicum L.   Plate 39

Erect to ascending annual quite similar in general aspect to the preceding species, but the sheaths lacking bristles on the margin, the flower spikes dense, erect, pink to purplish. This is a highly variable species with several recognized varieties.

On damp shores, in wet thickets, clearings, and in cultivated soil. Flowering late May to October.

DOCK-LEAVED SMARTWEED

Polygonum lapathifolium L.   Plate 39

Quite similar to the 2 preceding species in general aspect, the sheaths without bristles on the margin, the flower spikes usually arching or drooping at the tip. A highly variable species.

On wet shores, in thickets and clearings. Introduced from Europe. Flowering July to November.

PLATE 40

Buckwheat (*Fagopyrum sagittatum*)

Climbing Buckwheat (*Polygonum cilinode*)

calyx is 8–10 mm. long, and has paperlike pinkish to yellowish wings. It grows in damp thickets and river bottoms, along shores, and in low woods.

BUCKWHEAT

Fagopyrum sagittatum Gilib.　　　　　　　　　　Plate 40

Erect annual 2–6 dm. tall. Flowers white, in dense compound racemes. Petals lacking; calyx petallike, 5–parted; stamens 8, alternating with yellow, honey-bearing glands; styles 3; achenes 3-sided, smooth and shining. Leaves alternate, triangular with heart-shaped or hastate base, the sheaths semicircular.

In waste places and old fields, along roadsides. Spreading from or persistent after cultivation. Flowering June to September.

This species is the source of buckwheat flour.

JOINTWEED

Polygonella articulata (L.) Meisn.　　　　　　Plate 37

Erect, branching, heathlike, jointed annual up to 6 dm. tall, the stems and leaves quite similar in appearance. Flowers tiny, rose to white, solitary on short pedicels which rise from the sheathing stipules. Corolla lacking; calyx petallike, 5-parted, persistent around the achene, stamens 8, styles 3. Leaves alternate, needlelike, jointed at the base, and readily falling.

In dry sands, open ground, jackpine plains, and along lake shores. Flowering July and August.

GOOSEFOOT FAMILY. CHENOPODIACEAE

This is a family of wide distribution, with more than 100 genera and 1400 species; 7 genera occur in Michigan. The family is of some economic importance: garden and sugar beets, spinach, and Swiss chard are common foods; pigweed and Russian thistle are troublesome weeds; *Kochia* is grown as an ornamental.

The family is characterized by its minute flowers. The perianth is bractlike and lacks petals; there are 5 sepals, 5 stamens, and a single pistil.

STRAWBERRY-BLITE, INDIAN-PAINT

Chenopodium capitatum (L.) Aschers.　　　　　Plate 41

Glabrous, erect annual up to 6 dm. tall, simple or branching. Flowers very small, borne in globose clusters in the axils of the leaves (or the clusters confluent, without intervening leaves, near top of stem); in fruit the clusters become large, juicy, and bright red, and are very conspicuous; seed minute, black. Leaves alternate, bright green, triangular to somewhat arrow-shaped, long-petioled, the margin wavy or with large irregular teeth.

In woods, clearings, burns, usually in light soil. Flowering June to August.

PIGWEED, LAMB'S-QUARTERS, GOOSEFOOT

Chenopodium album L.　　　　　　　　　　　Plate 41

Mealy, erect annual up to 2 m. tall. Flowers small, greenish, often becoming reddish in fall, borne in small clusters in terminal or axillary panicles.

103

PLATE 41

Strawberry-blite (*Chenopodium capitatum*)

Pigweed (*Chenopodium album*)

Leaves alternate, green or (often) covered with a white meallike powder, lanceolate or somewhat rhombic, wedge-shaped at base, 3–10 cm. long, the larger leaves usually coarsely toothed.

In waste ground and dry woods, along roadsides, in fields and gardens. Introduced from Europe. Flowering June to October.

This is a common and troublesome weed, but it is sometimes cooked and served as "greens."

Some quite similar very common weeds (called Pigweed or Tumbleweed) belong to the genus *Amaranthus* in the closely related Amaranth Family. In this latter family the tiny flowers have dry bracts at the base.

FOUR-O'CLOCK FAMILY.   NYCTAGINACEAE

This small family of 28 genera and about 250 species is distributed mostly in the tropics and subtropics. One genus and two species occur in Michigan. The only economic importance of the family is for ornamentals: Four-o'clock, Sand Verbena, and the subtropical woody vine, *Bougainvillea*, are the most familiar here.

Members of the family have the stems swollen at the joints; the calyx funnel-shaped or tubular, corollalike.

FOUR-O'CLOCK, UMBRELLA-WORT

Mirabilis nyctaginea (Michx.) MacM.   Plate 42

Glabrous, freely forking perennial up to 1.5 m. tall. Flowers pink to rose-purple, 1–5 in a broad, open, 5-lobed, calyxlike, membranous involucre up to 2 cm. in diameter; pedicels slender, short at first, elongating. Petals lacking; calyx corollalike, with a very short tube flaring above and united to the ovary below, opening in the morning, soon falling; stamens 3–5; pistil 1, the style threadlike, the ovary superior; achene angled. Leaves opposite, broadly ovate to oblong and heart-shaped at base, petioled, entire.

Usually in rich soil, along old roads and railways, on sandy and gravelly shores, on prairies. Flowering June to October.

M. hirsuta (Pursh) MacM. is quite similar but is generally smaller; it is glandular-hairy, with oblong to lanceolate sessile or short-petioled leaves. The cultivated Four-o'clock, *M. jalapa* L., has considerably larger white, yellow, purple-red, or variegated flowers, which open in the late afternoon.

POKEWEED FAMILY.   PHYTOLACCACEAE

This mostly tropical and subtropical family includes about 17 genera and 125 species; only one genus is native to Michigan. One or two genera are sometimes used for ornamentals, and Pokeweed, or Pigeonberry, is used for greens.

105

PLATE 42

Four-o'clock (*Mirabilis nyctaginea*)　　　Pokeweed (*Phytolacca americana*)

POKEWEED, PIGEONBERRY, INKBERRY
Phytolacca americana L. Plate 42

Stout, smooth, malodorous perennial with fleshy purple stems up to 4 m. tall from a large poisonous root up to 1.5 dm. in diameter. Flowers white, in racemes which appear to be opposite the leaves except at first. Petals lacking; sepals 5, petallike, white or pinkish, rounded; stamens 10; pistils 10, united into a ring, the ovary superior, green when young, forming a dark purple, flattened, juicy berry with a seed in each of the 10 cells. Leaves large, alternate, entire, petioled, oblong-lanceolate to ovate.

In rich low ground, open woods, or thickets, often along roads; especially abundant in recent clearings. In Michigan chiefly in the southern and central part of the Lower Peninsula. Flowering July to September.

Although the berries and roots are poisonous, the young leafy shoots are edible when well cooked and are sometimes used as greens. The plants are reportedly cultivated for food in France. The purplish-red juice of the berries gave rise to the name "Inkberry." The Indians prepared a dull red or magenta pigment from the dried and pulverized berries and used it for stamping designs on baskets (using dies cut from potatoes). A yellow dye was made from the leaves.

PURSLANE FAMILY. PORTULACACEAE

A family of 16 genera and more than 500 species, most abundant on the Pacific Coast and in South America. Two genera and less than a half-dozen species occur in Michigan. Several ornamentals belong to the family: the well-known Moss Rose (*Portulaca*), as well as *Talinum, Lewisia,* and *Calandrinia*. A common weed, Purslane, *Portulaca oleracea* L., is widespread and is used to some extent for salad greens and as a potherb.

Michigan representatives of the family are characterized by their fleshy leaves, flowers with 5 petals, 2 sepals, and a 1-celled ovary. The flowers open only in sunshine.

SPRING-BEAUTY
Claytonia virginica L. Plate 43

Fleshy perennial with 2–40 weak unbranched stems up to 20 cm. tall from a round, deep-seated tuber up to 5 cm. thick. Flowers pinkish or nearly white, borne on pedicels in loose terminal racemes with an herbaceous bract at the base of the lowest pedicel. Petals 5, pinkish or white with rose to dark pink veins; sepals 2, ovate, separate; stamens 5, pink to rose, attached to the claws of the petals; style 3-cleft above the single ovary; fruit an ovoid capsule, opening along 3 sutures to show the 3–6 shining dark seeds. Leaves a single opposite pair on each flowering stalk and a few basal ones, fleshy, linear to linear-lanceolate or linear-oblanceolate, up to 17 cm. long and 1 cm. broad.

In rich, rather open woods and thickets, along roads in woods and clearings. Flowering mid-April to late May.

107

PLATE 43

Broad-leaved Spring-beauty (*Claytonia caroliniana*)

Spring-beauty (*Claytonia virginica*)

This species often forms veritable carpets of bloom in the open woods of southeastern Michigan. In contrast to most members of the family, the flowers last for several days. The flowers of both of our Spring-beauties tend to face and follow the sun. They open only when the sun is shining but do not seem particularly sensitive to temperature changes. They close when picked and when the sun is hidden. Both species are satisfactory for the garden. They are especially effective in natural settings. The tubers are edible but too small to be of much importance as food.

BROAD-LEAVED SPRING-BEAUTY

Claytonia caroliniana Michx.   Plate 43

Greatly resembling the preceding species, but differing in having fewer flowering stems (1–8), slightly smaller flowers, broader leaves (about a third as broad as long), and the bract at the base of the lowest pedicel dry and membranous.

In sandy or rich woods, along streams in hardwood or mixed woods, alluvial thickets, or upland slopes. Flowering late April to mid-June.

PINK FAMILY. CARYOPHYLLACEAE

This primarily north-temperate family includes some 80 genera and more than 2000 species; 35 or more species occur in Michigan. Many ornamentals belong to the family, the florist's carnation (*Dianthus caryophyllus*) being perhaps the best-known. Baby's-breath (*Gypsophila*), Catchfly (*Silene*), Maltese Cross (*Lychnis*), Sweet William, Bouncing-Bet, and pinks are also familiar flowers. Several well-known weeds—Chickweed, Corn Cockle, Sleepy Catchfly, Bladder Campion—likewise belong to this family.

The family is characterized by opposite, entire, simple, mostly narrow leaves, often united at the base; usually swollen nodes; symmetrical flowers with 4–5 sepals and 4–5 usually notched petals; stamens the same as or twice the petals in number; and a single pistil with superior ovary. Although the leaves of many species of this family have parallel veins, the 4–5 sepals and petals readily distinguish the plants from the monocots.

CARYOPHYLLACEAE

1. Sepals nearly or entirely separate to base; petals not greatly narrowed at base 2
1. Sepals united into a tube or cuplike structure; petals having a long, narrow base 4
   2. Petals entire or nearly so, not notched at apex; leaves needlelike . . . . . . *Arenaria stricta*, Plate 44
   2. Petals notched or deeply cut at apex 3
3. Styles usually 3; capsule ovoid to oblong . . . *Stellaria media*, Plate 44
3. Styles usually 5; capsule cylindric . . . . *Cerastium arvense*, Plate 44

PLATE 44
Rock Sandwort (*Arenaria stricta*)
Field Chickweed (*Cerastium arvense*)   Purple Cockle (*Agrostemma githago*)
Common Chickweed (*Stellaria media*)

110

Rock Sandwort

Arenaria stricta Michx.   Plate 44

Low, spreading, loosely tufted perennial 15–25 cm. tall, the stems numerous, very leafy in the lower half, nearly naked above. Flowers white, about 8 mm. wide, borne on slender pedicels in loose, terminal or axillary, 3–30-flowered cymes. Stems, pedicels, flowers, and fruit drying and persisting on the plant, giving it a somewhat ragged appearance. Petals 5, obovate, attached with the stamens to a basal disk; sepals 5, 3-ribbed, about half as long as the petals; stamens 10, white; styles 3; capsule splitting into 3 segments, the seeds kidney-shaped, nearly black. Leaves opposite, rigid, linear or needlelike, at least the lower ones usually with a cluster of smaller leaves in the axil.

In wet sand, along bog margins, on sand dunes; frequent in the jackpine plains. Flowering late June through July.

Common Chickweed

Stellaria media (L.) Cyrillo   Plate 44

Small, densely matted annual or perennial with weak stems and threadlike branches. Flowers small, white, star-shaped. Petals 4–5, deeply cleft, shorter than the calyx, sometimes lacking; sepals 4–5, distinct; stamens 3–10; styles usually 3. Leaves ovate with rounded base; upper leaves sessile; lower leaves petioled, often fringed with hairs toward the base or on the petioles.

In lawns, along roadsides, and in moist waste ground, often forming continuous mats under shrubbery. Introduced from Europe. Flowering over a long period.

This widespread weed is difficult to eradicate. It is said that its seeds, if buried deeply, will retain viability for 30 years. Birds eat the capsules, seeds, and leaves. Indians used the plant in making medicine for sore eyes.

PLATE 45

White Campion (*Lychnis alba*)   Mullein-pink (*Lychnis coronaria*)

112

FIELD *or* MOUSE-EAR CHICKWEED

Cerastium arvense L.   Plate 44

Matted or tufted, grayish-green, often glandular perennial up to 4 dm. tall, the tough basal branches bearing withering but persistent leaves and many conspicuous axillary leafy tufts. Flowers white, few to many, borne on simple or freely-branching ascending stems. Petals 5, 2-lobed, 2–3 times as long as the sepals; sepals 5, separate; stamens 10; styles usually 5, opposite the petals; fruit a cylindric capsule equaling or exceeding the sepals in length, opening by 10 teeth. Leaves mostly on the lower 2/3 of the stem, sessile or nearly so, linear or narrowly ovate, 0.5–6.5 cm. long.

In gravelly, rocky, or sandy areas, abandoned fields, meadows, and grasslands. Flowering April to August.

Another common Chickweed, *C. vulgatum* L., is a short-lived perennial which has leafy basal offshoots and few or no axillary tufts; the hairy leaves are oblong; the petals are narrow, deeply cleft, and about the same length as the sepals, or slightly shorter.

PURPLE COCKLE, CORN COCKLE

Agrostemma githago L.   Plate 44

Tall, silky annual or biennial often 1 m. or more tall. Flowers purplish-red, spotted with black, 2.5–4 cm. wide. Petals 5, narrowed to a claw at the base, borne on the stem of the ovary; calyx ovoid and lobed at the apex, the lobes leaflike and longer than the petals; stamens 10, attached to the stem of the ovary; pistil 1, the styles 5, opposite the petals; capsule 1-celled. Leaves opposite, sessile, linear, silky.

In grain fields, along roadsides, and in waste places. Introduced from Europe; now a common weed. Flowering June to September.

WHITE CAMPION

Lychnis alba Mill.   Plate 45

Erect or ascending, glandular and sticky, unisexual biennial or short-lived perennial with 4–8 forking stems up to 12 dm. tall from a basal rosette. Flowers white, 2–2.5 cm. wide, borne in few-flowered cymes, opening in the evening. Petals 5, heart-shaped above and deeply cut; calyx tubular, inflated, ellipsoid in the staminate flowers, ovoid in the pistillate, 5-toothed; stamens 10, in 2 whorls, the outer whorl attached to the petals, the inner stamens more or less united at the base; capsules narrowed at the top; styles 5, alternate with the petals. Stem leaves opposite, sessile, lance-oblong, entire, hairy; the basal leaves petioled.

In waste places, along roads, and in fields. Introduced from Europe. Flowering late May to September.

This persistent weed of field crops is a frequent contaminant of clover and forage-grass seed. It is easily confused with Night-flowering Catchfly, *Silene noctiflora* L., which has smaller perfect flowers with narrower corolla lobes and only 3 styles.

MULLEIN-PINK, ROSE CAMPION

Lychnis coronaria (L.) Desr.   Plate 45

Erect, densely white-woolly perennial up to 1 m. tall, the stems conspicu-ously swollen at the nodes. Flowers few, showy, purplish-red, about 3.5 cm.

PLATE 46

Sleepy Catchfly (*Silene antirrhina*)

Starry Campion (*Silene stellata*)

Bladder Campion (*Silene cucubalus*)

114

PLATE 47

Deptford Pink (*Dianthus armeria*)   Bouncing Bet (*Saponaria officinalis*)

wide, borne on stiffly erect peduncles. Petals 5, purplish-red, becoming white at the base; calyx with prominent ribs and twisted, linear, pointed teeth, becoming inflated. Leaves densely hairy, almost velvety in appearance, thick, the veins obscure except for the mid-rib, the stem leaves opposite, oblong to ovate, sessile; rosette leaves spatulate, narrowed to winged petioles.

Along roads, in fields, rocky woods, clearings. Introduced from Europe. Flowering June to August.

This attractive plant is a garden escape which is now thoroughly naturalized throughout the United States.

STARRY CAMPION, WIDOW'S-FRILL
Silene stellata (L.) Ait. f.   Plate 46

Perennial with several stiff unbranched stems up to 8 dm. tall. Flowers white, borne in a loose panicle, the petals fringed; calyx bell-shaped, somewhat inflated. Leaves mostly in whorls of 4, linear-lanceolate to ovate-lanceolate.

In woods and clearings. Flowering July to September.

BLADDER CAMPION
Silene cucubalus Wibel   Plate 46

Erect or partly decumbent, whitish, glabrous perennial up to 4.5 dm. tall, the stems branching at the base. Flowers white or occasionally pinkish, about 2 cm. long, borne on long peduncles in loose, spreading panicles. Petals 5, attached with the stamens to a disk at the base of the ovary, narrowing to a slender claw at the base, the blade broad and cleft at the apex; calyx greatly inflated, 5-toothed, whitish with 20 greenish or light brown veins connected by a network of veinlets; stamens 10, borne on the disk; pistil 1, the ovary stalked, the styles 3; capsule 1-celled, opening at the apex, stalked, covered by the greatly inflated calyx. Leaves opposite, sessile, lance-ovate to narrowly oblong.

Along roads, on gravelly shores, borders of fields, in meadows, and waste places. Introduced from Europe; now a common weed. Flowering April through August.

SLEEPY CATCHFLY
Silene antirrhina L.   Plate 46

Erect or ascending annual or biennial up to 8 dm. tall, usually with dark glutinous spots on the stem. Flowers pink or purplish (sometimes partly white), borne on slender pedicels in loose spreading panicles. Petals small, soon falling, sometimes lacking; calyx spindle-shaped, not inflated, 5-toothed, the teeth often purple; stamens 10; styles 3; capsule nearly sessile, closely covered by the calyx. Leaves opposite, sessile, lanceolate, oblanceolate, or linear.

In dry or rocky open woods, fields, waste places, in sandy soil, and jack-pine plains. Flowering May to September.

BOUNCING BET, SOAPWORT
Saponaria officinalis L.   Plate 47

Nearly glabrous, sparingly branched perennial 3–6 dm. tall, spreading rapidly by branching, underground runners to form dense colonies. Flowers white or pinkish to pinkish lavender, frequently double, about 2.5 cm. wide, borne in dense terminal corymbs. Petals 5, obcordate shallowly notched at the apex and extending into a long narrow claw; calyx long, tubular, 5-toothed at the apex; stamens 20; pistil 1, the styles 2, long and threadlike; pod shorter than the calyx. Leaves sessile, opposite, narrowly lanceolate to ovate, strongly 3-veined.

Along roadsides and railroads, on sandy open ground, and in waste places. Introduced from Europe; now a common weed. Flowering late July and August (sometimes a few flowers as late as October).

This species has long been known for its therapeutic properties. The ancient Greeks and Romans cultivated it for medicine and as a soap. The crushed leaves and stems make a soapy lather.

DEPTFORD PINK

Dianthus armeria L.   Plate 47

Stiff, simple or sparsely branched, somewhat hairy annual or biennial up to 8 dm. tall. Flowers few, showy, red or roseate with white dots, borne in flattish terminal clusters which are subtended by strongly ribbed, narrow bracts. Petals 5, toothed on margin, attached to the stem of the ovary; calyx long, cylindrical, 5-toothed, with narrow basal bracts which are about as long as the tube; stamens 10, pistil 1; styles 2; capsule opening at the apex by 4 teeth, the seeds flattish. Stem leaves 5–10 pairs, opposite, linear to linear-lanceolate, entire, 3–8 cm. long, 2–8 mm. wide; basal leaves numerous.

In dry fields, along roads, and on dry sandy shores. Introduced from Europe. Flowering May to July.

WATER LILY FAMILY. NYMPHAEACEAE

This aquatic, cosmopolitan fresh-water family includes 8 genera and about 90 species. Less than a dozen species occur in Michigan. These plants are used to some extent for ornamentals. The Sacred Lotus of India, Tibet, and China, *Nelumbo nucifera,* with its large showy pink flowers, is used in large formal pools.

The water lilies have submerged, horizontal rootstocks. They give rise to long petioles and peduncles which permit the leaves and flowers to float on the surface or to rise above the surface of the water. The solitary, showy flowers have few sepals, many petals (which in some species are so modified that they are difficult to distinguish from the stamens), numerous stamens, and either a solitary, many-celled ovary or several separate pistils.

NYMPHAEACEAE

1. Flowers white . . . . *Nymphaea odorata,* Plate 49
1. Flowers yellow 2
   2. Leaf blades nearly round . . . . . . *Nelumbo lutea,* Plate 48
   2. Leaf blades broadly ovate, with deep sinus extending
     nearly to center . . . . *Nuphar advena,* Plate 49

AMERICAN LOTUS, YELLOW NELUMBO (Protected)

Nelumbo lutea (Willd.) Pers.   Plate 48

Large aquatic perennial, the petioles and peduncles up to 2 m. long from the buried rootstock, the flowers and leaves usually held well above the

PLATE 48
American Lotus (*Nelumbo lutea*)

surface. Flowers pale yellow, fragrant, up to 2.5 dm. broad. Sepals and petals quite similar, 20 or more; stamens numerous; pistils numerous, embedded in pits in the enlarged top of the receptacle, which becomes dry and hard; up to 10 cm. in diameter in fruit, the globular, nutlike fruits soon free. Leaves smooth, circular in outline, cup-shaped or depressed in the center where the petiole is attached, 3–6 dm. in diameter, the veins prominent.

In quiet streams, ponds, and lakes. Quite rare and known in Michigan from only a few localities. Flowering in August.

Another rare member of this family also has a leaf with no sinus or cut and the petiole is attached to the center. Watershield, *Brasenia schreberi* Gmel., has small, dull purple flowers with 4–18 separate pistils, and oval, floating leaves up to 10 cm. wide. The stems, petioles, and lower surfaces of the leaves are coated with a thick jelly.

The Indians believed that the American Lotus had mystic powers; they often kept tubers about as a protection against witches. They also dried and stored the tubers for winter use with boiled meat, corn, or hominy. The leaves were also eaten. The dried fruiting heads are often used in winter bouquets.

FRAGRANT WHITE WATER LILY
Nymphaea odorata Ait.　　　　　　　　　　　　　　　Plate 49

Aquatic perennial from an elongate continuous rootstock with branches that are neither constricted nor easily detached. Flowers solitary, showy, floating, white or rarely the outer petals rose, very fragrant, 5–15 cm. broad, open from early morning till noon for 3–4 days. Petals 17–32, in several rows, narrowly elliptic, the inner ones more like the stamens; stamens 36–100, large, conspicuous, variable, often somewhat petallike; ovary large, globose, the stigmas radiating from the center; fruit globular, maturing under water. Leaves floating or in shallow water above the surface, green above, usually purple beneath, nearly round, with a narrow sinus, up to 25 cm. in diameter, petiole purplish-green to red.

Along the margins of ponds and lakes, in marshes and along slow streams. (A dwarf form also occurs in bog pools.) Most common in the southern part of Michigan. Flowering June to September.

The Tuberous White Water Lily, *N. tuberosa* Paine, is quite similar in general aspect, but the rootstock has numerous readily detachable knotty tubers; the flowers are odorless or only faintly fragrant; the petals are broader and more rounded at the apex; the sepals are green outside; the leaf blades are usually green beneath, rarely purple; and the petioles are usually striped.

This species also grows in quiet or slow-moving water, pond margins, shallow bays and protected coves. It is more common in northern Michigan and flowers chiefly in July and August.

YELLOW POND-LILY, COW-LILY
Nuphar advena (Ait.) Ait. f.　　　　　　　　　　　　Plate 49

Aquatic perennial with erect leaves (floating only in very deep water) held well above the water on nearly round petioles rising from a rootstock

PLATE 49
Yellow Pond-lily (*Nuphar advena*)
Fragrant White Water Lily (*Nymphaea odorata*)

creeping in the mud. Flowers bright yellow, solitary, usually raised above the water on round peduncles. Petals small, flattish, resembling and usually hidden by the stamens; sepals usually 6, large, concave, leathery, in 2 rows, deep yellow or greenish-yellow; stamens very numerous, straplike, borne in several circles; ovary large, many-celled, the stigma a broad circular disk with 7–25 rays; fruit berrylike, many-seeded. Leaves broadly ovate with a broad V- or U-shaped sinus at the base, the sinus 5–15 cm. wide, the 2 basal lobes nearly triangular; petioles round or nearly so.

In shallow, slow-running or stagnant water, in swamps and along the margins of ponds or lakes. More common in the southern part of Michigan. Flowering chiefly in June and July.

Another common Yellow Pond-lily or Bullhead-lily, *Nuphar variegatum* Engelm., is quite similar in general aspect but tends to be smaller; the sepals are tinged with purple at the base; the leaves are usually floating and have a deep, narrow closed sinus; the basal lobes are broad and rounded; and the petiole, somewhat flattened, is ridged or winged.

It grows in slow streams or ponds and occurs throughout Michigan, but is more common in the northern part. It flowers chiefly in July and August. Tubers of this species were harvested by Indian women or were obtained by raiding the hoards collected by muskrats. The tubers were eaten raw, roasted, boiled with meat, or used to thicken soups. The seeds were ground into meal for bread, used for porridge, or parched and eaten like popcorn.

BUTTERCUP FAMILY *or* CROWFOOT FAMILY. RANUNCULACEAE

This is a fairly large family and particularly important in the cool, temperate regions of the Northern Hemisphere. It includes about 35 genera and 1500 species, of which some 300 species are native to the United States; 14 genera are found in Michigan. The family is of some importance for ornamentals. Buttercups, Globe Flower (*Trollius*), Peony (*Paeonia*), Larkspur (*Delphinium*), Christmas Rose (*Helleborus*), Winter Aconite (*Eranthis*), Clematis, Columbine, and Meadow-rue are among the best-known of the garden species.

Most members of the family are herbaceous. The petals, sepals, stamens, and pistils are all separate; the petals are often lacking, in which case the sepals may be petallike. The stamens are usually numerous and spirally arranged; there are generally several to many one-celled pistils. The leaves are often deeply divided or compound, but in some species they are simple and merely toothed or shallowly lobed; the petiole is usually enlarged at the base, and there are seldom stipules present. The juice is acrid and, in many species, poisonous.

PLATE 50
Swamp Buttercup (*Ranunculus septentrionalis*)

RANUNCULACEAE

PLATE 51
Common Buttercup (*Ranunculus acris*)

124

SWAMP BUTTERCUP

Ranunculus septentrionalis Poir.   Plate 50

Coarse, fleshy perennial with soft, hollow, ascending or trailing stems up to 1 m. long, rooting and sending up leaves at the nodes, the roots thick and fibrous. Flowers few, bright yellow, 2–3 cm. wide. Petals 5, somewhat longer than the sepals; sepals 5, spreading, becoming reflexed; stamens and pistils numerous, the style long, nearly straight, the stigma at the tip; fruiting heads globose to ovoid; achenes pitted, wing-margined, beaked. Basal and lower leaves compound, the divisions in 3's, the leaflets stalked, cleft, sharply toothed, the stipules conspicuous, brown, and leathery.

In open or shady places, alluvial thickets, woods, meadows, and marshy shores, along stream banks. Flowering April to July.

Creeping Buttercup, *R. repens* L., a common and somewhat similar species, also has creeping stems, but the style is short and has the persistent stigma down one side. It was introduced from Europe.

KIDNEY-LEAF *or* SMALL-FLOWERED BUTTERCUP

Ranunculus abortivus L.   Plate 52

Glabrous perennial with 1–3 stems up to 7 dm. tall, branching above. Flowers few to many, less than 1 cm. wide, pale yellow, the petals shorter than the sepals; achenes nearly round, shining. Stem leaves variable, simple or divided into lanceolate or linear segments, the upper leaves sessile, the lower stem leaves petioled; basal leaves simple and kidney-shaped to nearly round, or (less commonly) 3-lobed, cleft, or compound.

In low woods, thickets, and clearings, and on damp slopes. Flowering April to July.

COMMON *or* TALL BUTTERCUP

Ranunculus acris L.   Plate 51

Erect, branching, many-stemmed perennial, up to 1.3 m. tall from a short, thickish, erect rootstock. Flowers bright yellow, borne on freely branching terminal peduncles. Petals twice as long as the sepals, glossy above, dull beneath; style short and curved, the stigma persistent, covering one side of the style; achene smooth, flattened, the beak nearly central. Basal leaves large, long-petioled, 5–7-divided to the base, the divisions cleft and toothed; stem leaves similar but less divided, sessile or with petioles sheathing at the base.

In fields and clearings, along roadsides, in meadows and pastures. Introduced from Europe. Flowering May to August.

This common species often colors whole fields yellow in late June and is reputedly the cause of most buttercup poisoning in cattle. Cows poisoned by buttercups may produce milk with a reddish color or bitter taste. The poison is broken down when the plants are dried, so that buttercups cause no trouble in hay.

EARLY BUTTERCUP

Ranunculus fascicularis Muhl.   Plate 52

PLATE 52

126

Kidney-leaf Buttercup
(*Ranunculus abortivus*)

Early Buttercup
(*Ranunculus fascicularis*)

White Water-buttercup
(*Ranunculus longirostris*)

Yellow Water-buttercup
(*Ranunculus flabellaris*)

Small perennial, with weak silky stems up to 2 dm. tall from thickened roots. Flowers 2–8 on a stem, 1–3 cm. wide, pale yellow. Petals 5 or more; fruiting heads globose, 5–8 mm. long; achenes slightly flattened, having a narrow wing and a long, straight or curved beak. Basal leaves pinnately 3–5-parted and having linear to oblong lobes.

In thin soil in open woods and thickets, on exposed hills or calcareous ledges. Flowering late April to early June.

The less common Hairy Buttercup, R. *hispidus* Michx., is quite similar, but it has palmately divided leaves and thicker fruiting heads (7–11 mm. in diameter).

Yellow Water-buttercup *or* Crowfoot
Ranunculus flabellaris Raf.   Plate 52

Amphibious, submerged or floating species with stout, hollow, elongate stems. Flowers golden yellow, 1–7 on branching stems above the water, 1.5–2.5 cm. wide. Petals 5–8, nearly twice as long as the sepals; sepals greenish to yellowish-green; fruiting head globose, the achenes having a corky thickening at the base and along the margin. Leaves twice compound, the divisions in 3's, narrow to almost threadlike, flabby, up to 7 cm. long. Strand or shore plants have shorter stems and thicker leaves.

In quiet water or on muddy shores. Flowering May to June.

White Water-buttercup
Ranunculus longirostris Godr.   Plate 52

Aquatic or amphibious, the stems elongate in water, shorter and rooting at the nodes in mud. Flowers white, solitary, 1–2 cm. broad. Petals and sepals 5; achenes ridged, the beak long. Leaves very finely and deeply divided into stiff threadlike segments; stipules united to the petioles for at least 3/4 their length.

In shallow, usually calcareous, waters of rivers, lakes, and ponds. Flowering May to September.

The other two species of white buttercup or crowfoot occurring in Michigan are distinguished by rather slight technical differences.

Early Meadow-rue, Quicksilver-weed
Thalictrum dioicum L.   Plate 53

Delicate perennial up to 6 dm. tall. Flowers greenish or straw-colored, unisexual, borne in axillary or terminal panicles, the individual flowers small and inconspicuous but the panicles graceful and attractive. Staminate flowers with 4–5 small, thin, oblong to oval, green, straw-colored, or purplish sepals; stamens numerous, at first erect and brownish but soon yellow and drooping on threadlike filaments. Pistillate flowers with 4–5 smaller, firm, green or purple sepals; pistils 8–20, the stigma threadlike; achenes ellipsoid with a short point, ridged. Leaves 1–3 below the flowers, 2-3 times 3-parted, the leaflets with rounded teeth or lobes, stalked; upper leaves with green, crescent-shaped stipules; not fully expanded at flowering time.

In rich rocky woods and ravines and on slopes. More common in the southern part of the state. Flowering late April to May.

This and other species of Meadow-rue are often cultivated for the attractive light-green foliage and the feathery flower clusters.

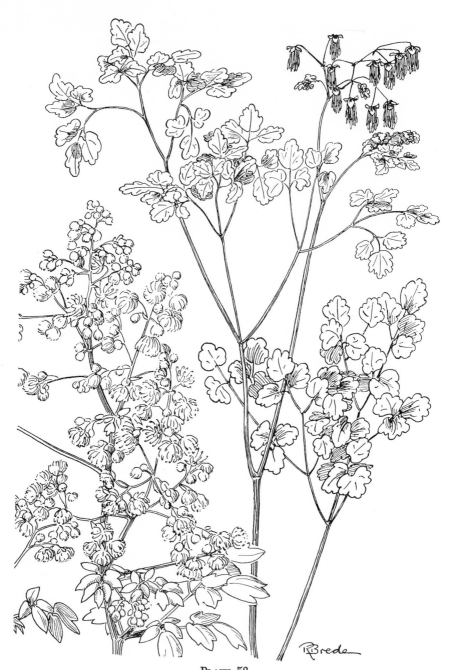

PLATE 53
Purple Meadow-rue (*Thalictrum dasycarpum*)
Early Meadow-rue (*Thalictrum dioicum*)

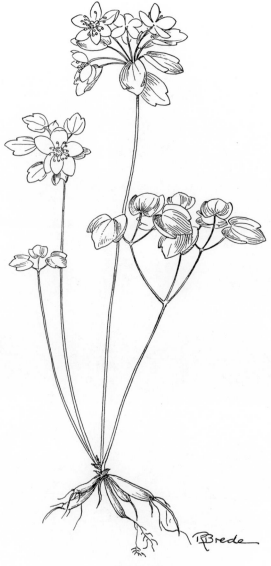

PLATE 54

Rue Anemone (*Anemonella thalictroides*)

PLATE 55

Round-lobed Hepatica
(*Hepatica americana*)

Sharp-lobed Hepatica
(*Hepatica acutiloba*)

PURPLE MEADOW-RUE
Thalictrum dasycarpum Fisch. & Lall.   Plate 53

Considerably more robust than the preceding species, this plant may be 2 m. or more in height, with many thick, often purplish stems, which give it the name Purple Meadow-rue. Flowers chiefly unisexual, borne in large whitish panicles, usually well above the leaves. Leaves 3–4 times compound; stem leaves 3–7, the upper ones sessile or nearly so, their ovate stipules brown, the leaflets entire or with 2–3 lobes, well developed at flowering time.

In damp soil, along streams, in swamps, damp thickets, and meadows. Flowering June and July.

Though not colorful, this species is attractive because of the large, striking panicles. It can be easily grown in a damp location but requires lots of space. The ripening seeds have a delicate odor which the Indians used for perfume, rubbing the seeds over their clothing.

RUE ANEMONE
Anemonella thalictroides (L.) Spach   Plate 54

Delicate, glabrous, weak-stemmed perennial up to 3 dm. tall. Flowers delicate pink or white, 2 or more in a loose umbel above a whorl of leaves (involucre), 1–2 cm. broad. Petals lacking; sepals petallike, 5–10 (usually 7–8), white or pink (in one rare form green and leaflike); stamens numerous, small; pistils 4–15, achenes ovoid with 8–10 ribs. Leaves on the stem in a whorl forming an involucre, the leaves compound, the divisions in 3's, the leaflets rounded, heart-shaped at the base, 3-lobed at the apex, not fully expanded at flowering time, petioled; basal leaves similar.

In open woods and thickets, along roadsides. Flowering late April to early June.

This species makes a charming addition to the wildflower garden. Forms in which there are extra sepals or in which the sepals are 3-lobed are particularly attractive. The small starchy tubers grow in a cluster and resemble miniature sweet potatoes. They are edible when cooked but are much too small to use conveniently.

Because of the general similarity this species is sometimes confused with False Rue Anemone and Wood Anemone, but both of those species have solitary flowers. The latter also has sharply toothed leaves.

ROUND-LOBED HEPATICA, LIVER-LEAF
Hepatica americana (DC.) Ker   Plate 55

Low, hairy perennial seldom over 1.5 dm. tall. Flowers blue, lavender, purple, maroon, pinkish, or whitish, closing in cloudy weather and at night, solitary on hairy flowering stems with a calyxlike involucre of 3 round-tipped bracts just below the flower. Petals lacking; sepals usually 6 or 7, petallike; stamens numerous, small, of unequal lengths; pistils several; achenes oblong, pointed, hairy. Leaves usually broader than long, heart-shaped at the base and having 3 broad, blunt to rounded lobes, appearing after the flowers and persisting until the following spring, the old leaves frequently purplish red.

In dry woods, on sandy slopes and in thickets. Flowering principally in April and May.

131

R. Brede

PLATE 56

Red Windflower
(*Anemone multifida*)

Canada Anemone
(*Anemone canadensis*)
Wood Anemone
(*Anemone quinquefolia*)

132

This plant is fairly common in oak woods, where the clusters of flowers stand out well above the old leaves. It is an excellent garden plant and is as attractive as many cultivated species, both in flower and in leaf after the flowers are gone. It blooms with or just after Crocuses.

The Indians used Hepatica medicinally and as a charm to put on traps for fur-bearing animals.

SHARP-LOBED HEPATICA

Hepatica acutiloba DC.   Plate 55

Very similar to the preceding species, but the blades of the leaves are usually longer than broad, the 3 divisions more sharply pointed and frequently notched or lobed; the involucral bracts are pointed, and the flowers tend to be showier.

In rich, often calcareous, woods. Flowering March to early May.

The two species of *Hepatica* seldom grow together naturally, probably because *H. acutiloba* does best in a less acid soil.

Anemone

1. Leaves cut into numerous long, narrow segments, flowers
usually red; plants of sandy or gravelly shores of the
Great Lakes . . . . *A. multifida,* Plate 56
1. Not as in alternate choice 2
  2. Plants usually 1–2 dm. tall, unbranched, having
a single flower; leaves compound . . . . *A. quinquefolia,* Plate 56
  2. Usually much taller and coarser, branched, and having
more than 1 flower; leaves deeply cut, but not compound 3
3. Leaves of flowering stem sessile or nearly so;
fruiting heads nearly globose . . . . . . *A. canadensis,* Plate 56
3. Leaves of flowering stem petioled; fruiting heads ovoid to cylindric . . 4
  4. Stem leaves typically 3; plants green . . . . *A. virginiana,* Plate 57
  4. Stem leaves typically 5–9 in a whorl, of 2 sizes;
plants grayish green . . . . *A. cylindrica,* Plate 57

RED WINDFLOWER

Anemone multifida Poir.   Plate 56

Freely branching, silky-hairy perennial, seldom over 3 dm. tall. Flowers solitary on erect peduncles, red, purplish, or yellowish inside and yellowish, greenish, purplish, or red outside. Petals lacking; sepals 5 (14–16 in one form), petallike; stamens many; pistils numerous, the styles threadlike, erect, often falling off in fruit; fruiting head short-cylindric (2 cm. long and 1 cm. thick) or nearly globose, woolly; achenes pubescent to woolly. Basal leaves long-petioled, 2–3 times divided or cleft into long, narrow, rather pointed segments; leaves of the involucre 3, like the basal leaves, petioled; the main peduncle leafless, the secondary peduncles with small petioled leaves resembling the basal leaves.

In dry, slaty or calcareous gravel, on ledges, and in sand, frequently on lake shores. Common on the sandy beaches of Lakes Michigan and Huron at the tip of the Lower Peninsula; also on Isle Royale. Flowering May to September (more profusely early in the season).

133

PLATE 57

Long-headed Thimbleweed   Thimbleweed
(*Anemone cylindrica*)   (*Anemone virginiana*)

134

Another colorful and very beautiful anemone, the Pasque-flower, *A. patens* L. var. *wolfgangiana* (Bess.) Koch, is reported to occur in the western part of the Upper Peninsula. It has large blue, purple, or lavender flowers, which are open and bell-shaped at first, resembling a crocus. The entire plant is covered with silky hairs, and the leaves are finely divided.

WOOD ANEMONE

Anemone quinquefolia L. var. *interior* Fern.   Plate 56

Small, unbranched perennial with a solitary slender stem 1–2 dm. tall. Flowers solitary, white, 1.5–2 cm. wide. Petals lacking; sepals usually 5 (4–9), petallike, often tinged with pink or crimson; stamens numerous; pistils few, hairy; fruiting head globose; achenes tipped with hooked styles. Basal leaf solitary, long-petioled, palmately compound, with 3–5 sharply toothed or cut leaflets (or those with 3 leaflets having the lower leaflets so deeply cut that there appear to be 5 leaflets); involucre usually of 3 (2–4) petioled leaves similar to the basal leaves.

In low or moist openings, thickets, open woods, and rich partially shaded ground. Flowering late April to mid-June.

CANADA *or* BROAD-LEAF ANEMONE

Anemone canadensis L.   Plate 56

Robust perennial with 1–2 usually freely branching stems up to 7 dm. tall, usually growing in clumps or patches. Flowers solitary on peduncles, white, 1.5–5 cm. wide. Petals lacking; sepals 5, petallike, white, oblong or ovate, unequal; stamens numerous, conspicuous; pistils numerous, glabrous or somewhat hairy; fruiting heads globose; achenes flat, broadly wing-margined, beaked with a long, hairlike, pointed style. Primary involucre large, of 3 sessile, deeply 2–3-lobed, coarsely-toothed leaves; secondary involucres of 2 smaller but similar leaves. Basal leaves 5–15 cm. broad, long-petioled, 5–7-parted nearly to the base, the divisions usually 3-cleft and coarsely toothed.

In damp thickets, open woods, and meadows, along gravelly, usually calcareous, shores, and in shallow ditches. Flowering late May to early August.

This species is more attractive than our other white-flowered anemones because of its more conspicuous, yellow-centered, brilliantly white flowers and its habit of growing in clumps. It makes a satisfactory garden flower, though it tends to spread too rapidly. The Indians used the crushed rootstocks on wounds and hemorrhages and in infusions for treating infections. They also used this plant for a tea to relieve lung congestion.

THIMBLEWEED, TALL ANEMONE

Anemone virginiana L.   Plate 57

Stiffly erect, greenish perennial up to 1 m. tall. Flowers solitary on long peduncles, white, greenish-yellow, or red-tinged, 1.5–3.8 cm. wide. Petals lacking; sepals 5, petallike (sometimes leathery); stamens numerous, the styles strongly spreading at maturity, persistent; fruiting heads 12–15 mm.

PLATE 58

Purple Clematis   Virgin's Bower, Clematis
(*Clematis verticillaris*)   (*Clematis virginiana*)

thick, woolly, ovoid or somewhat thimble-shaped, the achenes woolly. Basal leaves long-petioled, hairy, deeply palmately lobed and cleft, the divisions convex, the margins slightly rounded on the sides at the base, the involucre usually of 3 (2–5) short-petioled smaller leaves; the main peduncle leafless, the secondary peduncles usually with a pair of small leaves near the middle.

In dry or rocky open woods, thickets, and clearings. Flowering late June to September.

Long-headed Thimbleweed. Long-headed Anemone

Anemone cylindrica Gray

Plate 57

Similar to the preceding species, but the plants grayish-green; the involucre usually of 5–9 leaves, 3 of which are noticeably larger than the others; the secondary peduncles usually lacking involucres; the fruiting heads cylindric (typically more than twice as long as thick); the styles pointed, crimson, the tips recurved.

In dry open soil, along roadsides, on dry and rocky lake shores, and in dryish open woods.

A third Thimbleweed, *A. riparia* Fern., resembles the two preceding species in size and habit and is difficult to distinguish from them. It has 3 involucral leaves, with the segments wedge-shaped in general outline and the margins straight or nearly so toward the base. The styles at maturity are curved upward and the mature fruiting heads are 7–11 mm. thick.

Virgin's Bower, Clematis

Clematis virginiana L.

Plate 58

Perennial vine with freely branching stems 2–3 m. long, trailing or climbing over shrubs, trees, and fences by twisting the petioles around the support. Flowers unisexual, creamy white, borne in large cymose clusters from the leaf axils, about 2 cm. wide. Petals lacking; sepals 4, separate; staminate flowers with numerous stamens; pistillate flowers with a cluster of silky, long-styled pistils surrounded by sterile stamens and the sepals; achenes brown or reddish with long, whitish, feathery, somewhat curly styles 2 cm. or more long, forming conspicuous fluffy masses. Leaves opposite, 3-foliolate, the leaflets thin, ovate, often heart-shaped at the base, toothed or lobed.

In moist places, lowlands, damp thickets, borders of woods and along streams. Flowering July to September. Fruits ripe in late summer and early fall.

Various species of *Clematis* are cultivated; some have very showy flowers which may be as much as 10–15 cm. in diameter.

Purple Clematis

Clematis verticillaris DC.

Plate 58

Woody-stemmed climber differing from the preceding species by having large (5–8 cm. broad) blue, mauve, or purple solitary flowers nodding in the axils of the leaves; the sepals covered with long soft hairs; the achenes with long, softly hairy styles, borne in a dense cluster.

In rocky open woods and on slopes. Flowering May to June.

PLATE 59
Golden Seal
(*Hydrastis canadensis*)

Goldthread
(*Coptis groenlandica*)

False Rue-anemone
(*Isopyrum biternatum*)

138

FALSE RUE-ANEMONE
Isopyrum biternatum (Raf.) T. & G.   Plate 59

Slender, glabrous perennial up to 4 dm. tall from fibrous or somewhat tuberous roots. Flowers white, solitary from the axils or terminal, 1–1.5 cm. wide. Petals lacking; sepals 5, petal-like, soon falling; stamens up to 40; pistils 4 (3–6); follicles spreading at maturity, oblong, pointed, sessile, the seeds 2–5, smooth. Leaves alternate, 2–3 times compound, the leaflets roundish, 2–3-lobed.

In rich moist woods or thickets. Flowering April and May.

MARSH MARIGOLD, COWSLIP
Caltha palustris L.   Color Plate 6

Glabrous, decumbent or erect perennial often forming low rounded mounds, the stems clustered, branching, short at flowering time but later up to 7 dm. tall. Flowers bright yellow, 3–4 cm. wide, borne in loose cymose clusters mostly above the leaves. Petals lacking; sepals 5–10, petallike, green at first, becoming bright yellow to yellow-orange; stamens numerous; pistils 5–10, separate; follicles compressed, many-seeded, spreading. Leaves nearly kidney-shaped or round, with a deep sinus, margin crenate, toothed or nearly entire; upper leaves smaller and short-petioled or sessile.

In wet places, low meadows, along streams, in swamps and wet woods. Often occurring in great profusion. Flowering late April to mid-June.

It is said that this species has more than 25 common names. The leaves and stems are edible when cooked, but are poisonous when raw. The plant is so acrid that animals usually avoid it. The Indians used the boiled, mashed roots for treating running sores.

GOLDTHREAD, CANKER-ROOT
Coptis groenlandica (Oeder) Fern.   Plate 59

Small, stemless, evergreen perennial up to 15 cm. tall from a golden-yellow, threadlike rootstock. Flowers solitary, white, about 1 cm. wide. Petals 5–7, small, thick and fleshy, club-shaped, dull greenish to yellow, and not always easily recognizable as petals; sepals 5–7, petallike, white, sometimes tinged with green below; stamens 15–25, white, small but conspicuous; pistils 3–9, pale yellowish-green, long-stalked, the styles elongate and frequently curled downward; follicles divergent, pointed. Leaves all basal, 3-foliolate, shiny on upper surface, 2.5–5 cm. wide, toothed, the leaflets obscurely 3-lobed.

Usually in acid, peaty soil, in bogs, low wet woods, cedar swamps, mossy woods.

A bright yellow dye can be made by boiling the rootstocks. Indians used a decoction of the rootstocks for treating sore gums and for lessening the pain of teething. The only other member of this genus grows in eastern Asia and differs from it only in minor respects.

WILD COLUMBINE, ROCK-BELLS, MEETINGHOUSES
Aquilegia canadensis L.   Color Plate 7

Slender, graceful, many-branched perennial up to 1 m. tall. Flowers 2.5–5 cm. long, scarlet and yellow, solitary, nodding at the ends of slender branches. Petals 5, bright red to pinkish outside, yellow inside, having a

139

PLATE 60

Red Baneberry
(*Actaea rubra*)

White Baneberry
(*Actaea pachypoda*)

short spreading lip and a slender spur nearly 2 cm. long with a nectar-filled terminal knob; sepals 5, petallike, reddish or greenish-yellow, 1 cm. or more long; stamens very numerous, small, projecting as a column well beyond the perianth; pistils 5, the styles long and thin; follicles erect, the seeds numerous, shiny. Leaves basal or alternate on the stem, 2-3 times compound, the divisions in 3's; basal leaves long-petioled, 10–20 cm. broad, the leaflets 2–5 cm. broad and sessile or with short stalks; upper leaves similar but smaller.

In sandy or rocky, open or partially shaded ground; frequent in open woods and thickets, on dry slopes and ledges with scanty soil; sometimes on springy slopes and in peat bogs. Flowering late April to mid-July.

This handsome plant, easy to grow and often cultivated, is visited by hummingbirds and large moths that can reach the nectar at the base of the long spurs. It is the only native Michigan columbine, but it has several color variations. The common garden Columbine, *A. vulgaris* L., often escapes and may grow wild for a time. It has blue, purple, pink, or white flowers with short, thick, recurved spurs. Several long-spurred varieties are also cultivated.

Wild Columbine was used in many ways by the Indians. Men rubbed it on the hands as a love charm. The pulverized seeds were also used as a "man's perfume" by some tribes. An infusion was made of the pounded seeds for treating headache and fever, and a remedy for stomach trouble was derived from the roots. The seeds were a commodity of intertribal commerce.

WHITE BANEBERRY, DOLL'S-EYES

Actaea pachypoda Ell.   Plate 60

Perennial up to 1 m. tall from a creeping rootstock. Flowers whitish, borne on thick red pedicels in a sub-cylindric raceme 5–20 cm. long, the pedicels becoming thicker in fruit, nearly as thick as the peduncle. Petals 4–10, small, flat, with slender claws, resembling modified stamens; sepals 4–5, soon falling when the flowers open; stamens numerous, the filaments slender; pistil 1, the stigma sessile, broad and caplike; berry white (red in one form), shining, subglobose, about 1 cm. long, the stigma persisting as a red or purple "eyespot." Leaves large, 2–3 times pinnately compound, the leaflets whitish beneath, ovate, sharply cleft and toothed.

In rich woods and thickets. Flowering May and June. Fruit ripe July to October.

The berries are reported to be poisonous, and the rootstock is a violent purgative.

RED BANEBERRY, SNAKEBERRY

Actaea rubra (Ait.) Willd.   Plate 60

Like the preceding species, but the pedicels are thin and remain so, the leaflets are less sharply toothed, the petals taper to the apex, and the berries are red (white in one form).

In woods and thickets. Flowering May and early June.

$\frac{1}{3}$

PLATE 61
May-apple (*Podophyllum peltatum*)

142

Both species of baneberry may have either red or white berries, but, regardless of the color of the berries, the species with thick red pedicels is *A. pachypoda,* or White Baneberry, and that with thin pedicels is Red Baneberry.

GOLDEN-SEAL, ORANGEROOT

Hydrastis canadensis L. Plate 59

Perennial with a single unbranched stem up to 4 dm. tall. Flower solitary, terminal, whitish. Petals lacking; sepals 3, petallike, falling off as the flower opens; stamens numerous, conspicuous; pistils 12 or more; fruit a raspberrylike head of small, 2-seeded red berries. Stem leaves 2, alternate near the top of the stem, palmately cut, sharply toothed; basal leaf similar, solitary, long-petioled, becoming 13–20 cm. broad.

In woods in rich damp leaf mold. In Michigan confined mostly to the southern part of the state. Flowering in May.

The rootstock and leaves of this species contain alkaloids which are poisonous but have medicinal value. Formerly quite abundant, the plant was so extensively collected for medical purposes that it is now rare, but it is sometimes grown commercially.

BARBERRY FAMILY.   BERBERIDACEAE

This family of perennial herbs and shrubs includes 10 or 12 genera and about 200 species, mostly of north temperate regions. Three species, in three genera, are native to Michigan. Several members of the family are used as ornamentals, Barberry and Oregon Grape, for example, being well-known shrubs.

It is difficult to characterize the family, since the genera composing it are not closely related. In our genera the stamens (the same number as the petals or twice as many) are borne in two rows, those of the outer row being opposite the petals; there is a single pistil with superior ovary; the petioles are usually dilated at the base. In *Podophyllum,* the anthers open by longitudinal slits; in the other genera, they open by pores.

MAY-APPLE, MANDRAKE

Podophyllum peltatum L. Plate 61

Low, erect perennial 3–5 dm. tall with 1 or 2 large, umbrellalike leaves from rootstocks that creep just below the surface and often form large colonies. Flowers solitary, drooping on stout peduncles from the fork between the leaves, creamy to white, waxy, ill-scented, often with sickly-sweet odor. Petals 6 or 9, 2–3 cm. long; sepals 6, soon falling; stamens twice as many as the petals; pistil one, large, the ovary superior; berry large, 2–5 cm. long, lemon-shaped, becoming yellow, the pulp slightly acid, the seeds numerous. Leaves of the flowering stalk 2, umbrellalike, the stem attached to the middle, roundish in outline, deeply 3–5-parted; leaf of non-flowering plant only one, deeply 5–9-lobed.

In open woods and thickets in meadows, and along partly shaded roadsides. Flowering April to early June.

143

PLATE 62

Twinleaf
(*Jeffersonia diphylla*)

Blue Cohosh
(*Caulophyllum thalictroides*)

144

The rootstock and, to a lesser degree, other parts of this plant are bitter and contain a poisonous substance that is used in medicine. Some of the Michigan Indians dried, roasted, and boiled the roots and used the liquid, sweetened with maple sugar or honey, as a cure for rheumatism and liver ailments. The green fruit is harmful, but when ripe it is edible in moderate quantities—if one likes the flavor. Indians gathered the fruits before they were fully ripe and buried them in the ground to ripen, believing this improved the flavor. The fruits are occasionally used for preserves and in making beverages.

TWINLEAF

Jeffersonia diphylla (L.) Pers.   Plate 62

Low, unbranched perennial up to 3 dm. tall. Flowers white, solitary, terminal, about 2–3 cm. broad. Petals 8, white, oblong, flat; sepals usually 4 (3–5), petallike, falling off as the flower opens; stamens 8, prominent; pistil solitary, the ovary ovoid, the stigma 2-lobed; capsule pear-shaped, opening near the top by a peaked cap-like lid; seeds numerous, with a fleshy lateral appendage (aril). Leaves basal, becoming taller than the flower after flowering time, divided into two half-ovate leaflets and somewhat like an outspread butterfly in shape, up to 1 dm. wide when mature.

In rich damp woods. Rare. In Michigan found only in the southern part of the Lower Peninsula. Flowering April and May.

The genus name honors President Thomas Jefferson. The flowers resemble those of Bloodroot (*Sanguinaria canadensis* L.), but they are much shorter-lived and not quite so pretty; the two plants are easily distinguished by their leaves and juice. It is said that ants feed upon the seeds of Twinleaf and often carry them from one place to another, thus helping to spread the species.

BLUE COHOSH, PAPOOSE-ROOT

Caulophyllum thalictroides (L.) Michx.   Plate 62

Glaucous, unbranched perennial up to 1 m. tall. Flowers inconspicuous, greenish or yellowish, 1–1.5 cm. wide, borne in few-flowered, loose, terminal racemes or panicles. Petals 6, greenish, bronze, purplish, or yellowish, thick and glandlike, much smaller than the sepals, having a short claw at the base and kidney-shaped or hooded above, borne at the base of the sepals and opposite them; sepals 6, petallike, yellowish-green, ovate-oblong, spreading, having small basal bracts; stamens 6; pistil 1, the style short, the stigmatic surface a line along one side; seeds 2, appearing as a pair of blue, globose, pealike drupes when mature. Leaves usually 2, one placed a little below, the other just at the base of, the inflorescence; lower leaf large, 2–3 times compound in 3's, with the main divisions petioled; the upper leaf small (becoming larger after flowering) and with the leaflets 2–3-lobed, obovate, and wedge-shaped at base.

In rich woods. Flowering late May to mid-June.

POPPY FAMILY. PAPAVERACEAE

This group of nearly 50 genera and 750 species is divided into 2 families by some authorities and into 2 subfamilies by others. Many

PLATE 63
Bloodroot (*Sanguinaria canadensis*)

species, particularly poppies and bleeding-heart, are grown as ornamentals. Opium is derived from capsules of certain species of poppy, and seeds of some kinds are used in cakes and on breads. The seeds do not contain the narcotic compounds.

The family in Michigan is characterized by regular or irregular flowers with 4 or more distinct or slightly united petals, 2 or 4 sepals, 6 to many stamens, and a single pistil which forms a capsule.

PAPAVERACEAE

1. Plants with colored juice; flowers regular . . . . *Sanguinaria canadensis,* Plate 63
1. Plants with colorless juice; flowers irregular 2
   2. Plants stemless, leaves all basal . . . . . . *Dicentra cucullaria* or *canadensis,* Plate 64
   2. Plants with leafy stems . . . . . *Corydalis sempervirens,* Plate 65

BLOODROOT

Sanguinaria canadensis L.   Plate 63

Glabrous, stemless perennial seldom over 3 dm. tall at flowering time. Juice (latex) red to reddish-orange. Flowers white (pink in one form), solitary, lasting a very short time, 2.3–3.5 cm. wide. Petals 8–12 (more in the rare double form), borne in 2 or more rows; sepals 2, soon falling; stamens numerous; pistil 1, the capsule slenderly ellipsoid, 2 cm. or more long, 1-celled, many-seeded. Leaves enfolding the base of the flowering stem at first, soon expanding and finally overtopping the capsules, roundish, 10–25 cm. in diameter, palmately lobed or with merely a wavy margin, toothed or crenate, the veins (especially on the lower surface) prominent and orange-red.

In rich open woods or thickets. Flowering March to May (chiefly in April).

These attractive flowers are very susceptible to weather changes, opening in sunshine but closing up when it is cold or cloudy. Cold may cause the petals to fall even when the flower has been open only a few hours. The rootstock is very acrid and is distinctly poisonous. Indians used the juice for dyeing textiles, quills, and cane baskets. They also made a face paint and medicines from it.

Two other species with colored juice may be found. Both have bright yellow flowers and yellow juice. Wood-poppy, *Stylophorum diphyllum* (Michx.) Nutt., has large flowers (about 5 cm. wide), solitary or in few-flowered clusters; there are 4 petals which are crushed in the bud, 2 sepals, many stamens, and a single pistil with a long, hairy style; the pistil produces a bristly capsule. Celandine, *Chelidonium majus* L., an introduced weed, has much smaller flowers with a very short style and smooth capsule.

DUTCHMAN'S-BREECHES

Dicentra cucullaria (L.) Bernh.   Plate 64

Fernlike, stemless perennial 1.2–2.5 dm. tall from a cluster of small bulbs. Flowers nodding in a row on the flowering stem, often fragrant, white or rarely pinkish, tipped with cream or yellow, with 2 conspicuous diver-

PLATE 64

Dutchman's-breeches
(*Dicentra cucullaria*)

Squirrel-corn
(*Dicentra canadensis*)

148

gent spurs, resembling inverted, greatly inflated pantaloons. Petals 4, in 2 pairs, the outer pair longer than the pedicel, the inner pair at right angles and smaller, narrow, the tips enlarged, slightly crested, united to form an arch over the stamens; stamens 6, in 2 sets of 3; pistil solitary, the style slender, the stigma 2-lobed; capsule 1-celled, opening into 2 parts to the base, with 10–20 crested seeds. Leaves all basal, numerous, very finely dissected, the divisions in 3's, pale beneath.

In rich woods. Flowering in April, the plant usually disappearing by June.

SQUIRREL-CORN
Dicentra canadensis (Goldie) Walp. Plate 64

Greatly resembling and often growing with Dutchman's-breeches, but easily distinguished when in bloom by the heart-shaped rather than spurred base of the corolla and the more conspicuous crest on the inner petals. The small, grainlike, bright-yellow tubers are scattered instead of clustered. The sepals are often pinkish, tiny, and, as in the preceding species, so closely appressed to the corolla that they are easily overlooked.

In rich woods. Flowering in April, the plant disappearing by June.

This species tends to bloom a week or two later than the preceding one and thus is often in its prime when the other is fading. The flowers of Squirrel-corn resemble those of the common garden Bleeding-heart, which is native to Japan, but they are smaller and paler.

PALE CORYDALIS, PINK FUME-ROOT
Corydalis sempervirens (L.) Pers. Plate 65

Glabrous and glaucous, freely branched, erect annual or biennial up to 1 m. or more tall. Flowers numerous, pink (rarely white) tipped with yellow, 1–2 cm. long, borne in terminal clusters. Petals 4, in pairs, the uppermost of the outer pair with a spur at the base, the inner petals narrowed, keeled; sepals 2, small; stamens 6, in 2 unequal sets opposite the larger petals; pistil 1; capsule slender, 2–5 cm. long. Leaves much divided into toothed or entire segments; basal leaves shortpetioled, up to 12 cm. long, the upper leaves smaller, sessile.

In rocky places, on gravel slopes, and in recent clearings, often abundant on burnt-over areas. Flowering May to September.

When crushed these plants have a nitrous odor. Golden Corydalis, *C. aurea* Willd., has similar but golden-yellow flowers. It is a diffusely branched, often spreading, annual or biennial growing on rocky slopes, in open woods, and on the sandy shores of the Great Lakes. Both species of Corydalis are poisonous and are known to be fatal to sheep if eaten in quantity.

MUSTARD FAMILY. CRUCIFERAE

A large family of pungent or acrid, nonpoisonous plants comprising some 360 genera and 2500 species, distributed chiefly in the cooler regions of the Northern Hemisphere. Two dozen genera and a large number of species occur in Michigan. The family is of considerable importance for food crops and for ornamentals. Cabbage, cauliflower, broccoli, rutabaga, turnips, Brussels sprouts, radish, water cress, and kohlrabi, as well as mustard and horseradish, belong here. About 50 genera are cultivated for ornamentals, including Sweet Alyssum, Rock Cress, Stock, Rocket, Candytuft, Wallflower, and Honesty.

It is believed that many of the species have been weeds since prehistoric times, and that they spread over Europe and America as agriculture developed.

The members of this family are easily recognized by the flowers borne in bractless racemes, the 4 petals typically narrowed below into a claw, the 4 sepals, 6 stamens (2 shorter than the others), and the single pistil, usually with a 2-celled superior ovary. However, the classification of the species is difficult. Ripe capsules, as well as flowers, are necessary for the identification of most species.

CRUCIFERAE

1. Flowers yellow 2
1. Flowers not yellow 5

  2. Pods slender and cylindric 3
  2. Pods not slender and cylindric 4

3. Stem leaves clasping or having small
  ears at base . . . . *Barbarea vulgaris,* Plate 69
3. Stem leaves not as in alternate
  choice . . . . *Sisymbrium altissimum* or *officinale,* Plates 67, 68

  4. Pods plump, ellipsoid to nearly globose . . *Rorippa islandica,* Plate 68
  4. Pods flattened, circular in outline . . . *Alyssum alyssoides,* Plate 66

5. Plants fleshy, growing on shores of the Great Lakes;
  pods plump, in 2 sections . . . . . . *Cakile edentula,* Plate 67
5. Not as in alternate choice 6

  6. Plants aquatic, rooting readily at nodes;
  flowers white . . . . *Nasturtium officinale,* Plate 68
  6. Not as in alternate choice 7

7. Leaves palmately parted into 3 or more leaflets
  or segments . . . . . . *Dentaria diphylla* or *laciniata,* Plate 70
7. Leaves not as in alternate choice 8

  8. Flowering stem rising from a definite basal rosette . . . *Arabis,* 11
  8. Flowering stem not rising from a definite rosette 9

9. Lower and upper leaves different; marginal teeth,
  if present, blunt . . . . . *Cardamine bulbosa* or *pratensis,* Plate 70
9. Lower and upper leaves similar 10

  10. Flowers small, white, petals deeply cut in two
  at apex . . . . *Berteroa incana,* Plate 66
  10. Flowers large, usually purple or lavender; petals
  entire at apex . . . . *Hesperis matronalis,* Plate 69

11. Pedicels and pods erect, close to stem
at maturity . . . . *Arabis glabra,* Plate 71
11. Pedicels and pods not as in alternate choice 12
    12. Pods 7–11 cm. long, hanging down . . . *A. canadensis,* Plate 71
    12. Pods 2–4.5 cm. long, usually outspread at
    maturity . . . . *A. lyrata,* Plate 71

HOARY ALYSSUM

Berteroa incana (L.) DC.   Plate 66

Grayish-green, very hairy, stiffly erect annual up to 1 m. tall, sparsely branched above. Flowers small, white, numerous, borne on ascending pedicels in slender, terminal racemes. Blade of the petals deeply cut; pod flattened, oblong. Leaves alternate, lanceolate, with entire or slightly wavy margin.

In fields, along roads, and in waste places. Introduced from Europe; now a common weed. Flowering June to September.

Shepherd's-purse, *Capsella bursa-pastoris* (L.) Medic., is another white-flowered, common weed. It has triangular to inverted heart-shaped, flat pods. The upper leaves are sessile and arrow-shaped; those of the basal rosette are usually deeply pinnately cut. This widespread weed is reported to have been in Michigan as long ago as 1839. It is extremely variable; one author has described 63 forms.

ALYSSUM

Alyssum alyssoides L.   Plate 66

Low annual, up to 2.5 dm., simple or branched at the base, the stem, leaves, and fruits with star-shaped hairs. Flowers pale yellow to nearly white, about 2 mm. wide, the petals narrowly oblong, gradually narrowed to the base; pods borne on spreading pedicels, circular, flattened, each cell with 2 seeds. Leaves oblanceolate, 6–15 mm. long, entire.

In waste land. A common weed; introduced from Europe. Flowering May and June.

Golden-tuft, *A. saxatile* L., a related but attractive plant, is a low matted perennial with bright golden-yellow flowers which sometimes spreads from cultivation. The common garden Sweet Alyssum, *Lobularia maritima* (L.) Desv., may persist for some time after escaping from cultivation. It has honey-scented white or purple flowers.

SEA ROCKET

Cakile edentula (Bigel.) Hook.   Plate 67

Fleshy, spreading, somewhat reclining, glabrous, bushy perennial up to 3 dm. tall. Flowers lavender, 5–7 mm. wide, borne in compact terminal racemes; pod short, ovoid, 2-jointed, the upper joint the longer, flattened, and beaked; each joint 1-seeded or the lower seedless. Leaves alternate, sessile, fleshy, obscurely veined except for the midrib, oblanceolate to obovate, the margin wavy, toothed, or sometimes lobed, the lower leaves 7–12 cm. long.

On sandy or gravelly beaches, particularly on the shores of the Great Lakes. Flowering July to September.

PLATE 65
Pale Corydalis (*Corydalis sempervirens*)

152

PLATE 66

Hoary Alyssum
(*Berteroa incana*)

Alyssum
(*Alyssum alyssoides*)

PLATE 67

Sea Rocket
(*Cakile edentula*)

Tumble-mustard
(*Sisymbrium altissimum*)

154

The leaves and young stems have the pungent flavor of horse-radish. The Indians mixed the powdered roots with flour as an extender in times of food shortage.

TUMBLE-MUSTARD
Sisymbrium altissimum L.　　　　　　　　　　Plate 67

Coarse, erect, freely and loosely branching annual or biennial up to 1.7 m. tall. Flowers pale yellow, 7–12 mm. wide, borne in loose racemes that become greatly elongated after flowering begins; sepals straw-colored; pod slender, about the same thickness as the pedicel, 4.5–10.5 cm. long. Leaves petioled, deeply pinnately cut; segments of the upper leaves threadlike, those of the lower leaves broader, toothed.

In light soil in cultivated and waste land. Introduced from Europe. Flowering May to August.

The stems frequently break off near the ground at the end of the growing season, and the plants are blown considerable distances, scattering seeds as they go.

HEDGE-MUSTARD
Sisymbrium officinale (L.) Scop.　　　　　　　Plate 68

Stiffly branching annual up to 8 dm. tall, hairy at least below. Flowers pale yellow, about 3 mm. long, borne in spikelike racemes, the pedicels short, closely appressed to the stem, 2–3 mm. long at maturity, thickened (as wide as the pod at the summit); pod 10–15 mm. long, closely appressed to the stem. Lower leaves pinnately cut, the segments oblong to ovate; upper leaves sessile, arrow-shaped to lanceolate and entire.

In waste places. A common weed; introduced from Europe. Flowering May to October.

DAME'S ROCKET, MOTHER-OF-THE-EVENING
Hesperis matronalis L.　　　　　　　　　　　Plate 69

Biennial or perennial with 1 to several hairy, erect stems 6 dm. or more tall. Flowers lavender, rose-purple, or white (the white-flowered plants often the most numerous in a group), becoming fragrant in the evening, borne in loose terminal or axillary racemes. Claws of the petals longer than the sepals, the blade broad; sepals pale yellowish-green or purplish; pod cylindrical, slender, 5–14 cm. long. Leaves numerous, opposite or nearly so (no rosette), lanceolate, sharply toothed, having a short petiole.

In open woods and thickets and along roads and railroads. Introduced from Europe. Flowering May to August.

This species was formerly very popular in the garden; it has escaped from cultivation and become naturalized in many places.

YELLOW CRESS
Rorippa islandica (Oeder) Borbás　　　　　　Plate 68

Extremely variable simple or branched annual or biennial up to 1.3 m. tall. Flowers small (3–5 mm. wide), yellow, borne on elongate threadlike pedicels, and having small nectar glands; sepals loosely spreading,

PLATE 68

Hedge-mustard
(*Sisymbrium officinale*)

Yellow Cress
(*Rorippa islandica*)

Water Cress
(*Nasturtium officinale*)

156

longer than the petals; pedicels at maturity widely spreading; pods slenderly ellipsoid to nearly globose, 2–10 mm. long, 1–4 mm. thick, straight or curving; seeds minute. Leaves variable, lanceolate to oblong-ovate in general outline, pinnately divided or cleft, or merely toothed.

On wet shores, in damp openings and waste places. Flowering May to September.

WATER CRESS

Nasturtium officinale R. Br.   Plate 68

Aquatic, creeping or floating perennial, freely rooting at the nodes, often forming large floating mats. Flowers small, white, in racemes which are at first compact, soon elongating. Petals twice as long as the sepals, obovate; pistil cylindric, the style thick, the stigma slightly 2-lobed; pods 1–2.5 cm. long, 2-celled, with 2 rows of seeds in each cell. Leaves somewhat fleshy, alternate, pinnately compound, the leaflets 3–11, roundish, entire or the margin wavy, the terminal leaflet the largest.

In clear cold water and in swamps. Introduced from Europe; now widespread. Flowering April to October.

This is the species that is grown as the water cress of commerce. It is used in salads and sandwiches.

YELLOW ROCKET

Barbarea vulgaris R. Br.   Plate 69

Glabrous, many-stemmed biennial or perennial up to 8 dm. tall from a basal rosette of dark-green leaves, unbranched below, freely branching above. Flowers in terminal racemes, bright yellow, 5–7 mm. wide, the petals spreading above the sepals; pistil long and slender; pod 1.8–2.5 cm. long, on a slender pedicel, beaked, with seeds in a single row in each cell. Basal rosette leaves pinnately cut, the terminal lobe rounded and much the largest; stem leaves alternate, clasping, the upper ones nearly round or ovate and coarsely toothed or lobed.

In fields, cultivated ground, along roads and brooks, in woods and waste ground. Introduced from Europe. Flowering April to August.

TWO-LEAVED TOOTHWORT

Dentaria diphylla Michx.   Plate 70

Glabrous, stout, unbranched perennial up to 3 dm. tall at flowering time, the rootstock long, continuous, prominently toothed, often branched, the annual segments not (or only slightly) tapering at the ends. Flowers white, borne in a loose few-flowered raceme. Sepals green, linear, pointed, about half as long as the petals; pistil long and thin; pod flat, lanceolate, the seeds in a single row, rarely maturing. Stem leaves 2, nearly opposite, above the middle of stem, 3-foliolate, 10–15 cm. broad, the leaflets sessile, coarsely and bluntly toothed or lobed; basal leaves similar to stem leaves but the leaflets shorter and broader.

In rich damp woods. Flowering April to early June.

This species tends to grow in large masses and spreads rapidly from the rootstocks. The rootstocks are crisp and edible, with a mustard flavor.

157

PLATE 69

Yellow Rocket
(*Barbarea vulgaris*)

Dame's Rocket
(*Hesperis matronalis*)

158

CUT-LEAVED TOOTHWORT

Dentaria laciniata Muhl.   **Plate 70**

Low perennial from deep-seated yellowish-brown, readily separable, scarcely toothed tubers. Flowers white or purplish. Petals 1–2 cm. long, about twice as long as the sepals; pods lanceolate, long-pointed, 2.5–5 cm. long, including the beak. Leaves 3 (rarely 2), in a whorl or slightly separated on the stem, 3-foliolate, the leaflets simple to deeply 5–9-cleft.

In rich moist woods and on calcareous banks. Flowering March to May.

SPRING CRESS

Cardamine bulbosa (Schreb.) BSP.   **Plate 70**

Glabrous, simple or branched perennial from a short thick tuber, up to 5 dm. tall at flowering time. Flowers white, on spreading pedicels in a loose raceme. Sepals greenish with white margins; pods slenderly cylindric, tapering to a pointed apex. Stem leaves 4–14, scattered, ovate, rounded, or lanceolate, entire or sparsely and coarsely toothed, the upper leaves sessile; basal leaves few, oblong or kidney-shaped, or nearly round, long-petioled.

In low woods, moist ravines, around springs, and in wet meadows and shallow water. Flowering April to May.

C. douglassii (Torr.) Britt. is quite similar to *C. bulbosa*, but the stems are generally hairy and the flowers are a pinkish-purple.

CUCKOO-FLOWER

Cardamine pratensis L.   **Plate 70**

Variable, fibrous-rooted perennial up to 5 dm. tall. Flowers white (rarely rose), 6–17 mm. wide, the petals 3 times as long as the sepals. Leaves pinnately compound, the leaflets numerous, the margins entire or slightly toothed; lower leaves with long petioles and rounded leaflets; upper leaves with short petioles and oblong or linear leaflets, the terminal ones the narrowest.

In wet meadows, lawns, shallow water, bogs, springs. Introduced from Europe. Flowering May to July.

Pennsylvania Bitter Cress, *C. pensylvanica* Muhl., is somewhat similar, but the leaflets are usually run together along the stem, and the terminal leaflet is the largest. This species is said to be edible and to be an excellent substitute for water cress.

TOWER-MUSTARD

Arabis glabra (L.) Bernh.   **Plate 71**

Stoutish, erect biennial up to 1.2 m. tall, hairy at the base, smooth above. Flowers creamy or yellowish, borne in a slender straight raceme; pods slender, erect or nearly so, 4–9.5 cm. long, up to 1 mm. thick. Basal leaves spatulate or oblanceolate, entire or irregularly toothed; lower stem leaves overlapping, the upper ones less crowded, lanceolate or oblong, sessile or clasping.

In dry soil. Flowering May to June.

Several other species of *Arabis* are known from Michigan.

159

Cuckoo-flower
(*Cardamine pratensis*)

PLATE 70
Two-leaved Toothwort
(*Dentaria diphylla*)
Cut-leaved Toothwort
(*Dentaria laciniata*)

Spring Cress
(*Cardamine bulbosa*)

PLATE 71

Tower-mustard (*Arabis glabra*)

Sicklepod (*Arabis canadensis*)

Lyre-leaved Rock Cress (*Arabis lyrata*)

161

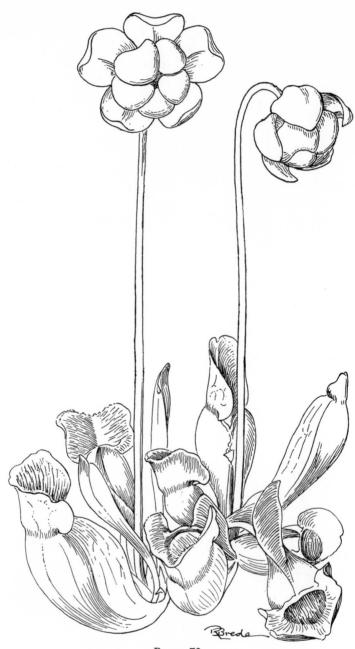

PLATE 72
Pitcher-plant (*Sarracenia purpurea*)

162

SICKLEPOD

Arabis canadensis L.

Plate 71

Simple or sparingly-branched biennial up to 9 dm. tall from a basal rosette, glabrous except for the sparsely hairy base. Flowers cream-white, borne in long, lax racemes, the pedicels soon drooping. Petals slightly longer than the sepals; pods flat, curved, 7–10 cm. long, hanging down, the seeds in 1 row, winged. Rosette leaves obovate to lanceolate, toothed or cut into backward-pointing segments, usually hairy on the midrib, soon wilting; stem leaves oblong-lanceolate to elliptic, tapering to the base, often finely toothed.

In rich woods, thickets, or on rocky banks. Flowering April to June.

LYRE-LEAVED ROCK CRESS

Arabis lyrata L.

Plate 71

Tufted, freely branching biennial or perennial up to 3.5 dm. tall from a basal rosette, hairy below. Flowers white, about 5 mm. broad, borne on slender, erect to spreading pedicels, the raceme elongating in maturity; pods spreading or somewhat ascending, linear, slightly flattened, 1.3–3 cm. long, the seeds in a single row. Rosette leaves spatulate to oblanceolate, 2.3–5 cm. long, usually pinnately lobed with the terminal lobe the longest; stem leaves scattered, spatulate to linear, tapering at the base.

In rocky places, gravels, and sands, on ledges or cliffs. Flowering April to September.

PITCHER-PLANT FAMILY.   SARRACENIACEAE

This family of bog-inhabiting plants comprises 3 genera and some 14 species in the Western Hemisphere; one species is native to Michigan. These plants are of considerable interest but are very difficult to grow. None is of economic value.

PITCHER-PLANT

Sarracenia purpurea L.

Plate 72

Low-growing, stemless perennial up to 7 dm. tall from a rosette of leaves. Flowers showy, purplish or wine-red (sometimes yellowish-green), nearly globose, 3.7–5.5 cm. broad, solitary and nodding at the end of the glabrous flowering stem. Petals 5, separate, incurved and arching over the style, fiddle-shaped, narrower than the sepals; sepals 5, ovate, usually greenish to deep purplish-red or maroon, often having 3 or 4 small, similarly colored bracts at the base; stamens numerous; pistil solitary, the ovary globular, 5-celled, the stalk of the style dilated at the top into a 5-rayed, greenish or yellowish umbrella-shaped structure, the rays protruding between the petals and bearing the small hooked stigmas on their lower surface. Leaves (often lasting more than one season) all basal, numerous, ascending, usually green, often veined with purple, somewhat pitcher-shaped or trumpet-shaped, curved, broadly winged, narrowed to a roundish petiole, hollow, with an upstanding or arching hood above the opening, 9.5–30 cm. long, nearly smooth outside and bristly on the inner side of the lid, the hollow usually partly filled with liquid and decaying insects.

In wet sphagnum, peat bogs, and tamarack swamps. Flowering May and June (sometimes until July).

This species is one of our most attractive bog plants. An Indian name for it means "frog-leggings." The leaves and roots were used medicinally. It is now thought that the decaying insects found in the hollow of the leaf provide food, not for the plant, but for the larvae of the flies that cross-pollinate the flowers.

SUNDEW FAMILY. DROSERACEAE

An insectivorous family of 4 genera and about 90 species, most of which grow in bogs. One species is almost cosmopolitan; the others occur in the Mediterranean region, Australia, and North America. In Michigan we have a single genus, with 4 species.

The family is characterized by rosettes of leaves, which are generally covered with sticky, insect-catching glands.

Drosera

1. Leaf blades nearly round, or broader than long . *D. rotundifolia*, Plate 73
1. Leaf blades longer than broad, linear or spatulate .　.　.　.　.　. 2

   2. Leaf blades linear, stipules adnate to base
     of petiole .　.　.　.　.　.　.　.　.　. *D. linearis*, Plate 73
   2. Leaf blades obovate to spatulate, stipules nearly
     free from base of petiole .　.　.　.　.　. *D. intermedia*, Plate 73

ROUND-LEAVED SUNDEW

Drosera rotundifolia L.　　　　　　　　　　　　　　Plate 73

Low-growing perennial from rosettes of sticky-haired leaves. Flowers white (rarely pink), borne in a 1–25 flowered, 1-sided raceme on a slender, leafless flowering stem which is usually simple but may be forked once, the undeveloped apex of the raceme nodding, so that the full-blown flower is always the highest; flowers opening only in sunlight. Petals 5, spatulate; calyx tube short, free from the ovary, usually 5 (4–8)-lobed; stamens 5; pistil 1, the ovary 1-celled; styles usually 3 or 5, deeply 2-parted so that there appear to be 6 or 10; capsule stalked, the seeds numerous, spindle-shaped. Leaves all basal, the blades nearly round, broader than long, coiled from the apex to the base of the petiole in bud, pale yellowish-green, the upper surface thickly covered with long gland-tipped reddish hairs which exude a sticky fluid that glitters in the sun; petioles long, hairy.

In bogs, peaty or moist acid soil, or wet sand. Flowering June to August.

LINEAR-LEAVED SUNDEW

Drosera linearis Goldie　　　　　　　　　　　　　　Plate 73

In general aspect somewhat like the preceding species, but the flowers 1–8, the leaves linear (up to 8 cm. long and 3 mm. wide), the petioles short, not hairy, and the stipules united to the base of the petiole.

In bogs, on limy shores, and in beach pools. Flowering June to August.

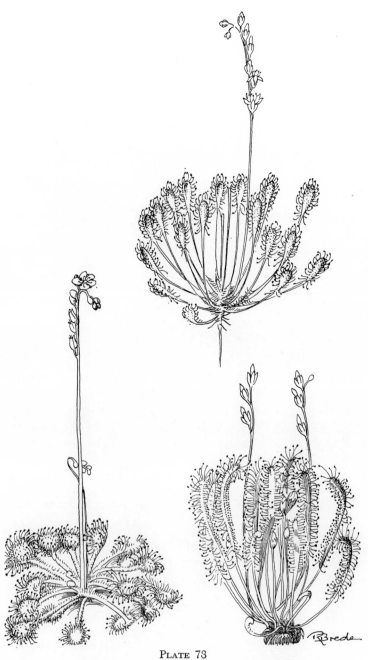

PLATE 73

Round-leaved Sundew
(*Drosera rotundifolia*)

Spatulate-leaved Sundew
(*Drosera intermedia*)

Linear-leaved Sundew
(*Drosera linearis*)

PLATE 74

Mossy Stonecrop
(*Sedum acre*)

Live-forever
(*Sedum purpureum*)

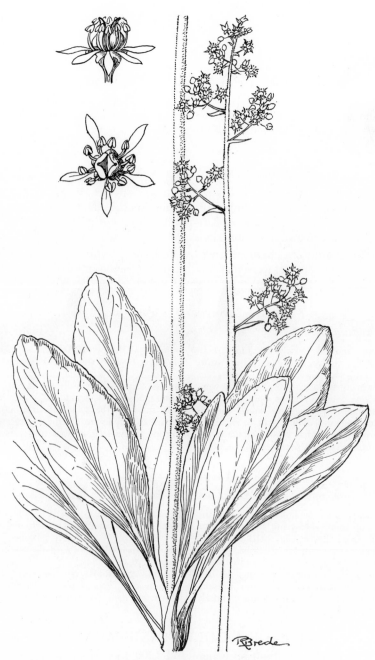

PLATE 75

Swamp Saxifrage (*Saxifraga pensylvanica*)

167

Drosera intermedia Hayne   Plate 73

Quite similar to the two preceding species but distinguished by the spatulate or obovate leaves with the stipules nearly free from the base of the petiole. In bogs and on wet shores. Flowering June to August.

Another, very similar, species, *D. anglica* Huds., also occurs here. It has narrow leaf blades 1.5–5 cm. long, and the stipules are united, except at the tip, to the base of the petiole.

ORPINE FAMILY.   CRASSULACEAE

A family of succulent herbs with over 500 species distributed over most of the world. A number of species, such as Hen-and-chickens (*Sempervivum*), Kalanchoe, Life-plant (*Bryophyllum*), and various sedums, are grown as ornamentals.

This family is characterized by fleshiness; symmetrical flowers borne in cymes; petals, sepals, and pistils the same in number (3–30); stamens the same number or twice as many; all parts separate.

MOSSY STONECROP, GOLD MOSS

Sedum acre L.   Plate 74

Low, matted, creeping and freely rooting, fleshy evergreen perennial forming mosslike carpets, the erect flowering stems 2–8 dm. tall. Flowers yellow, 1 cm. or more wide, borne on very short pedicels in small, forked, leafy racemes. Petals 4 or 5, separate, narrow, somewhat fleshy; sepals much shorter than the petals; stamens twice as many as the petals; follicles spreading, long-beaked, the seeds numerous. Leaves sessile, alternate, fleshy, thick and ovoid, usually closely overlapping, having a small spur at the base.

In sand, on rocks, and in dry, open places and in lawns. Introduced from Europe. Flowering in June and July.

LIVE-FOREVER

Sedum purpureum (L.) Link   Plate 74

Coarse, erect, succulent perennial, the usually many-flowering stems 2–8 dm. tall from fleshy, carrotlike tubers. Flowers in compact corymbs, purple-red to deep roseate; petals wide-spreading, 3 times as long as the sepals; nectar-bearing scales present, longer than broad; stamens nearly equaling the petals; follicles nearly erect. Leaves succulent, alternate or in whorls of 3, broadly oblong or elliptic, coarsely toothed, the larger ones 4–10 cm. long.

Along roadsides, on banks, or in open woods. Spread from cultivation. Flowering July to September.

SAXIFRAGE FAMILY.   SAXIFRAGACEAE

This family of about 80 genera and 1200 species has its best representation in the United States—principally in the West. Its chief economic importance is for ornamentals, Mock Orange (*Philadelphus*), Deutzia, Hydrangea, and Coral-bells (*Heuchera*) being well known. Currants and gooseberries are bush fruits of some importance.

The flowers are perfect and regular. The 5 (rarely 4) petals and sepals with the stamens (the same number as the petals or twice as many) are borne on the edge of a cuplike or saucerlike structure (hypanthium). There are usually 2 pistils, which may be separate or united. The leaves are opposite or alternate, are usually simple, and usually lack stipules. This family has many characters in common with the Rose Family, with which it is easily confused.

SAXIFRAGACEAE

1. Flowers borne in clusters 2
1. Flowers solitary . . . . . . *Parnassia glauca* or *parviflora*, Plate 77

  2. Petals with entire margins 3
  2. Petals with finely fringed margins . . *Mitella diphylla* or *nuda*, Plate 76

3. Basal leaves narrowly oblong to
   oblanceolate . . . . *Saxifraga pensylvanica*, Plate 75
3. Basal leaves cordate-ovate . . . . . . *Tiarella cordifolia*, Plate 76

SWAMP SAXIFRAGE

Saxifraga pensylvanica L.   Plate 75

Sticky-glandular perennial with stout flowering stems up to 10 dm. tall. Flowers yellowish, yellowish-green, or greenish, small, up to 1 cm. wide, borne on glandular pedicels in terminal panicles which are at first dense but soon elongate, becoming 1–6 dm. long. Petals 5, spreading, inserted at the top of the calyx tube; calyx tubular, with 5 lanceolate reflexed lobes which are 2–4 times as long as the tube; stamens 10; pistils 2, the ovaries adherent to the calyx tube, the styles short and thick; capsule inflated, many-seeded. Leaves in a basal rosette, thick, narrow, oval, ovate, obovate, or oblanceolate, 1–2.5 dm. long, obtuse at the apex and narrowed to a broad, clasping, often reddish petiole, shallowly crenate to entire, hairy, the midrib prominent beneath.

In swamps, wet meadows, and boggy thickets and on seepage banks. Flowering April to June.

FOAM FLOWER, FALSE MITERWORT

Tiarella cordifolia L.   Plate 76

Low perennial up to 2 dm. tall, the leaves all basal. Flowers small, white, borne in terminal racemes up to 14 cm. long, the flowering stalk and pedicels glandular-hairy. Petals 5, soon falling, inserted on the calyx tube between its lobes; calyx white, bell-shaped, with 5 lobes which resemble petals; stamens 10; pistil 1, with 2 uneven sides; capsule of 2 uneven parts which separate readily, few-seeded. Leaves all basal, petioled, heart-shaped-ovate, 5–12 cm. long when mature, smaller at flowering time, having stiff, spinelike hairs on both sides, the margin shallowly lobed and having rounded teeth.

In swampy woodlands and drier rich woods. Flowering in May and June.

There is considerable variation in this species, and several forms have been described. It often makes an extensive ground cover in woods. Alumroot, *Heuchera americana* L., is somewhat similar in aspect but is taller (up to 1 m.), the flowers are greenish or red-tinged, and there are only 5 stamens which, with the styles, extend well out of the flower. This species is also found in woods.

TWO-LEAVED BISHOP'S-CAP, MITERWORT, COOLWORT
Mitella diphylla L. Plate 76

Slender, stiffly erect, straight, stiffly hairy perennial with numerous unbranched stems which have a single pair of opposite leaves at or near the middle, rootstock stout, with stolons lacking. Flowers white, tiny, borne on very short, thick pedicels in a stiff, slender raceme. Petals 5, deeply and narrowly pinnately fringed or cut, alternate with the calyx lobes which appear petallike; calyx cuplike with 5 lobes, whitish; stamens 10, inserted on the calyx tube, not extending out of the flower; pistil 1; capsule opening wide and exposing the numerous blackish seeds at maturity. Stem leaves sessile or nearly so, ovate, palmately 3–5 lobed; basal leaves petioled, wider and more heart-shaped at the base, pointed at the apex, hairy and prominently veined beneath.

In rich, loamy and rocky, usually moist woods. Flowering in April and May.

NAKED MITERWORT, BISHOP'S-CAP
Mitella nuda L. Plate 76

Small, stiffly erect perennial up to 2 dm. tall, the rootstocks and stolons threadlike, the flowering stalk usually leafless but occasionally having 1 or more petioled leaves. Flowers delicate, pale yellowish-green, 7–8 cm. wide, borne in a simple, stiff, slender raceme. Petals deeply and very narrowly pinnately cut, the threadlike segments spreading; calyx short, attached to the base of the ovary. Leaves nearly round in outline, heart-shaped at the base, having scattered, short, stiff hairs on both sides; margin deeply crenate.

In cool mossy woods or swamps. A common ground cover in swampy woods throughout Michigan. Flowering May to August.

GRASS-OF-PARNASSUS
Parnassia glauca Raf. Plate 77

Smooth perennial with flowering stems (usually leafless but sometimes with a single sessile leaf) up to 6 dm. tall. Flowers white or whitish, solitary, upright, terminal, 2.2–3.2 cm. wide. Petals 5, separate, spreading out nearly flat, white, strongly veined with greenish or yellowish, about 3 times as long as the sepals, each petal with a staminode at base; staminode deeply cleft into 3 gland-tipped, threadlike segments shorter than (or about as long as) the stamens; sepals 5, blunt, united very slightly at the base, becoming reflexed; stamens 5, alternate with the petals; pistil 1, the ovary green, ovoid, 1-celled; stigmas 4, sessile; capsule many-seeded. Basal leaves parallel-veined, ovate, broadly oval, or nearly round, rounded or heart-shaped at base, occasionally winged along the petiole, rather thick, 2.5–5 cm. long, long-petioled.

In low wet places, swamps, meadows, along roadsides and in ditches; in calcareous soils. Flowering July to October.

PLATE 76

Two-leaved Bishop's-cap (*Mitella diphylla*)
Naked Miterwort (*Mitella nuda*)
Foam Flower (*Tiarella cordifolia*)

171

PLATE 77

Grass-of-Parnassus
(*Parnassia glauca*)

Small-flowered Grass-of-Parnassus
(*Parnassia parviflora*)

172

PLATE 78

Wild Strawberry
(*Fragaria virginiana*)

Barren Strawberry
(*Waldsteinia fragarioides*)

Woodland Strawberry
(*Fragaria vesca*)

173

Parnassia parviflora DC.   Plate 77

Generally smaller plants than the preceding, the 1–25 flowering stems up to 3.5 dm. tall. Flowers white, 10–15 mm. broad, solitary at the top of the slender stems; sometimes one small, sessile clasping leaf at or below the middle. The staminode shorter than the stamens, cleft into 5–9 (or even more) threadlike segments, each tipped with a globular, clear-yellow gland; sepals very slightly united at base, spreading in flower, ascending and persisting in fruit. Basal leaves oval or oblong, narrowed at base, the blades 5 mm.–3.3 cm. long, petioled.

In wet calcareous soil. Frequent in roadside ditches along with *Lobelia kalmii* L. Flowering July and August.

ROSE FAMILY. ROSACEAE

A large, nearly cosmopolitan family of about 115 genera and over 3000 species, particularly abundant in Asia. This family is of considerable economic importance in temperate regions. The principal fruits are apple, apricot, pear, cherry, plum, prune, peach, nectarine, quince, blackberry, raspberry, and strawberry. Such well-known ornamentals as Spiraea, Cotoneaster, Pyracantha, Ninebark, Flowering Quince, Japanese Cherry, Hawthorn, and Rose belong to this family.

Most members of the family are easily recognized as such. The flowers are usually showy, the petals and calyx lobes are 5 each, the calyx often with an extra row of bracts, the stamens in multiples of 5, and the pistils 1 to many. The petals and stamens appear to be borne on the edge of a saucer-shaped or cup-shaped receptacle (hypanthium), and the petals usually extend out horizontally from the base. The leaves are alternate, often compound, and usually have stipules.

ROSACEAE

1. Leaves simple, palmately lobed . . . . *Rubus parviflorus*, Plate 85
1. Leaves compound 2

  2. Flowers rose . . . . *Rosa palustris*, Plate 88
  2. Flowers not rose 3

3. Plants stemless, leaves and flowering stalk from base of plant . . . 4
3. Plants having leafy stems 5

  4. Flowers white . . . . . . *Fragaria virginiana* or *vesca*, Plate 78
  4. Flowers yellow . . . . *Waldsteinia fragarioides*, Plate 78

5. Flowers borne in very slender spikes; calyx bearing a band
  of stiff, hooked bristles . *Agrimonia grypoepala* or *parviflora*, Plates 86, 87
5. Flowers borne in a loose cluster; calyx not bristly 6

  6. Fruiting heads of achenes with short styles,
    soon falling off . . . . *Potentilla*, p. 177
  6. Fruiting heads of achenes with long, feathery,
    persistent styles . . . . *Geum*, p. 183

PLATE 79

Marsh Cinquefoil
(*Potentilla palustris*)

Shrubby Cinquefoil
(*Potentilla fruticosa*)

175

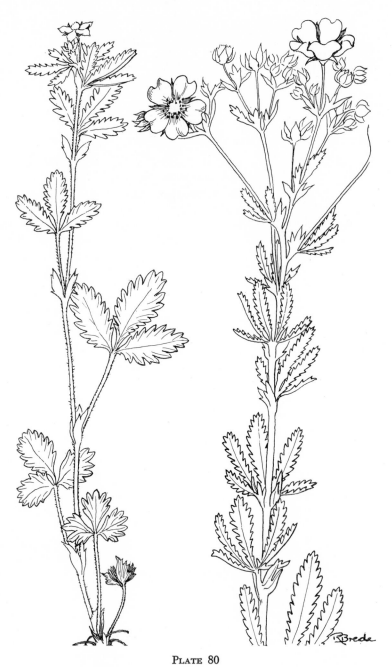

PLATE 80

Rough Cinquefoil
(*Potentilla norvegica*)

Rough-fruited Cinquefoil
(*Potentilla recta*)

176

WILD STRAWBERRY

Fragaria virginiana Duchesne   Plate 78

Stemless, tufted perennial up to 3 dm. tall, usually with several runners. Flowers white, in loose, few-flowered cymes. Petals 5, obovate or obcordate, inserted on the calyx; calyx deeply cleft into 5 ovate hairy lobes and with a smaller bract in each sinus; stamens numerous, inserted on the calyx; pistils many, on a rounded, somewhat hairy receptacle, the achenes numerous, borne in pits on the surface of the enlarged red pulpy receptacle (the strawberry). Leaves basal except for one subtending the cyme, 3-foliolate, the leaflets obovate, thick, firm, hairy, coarsely toothed.

In fields, along roadsides, on open slopes, and in thin woods. Flowering April to June. Fruits ripe in early summer.

This is a variable species, and several varieties have been described. It is probably our best-known and most delicious wild fruit. The domestic strawberry is a cross between this species and a South American species, but it seldom has the special flavor of the well-ripened wild berry.

WOODLAND STRAWBERRY

Fragaria vesca L.   Plate 78

Similar to the preceding species but generally smaller; the flowers in a raceme; the calyx lobes spreading or reflexed; the leaves strongly veined above; and the achenes on the surface (not in pits) of the cone-shaped fruit.

In rocky woods and on ledges. Flowering May to August.

BARREN STRAWBERRY

Waldsteinia fragarioides (Michx.) Tratt.   Plate 78

Stemless tufted perennial up to 2 dm. tall from a stout creeping rootstock. Flowers yellow, 3–8 on a bracted flowering stem. Petals 5, obovate, inserted on the calyx tube and longer than the calyx lobes; bractlets on calyx minute, soon falling; stamens 8; pistils 2–6, the styles slender; receptacle dry, not becoming greatly enlarged in fruit; achenes 2–6, hairy. Leaves from the base, long-petioled, 3-foliolate, the leaflets obovate, incised or crenate.

In woods, thickets, and clearings. Flowering late April to June.

Potentilla

7. Leaves palmately compound 8
7. Leaves pinnately compound . . . . *P. arguta,* Plate 81
   8. Petals pale yellow, much longer than lobes of calyx . . *P. recta,* Plate 80
   8. Petals deep yellow, same length as, or shorter than, calyx lobes . . 9
9. Lower surface of leaves white-woolly . . . . *P. argentea,* Plate 81
9. Lower surface of leaves slightly hairy . . . . *P. intermedia,* Plate 82

SHRUBBY CINQUEFOIL
Potentilla fruticosa L. Plate 79

Bushy-branched shrub up to 1 m. tall. Flowers bright yellow, 2–3 cm. wide, solitary or few at the ends of branches. Petals 5, rounded to broadly elliptic; calyx flat, deeply 5-lobed, the lobes alternating with 5 narrower bracts; stamens numerous; pistils numerous, borne on a dry receptacle, the style soon falling; achenes long-hairy. Leaves numerous, short-petioled, pinnately compound, the 5–9 leaflets narrowly oblong.

In wet or dry open ground, especially in calcareous soils, in meadows, bogs, and on shores. Flowering June to October.

SILVERWEED, SILVER-AND-GOLD
Potentilla anserina L. Plate 82

Low, tufted perennial with slender, arching, many-jointed runners up to 8 dm. long. Flowers bright yellow, 1.8–2.7 cm. across, solitary on erect, hairy, often reddish, axillary peduncles. Petals 5, nearly round, attached with the stamens to the flattish disk. Leaves all basal, 4–4.5 dm. long, pinnately compound, nearly smooth on upper surface, densely hairy beneath, the leaflets 7–25, oblong or obovate, blunt at the apex, sharply toothed, the lower leaflets smaller than the upper.

On sandy or gravelly lake shores, in sandy fields or on banks. Very common on lake shores in Michigan. Flowering June to September.

OLD-FIELD CINQUEFOIL
Potentilla simplex Michx. Plate 82

Rather coarse, hairy perennial, erect and up to 5 dm. tall at flowering time, but the stem soon elongating, forking, arching, and rooting at the tips, the rootstock irregularly enlarged, up to 10 cm. long and nearly 2 cm. thick. Flowers bright yellow, about 1 cm. wide, 1 (sometimes 3) on slender, hairy peduncles from the axils or from a point opposite the origin of the petiole, the first flower usually from the axil of the second stem leaf. Petals obcordate. Leaves alternate, palmately compound, mostly well expanded at flowering time, the leaflets 5, green on both sides, hairy beneath, narrowly obovate or oblanceolate, sharply and coarsely toothed in the upper 3/4; basal leaves similar or with linear-lanceolate inrolled auricles.

In dry or moist soil, in open fields, thickets, open woods, and waste places. Flowering April to June.

MARSH CINQUEFOIL *or* FIVE-FINGER
Potentilla palustris (L.) Scop. Plate 79

Stout, erect perennial up to 6 dm. tall from a partly reclining, somewhat woody base. Flowers purple, 1.8–3 cm. broad, several in a loose terminal cluster. Petals ovate to lanceolate, much smaller than the calyx lobes and about the same length as the calyx bracts but broader, persistent; calyx

PLATE 81

Silvery Cinquefoil
(*Potentilla argentea*)

Tall Cinquefoil
(*Potentilla arguta*)

Three-toothed Cinquefoil
(*Potentilla tridentata*)

deeply 5-lobed, the lobes large, purple at least inside, alternating with 5 smaller bracts; pistils numerous, borne on a superior, hairy, conical receptacle which becomes spongy and partly enclosed by the calyx. Leaves alternate, long-petioled, pinnately compound; leaflets 5–7, oblong-lanceolate to oblanceolate, toothed, green on both sides, smooth or nearly so; upper leaflets close together.

Around lakes, in swamps and bogs, and along streams. Flowering June to August.

ROUGH CINQUEFOIL *or* FIVE-FINGER
Potentilla norvegica L. Plate 80

Stiffly hairy, erect or ascending annual, biennial, or (rarely) short-lived perennial 1–9 dm. tall, the stiff hairs spreading. Flowers yellow, borne in leafy cymes, the petals obovate and usually shorter than the calyx lobes, calyx enlarging in fruit. Lower leaves 3-foliolate, long-petioled, the leaflets obovate to oblanceolate, coarsely toothed, green, having some long stiff hairs but not woolly; upper leaves sessile, the leaflets usually narrow.

In waste places, along roads, in open meadows and clearings. Flowering June to October.

THREE-TOOTHED CINQUEFOIL
Potentilla tridentata Ait. Plate 81

Evergreen creeping perennial with somewhat trailing woody branches which give rise to ascending flowering stems up to 3 dm. tall. Flowers white (sometimes pinkish) in stiff, few- to many-flowered cymes. Leaves palmately compound, the 3 leaflets leathery, oblong wedge-shaped, tapering to base, entire except for 3 (sometimes 5) teeth at the apex, bright green, smooth.

In dry open places, in rocky, gravelly, or peaty soil. Flowering late May to October.

TALL CINQUEFOIL *or* FIVE-FINGER
Potentilla arguta Pursh Plate 81

Rather coarse, erect perennial up to 1 m. tall, covered with clammy brownish hairs. The flowers whitish or creamy, borne in rather compact cymes. Petals broadly ovate to nearly round; stamens 30 (sometimes 25), borne in 5 groups on the glandular disk; style thickened at the middle. Basal leaves pinnately compound; leaflets 7–11, oval to ovate, toothed, downy beneath.

In rocky or bushy places, on prairies, and in alluvial soils. Flowering June to August.

ROUGH-FRUITED CINQUEFOIL *or* FIVE-FINGER
Potentilla recta L. Plate 80

Stout, erect, hairy or hairy-glandular perennial 3–6 dm. tall, many branched above. Flowers pale yellow, 1.3–2.9 cm. wide, borne in loose terminal cymes. Petals broadly obcordate, with a deep, rounded notch; calyx lobes 5, broader than the bracts, spread out flat when the flower is in bloom, but upright and enclosing the bud at first and becoming so again to cover the maturing seeds; style terminal, shorter than the mature smooth achene. Basal leaves palmately compound, the leaflets 5–7, oblanceolate, often glandular, with 7–17 long-pointed teeth; petioles long and hairy.

Along roadsides and in fields and waste places. A common weed; introduced from Europe. Flowering late July through August.

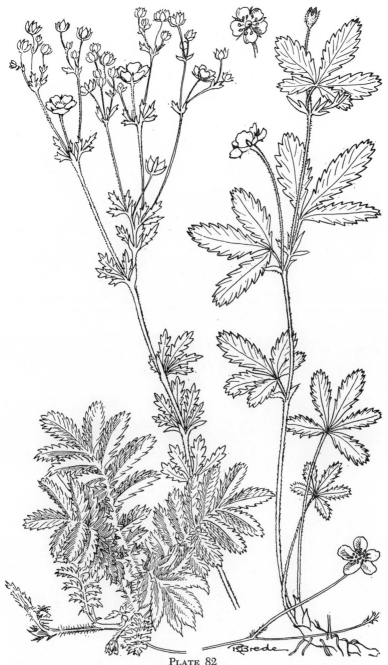

PLATE 82
Gray Cinquefoil
(*Potentilla intermedia*)
Silverweed
(*Potentilla anserina*)

Old-field Cinquefoil
(*Potentilla simplex*)

181

PLATE 83

White Avens
(*Geum canadense*)

Purple Water Avens
(*Geum rivale*)

182

SILVERY CINQUEFOIL

Potentilla argentea L. Plate 81

Erect or ascending, loosely clustered perennial up to 3 dm. tall, branched above. Flowers yellow, 8–10 mm. wide, borne in loose cymes. Pistils and achenes smooth, the style thickened, about the same length as the achene (or shorter). Leaves, except the uppermost, petioled, palmately compound; leaflets usually 5, green on upper surface, white-woolly beneath, sessile, oblanceolate to obovate, narrowed at the base and pinnately incised, the teeth long and sharp, the margins inrolled; withered stipules persistent.

In dry open ground. A common weed; naturalized from Europe. Flowering June to early August.

GRAY CINQUEFOIL or FIVE-FINGER

Potentilla intermedia L. Plate 82

Quite similar to the preceding species but tending to be larger; the inflorescence more freely branched; the leaflets grayish, hairy beneath, and less deeply cut; the plants shorter-lived.

Along roadsides and in waste places. Flowering May to August.

Geum

1. Petals white 2
1. Petals yellowish to purplish . . . . *G. rivale*, Plate 83
   2. Petals as long as, or longer than, calyx lobes; peduncles slender . . . . *G. canadense*, Plate 83
   2. Petals much smaller than calyx lobes; peduncles stout . . . . *G. laciniatum*, Plate 84

PURPLE WATER AVENS

Geum rivale L. Plate 83

Hairy, spreading or ascending, sparsely branched perennial up to 1 m. tall. Flowers several, nodding, yellow suffused and veined with purple, about 2 cm. wide. Petals 5, obcordate, constricted at apex, contracted to a claw at the base; calyx hairy, purple, bell-shaped, with 5 erect lobes and a small bract in each sinus; achenes borne on a dry, cylindrical receptacle, the styles elongating greatly, the plumose upper section soon falling from the persistent, stiff basal section. Basal leaves pinnately compound, the terminal 1–3 leaflets much larger than the others; stem leaves 3-foliolate or 3-lobed, coarsely toothed; stipules leaflike, green or purplish.

In wet meadows and bogs. Flowering May to August.

The Indians made a beverage from the fragrant rootstocks. Two species of yellow avens occur in Michigan. The flower structure and characteristic tailed achenes are similar to those of the above species. *G. aleppicum* Jacq. var. *strictum* (Ait.) Fern. has basal leaves in which the terminal and side segments are about the same size and are narrowed to the base. In *G. macrophyllum* Willd. the terminal segment of the leaf is conspicuously larger than the lateral ones and the base is heart-shaped or truncate. Both species grow in moist or wet soil in roadside ditches, thickets, and clearings, and flower from June to August.

PLATE 84
White Avens (*Geum laciniatum*)

PLATE 85
Thimbleberry (*Rubus parviflorus*)

PLATE 86
Agrimony (*Agrimonia gryposepala*)

186

WHITE AVENS

Geum canadense Jacq.
Plate 83

Variable, smooth to slightly hairy, slender, erect perennial up to 1.2 m. tall from a basal rosette. Flowers white, about 1 cm. in diameter, solitary on threadlike, hairy or glandular peduncles. Petals spreading, equaling or exceeding the calyx lobes in length, 5–9 mm. long, 2–4.5 broad; calyx tube saucer-shaped, deeply 5-lobed with bractlets at each sinus; stamens many; pistils several to many, borne on a broad, densely hairy receptacle; fruiting heads spherical; achenes 30–160; styles jointed, elon-

gating after flowering, the bearded upper segment falling off, leaving the stiff, hooked lower segment attached to the achene. Basal leaves long-petioled, simple or with 3 (sometimes 5 or 7) leaflets; lower stem leaves short-petioled or sessile, mostly with 3 leaflets; upper stem leaves 3-cleft to simple, sharply toothed; stipules 1–2 cm. long.

In rich open woods, borders of woods, and thickets, along roadsides and in fields throughout Michigan. Flowering June to early August.

WHITE AVENS

Geum laciniatum Murr.
Plate 84

Similar to the preceding species, but with the peduncles stout and hairy, the receptacle smooth or only sparsely hairy, and the petals much smaller than the calyx lobes, 2–5 mm. long,

1–2 mm. wide.

In damp thickets, meadows, and along roadsides only in the southernmost part of Michigan. Flowering June and July.

THIMBLEBERRY

Rubus parviflorus Nutt.
Plate 85

Erect, branched shrub up to 2 m. tall. Flowers showy, white, 3–5 cm. across, borne in a large, few-flowered corymb. Petals 5, spreading, oval; calyx lobes long-hairy, with a long slender appendage; stamens numerous; pistils many, borne on an elongate, spongy receptacle, each forming a small, juicy, 1-seeded fruit, these together forming the tart, flattened thimble-

shaped berry which separates readily from the receptacle. Leaves alternate, palmately 3–5 lobed, heart-shaped at base, the lobes all about the same length, irregularly coarse-toothed, sparsely hairy on both sides.

In rocky woods and thickets and on shores. Often forming the ground cover in open woods in northern Michigan. Flowering June and July.

The Purple-flowering Thimbleberry, *Rubus odoratus* L., which occurs only in the Lower Peninsula, is quite similar but has rose-purple flowers and a dry, insipid berry. The tart, juicy Thimbleberries are often made into jam or eaten fresh. The Indians used them fresh or pressed them into cakes, which were then dried. They also ate the young, tender shoots as a vegetable.

AGRIMONY

Agrimonia gryposepala Wallr.
Plate 86

Erect, branching, minutely glandular perennial, up to 1.8 m. tall. Flowers yellow, rather small, borne in slender, spikelike terminal and axillary ra-

cemes, the peduncles short, each subtended by a deeply cleft, hairy-margined bract. Petals 5, inserted on the disk; calyx tube top-shaped, with

PLATE 87
Small-flowered Agrimony (*Agrimonia parviflora*)

188

a band of stiff, hooked bristles around the top, the 5 lobes ovate, pointed; stamens 5–15; ovary inferior; styles 2; fruit dry, the hardened calyx tube enclosing the 2 achenes, the hooked bristles hardened and persisting. Leaves mostly below the middle, alternate, widely separated, petioled, pinnately compound with small leaflets between the larger ones, the large leaflets usual- ly 7 (or 5), thin, bright green, oblong-lanceolate to narrow-obovate, coarsely toothed, glabrous or with scattered long hairs on the veins beneath; having a disagreeable odor when crushed; stipules large and leaflike.

In woods and thickets, and along the borders of woods. Flowering July and August.

SMALL-FLOWERED AGRIMONY

Agrimonia parviflora Ait.   Plate 87

Quite similar to the preceding species in aspect, but the larger leaflets 11–15 on the middle and upper leaves, the leaflets softly hairy beneath, the stem of the inflorescence densely hairy, and the fruits only 4–5 mm. long.

In damp thickets and on rocky slopes. Flowering August and September.

WILD ROSE, SWAMP ROSE

Rosa palustris Marsh. L.   Plate 88

Freely branching, spiny shrub up to 2 m. tall, the spines short, usually recurved. Flowers showy, fragrant, rose, 5–7.5 cm. across. Petals 5, broadly ovate or somewhat obcordate; calyx tube urn-shaped, the 5 lobes very long, pointed; stamens numerous; pistils many, separate; fruit (hip) fleshy, the calyx tube enclosing the achenes, the sepals falling from the mature fruit. Leaves alternate, compound, odd-pinnate, the leaflets 5–9 (usually 7), finely toothed; stipules usually adherent to the base of the petiole.

Along swamps, stream borders, roadsides, on beaches, in wet thickets, dry open places, or in woods. Flowering May to July.

Several species of wild rose, often difficult to distinguish, occur in Michigan. The species of this genus vary greatly and hybridize readily.

The hips of various species were often eaten by the Indians, and they may be used for jelly making. They constitute a source of vitamins, particularly vitamin C, for which they were used in England during the World War. Roses have been in cultivation since ancient times and are probably our best-known ornamental plants.

PEA FAMILY.   LEGUMINOSAE

The Pea Family, in the broadest sense, is one of the largest of the flowering-plant families. It has over 500 genera and 1300 species, placing it third in size (below the Sunflower and Orchid families). In economic importance it is second only to the grass family. Garden peas, beans, soybeans, lentils, and peanuts, all widely-used table foods, belong to this family. The clovers, alfalfa, soybeans, and vetch are important both as forage and fodder plants. Peas are also important as rotation crops to increase the nitrogen content of the

PLATE 88
Wild Rose (*Rosa palustris*)

190

soil. Well over 100 species of the family are grown for ornamentals, among the most common ones being Sweet Pea, Lupine, Red-bud, and Wisteria. Kentucky Coffee-tree, Locust, and Honey-locust are trees which are often grown in Michigan. Many members of the family are poisonous; loco weeds in particular cause a heavy loss of livestock in the western mountains.

The family is characterized by usually irregular flowers, which are butterflylike ("papilionaceous"), with a large upper petal or "standard," two side petals or "wings," and 2 petals united into a "keel"; the stamens usually 10; the simple pistil ripening into a pod or legume which opens along 2 sides. The 10 stamens may be arranged in one of 3 fashions: the filaments distinct and separate, the filaments all united into a tube around the pistil (monadelphous) or the filaments of 9 stamens united into a tube, the tenth filament free (diadelphous). The leaves are usually compound and have stipules.

LEGUMINOSAE

PLATE 89
Partridge-pea (*Cassia fasciculata*)

192

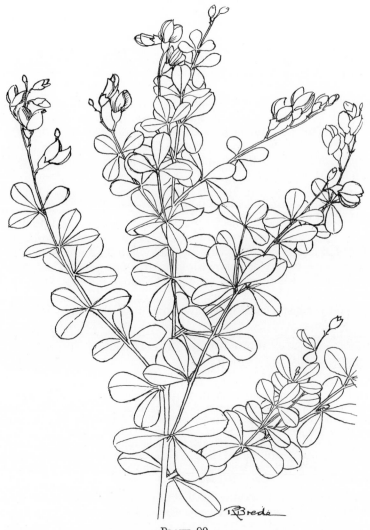

PLATE 90
Wild Indigo (*Baptisia tinctoria*)

PARTRIDGE-PEA, GOLDEN CASSIA

Cassia fasciculata Michx.   Plate 89

Nearly erect, rather slender annual up to 9 dm. tall. Flowers yellow or sometimes white, nearly regular, 1–6 in short, axillary, bracted racemes. Petals 5, often with a purple spot at the base, slightly unequal in size, 1–2 cm. long, spreading; sepals scarcely united at the base; stamens 10, distinct, very unequal, the anthers much longer than the filaments; pod linear, oblong, 4–13-seeded. Leaves pinnately compound, sensitive to touch, the leaflets 10–18 pairs, oblong, 1–2 cm. long, stipules persistent, streaked, folding upward when touched.

In moist or dry, usually sandy soil, on prairies and in open woods, along roadsides, and in old fields. Occurs only in the southern part of the state. Flowering July to September.

Wild Senna, *Cassia marilandica* L., with 4-10 pairs of larger leaflets (2-5 cm. long) is more common in southern Michigan. It grows up to 2 m. tall, and the flowers are borne in racemes from the axils of the leaves, the flowers are 10-15 mm. long, the 3 upper stamens lack normal anthers, and the segments of the legumes are much shorter than broad.

Goat's-rue, Catgut or Rabbit-pea, *Tephrosia virginica* (L.) Pers., is another erect pea with pinnately compound leaves, but in this there is an odd terminal leaflet in addition to the pairs of leaflets, and the leaves are not sensitive to touch. This species grows to be up to 6 dm. tall and is covered with long silky hairs. The numerous large flowers have yellow or yellowish standards and pink to pale purple wings. They are borne in compact terminal racemes. This is an attractive native species which grows in dry, sandy woods and openings and is conspicuous on sandy plains in southwestern Michigan.

WILD INDIGO, RATTLEWEED

Baptisia tinctoria (L.) R. Br.   Plate 90

Slender, smooth, bushy-branched perennial up to 1 m. tall, somewhat glaucous when young. Flowers yellow, 1–1.3 cm. long, borne in numerous, loose, terminal racemes. Standard and wings about the same length, the sides of the standard turned back, the petals forming the keel nearly separate, straight; stamens 10, separate; ovary and pod stalked, the pod papery to woody, inflated, 8–15 mm. long. Leaves 3-foliolate, the leaflets usually 1–2 cm. long, obovate, wedge-shaped at base, blackening on drying, minute stipules.

In dry, open woods and clearings. Flowering late May to September.

Indian children used the dried stalks with the inflated seed pods as rattles. The young shoots were eaten like asparagus. This species makes a showy garden plant, but is somewhat difficult to transplant. It needs acid soil.

Cream False Indigo, *B. leucophaea* Nutt., has cream-colored flowers borne in somewhat one-sided drooping racemes, and the stipules are up to 4 cm. long, conspicuous, and leaflike. White or Prairie False

194

Indigo, *B. leucantha* T. & G., has white flowers, sometimes tinged with purple, borne in stout, erect racemes; the stipules are slender, 5–10 mm. long and soon falling.

WILD LUPINE

Lupinus perennis L. var. *occidentalis* S. Wats.   Color Plate 8

Erect, bushy, hairy, many-stemmed, freely branching perennial up to 1 m. tall. Flowers usually blue or violet (rarely pinkish or white), about 1 cm. long, borne on short pedicels in loose terminal racemes. Standard nearly round, the sides turned back, wings completely covering the keel; keel curved; calyx strongly 2-lipped and very hairy; stamens 10, the filaments united into a closed tube for half their length; pistil solitary, the ovary superior, covered with long, soft, silky hairs, the style long, tapering, curved, the stigma appearing as a terminal fringe; pod 3–5 cm. long, hairy, the 2 halves coiling after opening. Leaves alternate, compound, circular, the 7–11 leaflets radiating from the top of the petiole like the spokes of a wheel; leaflets narrow, oblanceolate to obovate, abruptly tipped, entire.

In open woods and clearings, usually in dry sandy soil. Flowering April to July.

This is the only Michigan representative of this genus, which is so well known in the West. Some species are known as Bluebonnet in Texas. Several species of Lupine are cultivated for ornament, but they tend to die out in Michigan gardens.

Trifolium

1. Flowers white, pink, or rose to red 2
1. Flowers yellow . . . . *T. agrarium*, Plate 91

   2. Stems creeping, flowers white . . . . *T. repens*, Plate 91
   2. Stems erect or ascending 3

3. Heads pink and white; their stalks leafless . . . *T. hybridum*, Plate 91
3. Heads red, having a pair of leaves at base . . . . *T. pratense*, Plate 91

YELLOW CLOVER, HOP CLOVER

Trifolium agrarium L.   Plate 91

Glabrous or hairy, trailing or ascending, many-branched annual up to 5 dm. tall. Flowers yellow, becoming brown, borne on short pedicels in short-cylindric, 1–2-cm. long heads. Corolla brown and distinctly streaked in age, calyx 2-lipped; pod straight. Leaves petioled, 3-foliolate; leaflets sessile or nearly so; stipules linear.

Along roadsides, in waste places and dry fields. Flowering May to September.

Two other, less common but quite similar, yellow clovers have stalked terminal leaflets. The yellow clovers can be distinguished from the similar Black Medick, *Medicago lupulina* L., by their straight pods and 2-lipped calyx.

PLATE 91

Red Clover
(*Trifolium pratense*)

Alsike Clover
(*Trifolium hybridum*)

Yellow Clover
(*Trifolium agrarium*)

White Clover
(*Trifolium repens*)

PLATE 92

White Sweet Clover
(*Melilotus alba*)

Yellow Sweet Clover
(*Melilotus officinalis*)

197

WHITE CLOVER

Trifolium repens L. — Plate 91

Low, smooth perennial with long creeping stems. Flowers white, becoming brown, borne on pedicels in dense globose solitary heads 1.5–2.3 cm. in diameter. Corolla butterfly-like, the petals separate, 2–3 times as long as the calyx; standard oblong to ovate, not spreading, claws of the petals more or less united with the stamen tube below; calyx 5-cleft, the teeth bristle-tipped, similar, nearly equal; 10th stamen free; pistil 1, the legume usually 4-seeded. Leaves palmately 3-foliolate, long-petioled; leaflets broadly obovate, attached at the same point, finely toothed.

In fields, waste ground, open pastures, and woods. Flowering May to October.

This clover is commonly planted in lawns and as a forage crop. Like all other clovers in Michigan, it is an introduced species.

ALSIKE CLOVER

Trifolium hybridum L. — Plate 91

Quite similar to White Clover but differs by having leafy erect or ascending stems up to 5 dm. tall; the pink and white heads borne on peduncles which are longer than the subtending leaves.

Along roadsides and in clearings. Naturalized from Europe. Flowering June to October.

RED CLOVER

Trifolium pratense L. — Plate 91

Erect, partially reclining, or ascending biennial or perennial up to 8 dm. tall. Flowers magenta to nearly white, 13–20 mm. long, borne in dense globose to ovoid heads, the heads sessile or on peduncles, which are subtended by a pair of more or less hairy, opposite leaves. Leaves alternate, the lower ones long-petioled, the upper ones short-petioled to sessile, palmately 3-foliolate; the leaflets short-stalked, oval to cuneate-obovate, finely toothed; stipules oblong.

In clearings and old fields and along roadsides. Flowering May to August.

Extensively grown for hay.

WHITE SWEET CLOVER

Melilotus alba Desr. — Plate 92

Erect annual or biennial 1–3 m. tall, fragrant on drying. Flowers small, white, borne in long, narrow, spike-like, often 1-sided racemes from the axils of the upper leaves. Standard nearly round, a little longer than the wings; wings fastened to the keel; calyx tube bell-shaped, the lobes nearly equal; the 10th stamen free, the anthers all alike; pod ovoid, straight, leathery, wrinkled, longer than the calyx. Leaves 3-foliolate, the terminal leaflet stalked; leaflets narrowly oblong, pinnately veined, the veins ending in the teeth.

Along roads, ditches, and fences and in waste places. This common species was introduced from Europe as a forage and honey plant and is now widespread. Flowering May to October.

PLATE 93
Canada Beggar's-tick (*Desmodium canadense*)

199

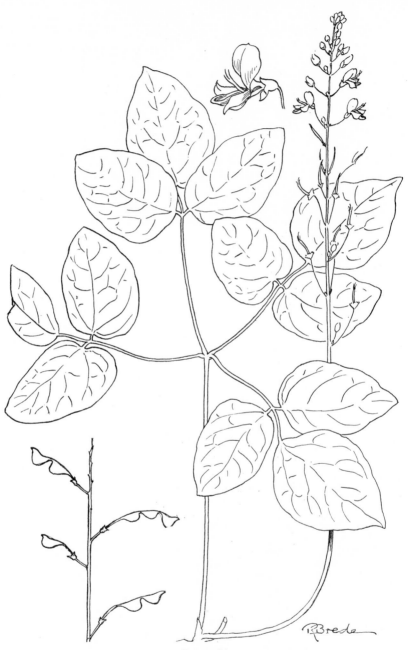

PLATE 94
Naked-stemmed Beggar's-tick (*Desmodium nudiflorum*)

YELLOW SWEET CLOVER

Melilotus officinalis (L.) Lam.   Plate 92

Very similar to the preceding species but usually not as tall; the flowers yellow and the standard nearly the same length as the wings.

In waste or cultivated ground. Flowering May to October.

Two other common introduced clovers with toothed 3-foliolate leaves and the terminal leaflet stalked are naturalized in Michigan: Black Medick, *Medicago lupulina* L., is a creeping, prostrate annual. The small yellow flowers are crowded into a compact head, and the ovaries and pods are kidney-shaped. The pods are black when mature. Alfalfa, *M. sativa* L., one of our most valuable forage plants, is a weak-stemmed perennial with blue, blue-violet, or whitish flowers in short cylindric heads. The pod is coiled into a loose spiral of 1–3 turns.

CANADA BEGGAR'S-TICK, TICK-TREFOIL, TICK-CLOVER

Desmodium canadense (L.) DC.   Plate 93

Erect, hairy perennial up to 1.3 m. tall. Flowers rose-purple changing to blue, 8.5–14 mm. long, borne on densely hairy, often sticky pedicels in racemes, the lanceolate to lance-ovate bracts conspicuous before flowering but then soon falling. Standard rounded to ovate; wings very slightly adherent to the curved keel; calyx 2-lipped; the 10th stamen free; pod flattened, composed of jointed, 1-seeded divisions which are densely covered with small hooked hairs. Leaves 3-foliolate, alternate, borne on the stem up to the inflorescence, with stipules; leaflets lance-ovate, thick, hairy on both surfaces, paler beneath, the larger leaflets 4.8–10.5 cm. long.

In open woods and waste places. Flowering July and August.

Everyone who has hiked in the woods and fields of southern Michigan is familiar with the fruits of this and related species, which cling so tenaciously to clothing, especially to wool socks.

NAKED-STEMMED BEGGAR'S-TICK

Desmodium nudiflorum (L.) DC.   Plate 94

Erect or ascending perennial up to 2 m. tall, usually forked at the base, giving rise to a leafless flowering stem and a leafy stem. Flowers rose to purple, rarely white, borne on slender, finely hairy pedicels in racemes. Calyx obscurely 2-lipped; stamens 10, all united into a tube; pod with 1–4 sections, densely covered with hooked hairs, the stipe longer than the pedicel. Leaves 3-foliolate, whorled at the apex of the leaf stem; terminal leaflets obovate to rhombic, 4.5–12 cm. long, finely downy above, glaucous and with some long hairs below; stipules soon falling.

In woods. Flowering July and August.

The several other species of *Desmodium* occurring in Michigan are distinguished mainly by their stipules and fruits. *D. glutinosum* (Muhl) Wood, with the leaves crowded at the middle of the stem, is especially noticeable in the woods of the Lower Peninsula.

PLATE 95

Round-headed Bush-clover   Purple Bush-clover   Hairy Bush-clover
(*Lespedeza capitata*)   (*Lespedeza violacea*)   (*Lespedeza hirta*)

Lespedeza

1. Flowers white to cream or yellowish, borne in dense
   heads or racemes 2
1. Flowers purple, borne in loose, few-flowered
   racemes . . . . *L. violacea*, Plate 95
   2. Flowers in very dense, subglobose heads, peduncles
      shorter than subtending leaf, or lacking . . . . *L. capitata*, Plate 95
   2. Flowers borne in spikelike racemes on peduncles
      longer than subtending leaf . . . . *L. hirta*, Plate 95

PURPLE BUSH-CLOVER
Lespedeza violacea (L.) Pers.   Plate 95

Freely branching, upright or spreading, glabrous to somewhat hairy perennial 4–8 dm. tall. Flowers purple, 7–10 mm. long, the keel often the longest part; borne in few, loose, few-flowered racemes which are much longer than the subtending leaves; unpetaled flowers numerous, in sessile or nearly sessile clusters in axils of leaves. Leaves few, 3-foliolate, the petioles slender, often nearly as long as the leaflets; leaflets elliptic, 1–4 cm. long and about half as wide.

In dry woods, thickets, and openings. Flowering August to October.

ROUND-HEADED BUSH-CLOVER
Lespedeza capitata Michx.   Plate 95

Erect, stiffish perennial with simple or sparsely-branched stems up to 1.2 m. tall. Flowers creamy-white, borne in many dense, subglobose heads or spikes which form a compact inflorescence, the heads sessile or on short peduncles which are usually shorter than the subtending leaves. Flowers of 2 kinds, those lacking petals rare and hidden among the petaled ones; petaled flowers with a purple spot at the base of the standard; calyx very hairy, 7–13 mm. long, 5-cleft, the slender lobes nearly equal; the 10th stamen free; pod flat, 1-seeded, shorter than the calyx. Leaves 3-foliolate, petioles 2–5 mm. long; leaflets oblong to lance-linear, thickish, downy, without stipules.

In dry open places. Flowering late July to September.

The seeds of some species of bush-clover, particularly the introduced Korean Lespedeza, *L. stipulacea* Maxim., provide food for the bobwhite, but are not attractive to other birds.

HAIRY BUSH-CLOVER
Lespedeza hirta (L.) Hornem.   Plate 95

Stout, usually erect, simple or branched perennial up to 1.5 tall, covered with spreading hairs. Flowers whitish to yellowish, purple at the base, the petaled flowers in cylindric, spikelike racemes which form a rather spreading inflorescence, the peduncles longer than the subtending leaves, the unpetaled flowers often in separate clusters. Leaves definitely petioled, 3-foliolate, the leaflets rounded obovate to lanceolate.

In dry soils. Flowering July to October.

PLATE 96

American Vetch
(*Vicia americana*)
Tufted Vetch
(*Vicia cracca*)

Hairy Vetch
(*Vicia villosa*)

Vicia

1. Racemes as long as, or longer than, subtending leaves; leaflets 6–12 pairs 2
1. Racemes shorter than subtending leaves; leaflets 4–9 pairs . . . . *V. americana*, Plate 96

2. Plants sprawling, stems weak, with spreading hairs . . . . *V. villosa*, Plate 96
2. Plants nearly erect, stems quite stiff, with tiny appressed hairs . . . . . . *V. cracca*, Plate 96

AMERICAN VETCH
Vicia americana Muhl.
Plate 96

Glabrous or nearly glabrous climbing or trailing perennial with stems up to 1 m. long. Flowers 3–9, bluish-purple to rose-purple, 1.5–2 cm. long, in racemes which are shorter than the subtending leaves. Calyx oblique, the lower teeth narrow and tapering, the upper teeth short and broad; pods 2.5–3.5 cm. long. Leaflets 4–9 pairs, nearly opposite, oblong-ovate to elliptic, 1.5–3.5 cm. long and less than half as broad.

On damp or gravelly shores, in thickets and meadows. Flowering May to July.

HAIRY VETCH, WINTER VETCH
Vicia villosa Roth
Plate 96

Grayish, long-hairy, weak, climbing or partly reclining perennial, with tough, ridged stems up to 1 m. long. Flowers 10–30, violet, violet and white, or sometimes all white, 12–20 mm. long, strongly overlapping in compact, 1-sided racemes which equal or overtop the subtending leaves. Standard overlapping the wings, the blade less than half as long as the claw; wings attached to the middle of the keel; wings and keel often whitish; calyx irregular, 5-toothed, the upper side enlarged and the pedicel seeming to be attached to the lower surface (instead of at base or ends); stamen tube oblique at apex, the 10th stamen free; style threadlike, with a tuft or ring of hairs at the apex; pod beaked, 1–3 cm. long. Leaves even-pinnate with a forking tendril at the end; leaflets 6–12 pairs, oblong-elliptic, abruptly pointed, obscurely veined; stipules hairy, half arrow-shaped.

In fields and along roadsides. Introduced from Europe as a forage plant; now naturalized and widespread. Flowering June to September.

Wood Vetch, *V. caroliniana* Walt., is another weak, trailing or climbing vetch. It has 7–20 white to pale-blue flowers borne in a loose raceme which is as long as or longer than the subtending leaf. The calyx is nearly regular, with the teeth nearly equal. This species grows in rich woods, in thickets, and on shores, and flowers from April to June.

TUFTED VETCH, CANADA-PEA
Vicia cracca L.
Plate 96

Quite similar to the preceding species, but the plants greener, less hairy, the hairs when present appressed, and the plants generally stronger and more upright in appearance. This species often stands without support, forming large, roundish patches. The racemes are stiffer, the blade of the standard

PLATE 97

Cream-colored Vetchling
(*Lathyrus ochroleucus*)

Marsh Pea
(*Lathyrus palustris*)

Beach Pea
(*Lathyrus japonicus*)

206

is nearly as long as the claw, and the calyx is merely rounded on the upper side. The leaflets tend to be narrower and upstanding.

In fields, waste places, and thickets, on shores, and along roadsides. Naturalized from Europe. Flowering May through August.

Lathyrus

1. Flowers blue, purplish, or rose-purple, rarely white 2
1. Flowers cream to yellowish-white . . . . . . *L. ochroleucus,* Plate 97

    2. Stipules nearly as large as leaflets, having 2 basal lobes . . . . *L. japonicus,* Plate 97
    2. Stipules not as large as leaflets, having only 1 basal lobe . . . . *L. palustris,* Plate 97

CREAM-COLORED VETCHLING

Lathyrus ochroleucus Hook.   Plate 97

Smooth, more or less trailing or climbing perennial with wingless, sometimes angled, green or purplish-red stems up to 1 m. long. Flowers cream or yellowish-white, 12–18 mm. long, in 5–10-flowered racemes which are much shorter than the subtending leaves. Calyx irregular, the lower teeth considerably longer than the upper. Leaflets 2–3 (sometimes 4) pairs, thin, ovate, somewhat glaucous below; stipules half heart-shaped, about half as long as the lower leaflets.

In dry or moist woods, on rocky banks or slopes. Flowering in May and June.

The introduced Yellow Vetchling, *L. pratensis* L., has bright yellow flowers and only 2 leaflets.

BEACH PEA

Lathyrus japonicus Willd. var. *glaber* (Ser.) Fern.   Plate 97

Somewhat fleshy, stiffly branching, climbing or partially erect, glaucous perennial with stout, sharply angled stems up to 1.5 m. long. Flowers butterflylike, deep rose-purple, blue-violet, or crimson, 1.2–3 cm. long, in stout 4–10-flowered racemes which are usually shorter than the subtending leaves, the pedicels short, stout and arching. Standard broad; wings only slightly coherent with the upwardly curved keel; calyx irregular; stamen tube not oblique at the apex, the 10th stamen free; style bearded along the inner side (next to the free stamen); pods brown, 3–7 cm. long. Leaves pinnately compound with a forking tendril at the end; leaflets thin, very firm, sessile, elliptic to obovate, blunt and with an abrupt point at the apex, smooth and glaucous, 1–7 cm. long, entire; stipules broadly ovate with 2 basal lobes, nearly as large as the leaflets.

On sandy or gravelly shores and beaches; common on the shores of the Great Lakes. Flowering in July and August.

This species, of which a number of varieties have been described, is circumpolar in distribution. The fresh stalks and young sprouts were used as food by the Indians.

MARSH PEA, VETCHLING

Lathyrus palustris L.   Plate 97

PLATE 98

Hog-peanut
(*Amphicarpa bracteata*)

Groundnut
(*Apios americana*)

208

Slender, climbing perennial with weak stems up to 1 m. long. Flowers purple, rose-purple, violet, or whitish, 1–2.5 cm. long, borne in racemes which are nearly as long as or slightly longer than the subtending leaf. Leaflets 2–5 pairs, firm, linear to ovate; stipules with only one lobe at base, pointed at both ends.

On lake shores, in meadows and damp thickets. Flowering June to September.

The shelled peas were cooked and eaten by the Indians. However, recent studies have shown that at least some species of *Lathyrus* are poisonous, and it is therefore inadvisable to eat wild peas. The familiar garden Sweet Pea belongs to this genus. Two rather common everlasting or perennial peas are quite striking and frequently grow wild. *L. latifolius* L. may be high-climbing. It has broadly winged stems; 2 lanceolate, oblong, or oval leaflets 4–9 cm. long; and conspicuous purple, pink, or white flowers about 2.5 cm. long, borne in 4–10-flowered racemes. *L. sylvestris* L. is quite similar, but the 2 leaflets are narrowly lanceolate and 1–1.5 dm. long; the flowers are about 1.5 cm. long.

GROUNDNUT, WILD BEAN

Apios americana Medic.   Plate 98

Perennial twining herb from slender rootstock with numerous tuberous enlargements resembling a string of beads; juice milky. Flowers reddish-brown, purplish-brown, or mauve, about 1 cm. long, borne in short, dense, often branching racemes from the axils of the leaves, fragrant, the odor somewhat like that of violets, the peduncle shorter than the leaves. Standard round, bent backward; wings oblique, adherent to the keel, elon-gated, incurved, and horseshoe-shaped, broadest at the base; calyx 2-lipped, with 4 teeth very small, the other about as long as the tube; 10th stamen free; ovary coiled; pod slightly curved or straight, 5–10 cm. long. Leaves pinnately compound, the leaflets usually 5–7, ovate-lanceolate, pointed at apex, rounded at base, 2.5–7 cm. long.

On lake shores, in moist rich thickets, and along streams. Flowering July to September.

Groundnuts are considered one of our best wild foods by some authorities and are said to be good raw, boiled, or roasted. They reportedly were eaten by the Pilgrims and constituted an important food for the Indians.

HOG-PEANUT

Amphicarpa bracteata (L.) Fern.   Plate 98

Low, twining or trailing perennial with brown, threadlike stems up to 2.6 m. long. Flowers of 2 kinds, the petaled ones pale lilac or purple to white, 9–13 mm. long, borne in nodding 2–13-flowered racemes from the upper axils. Standard narrowed to the base, longer than the wings and keel; calyx slightly irregular, the tube short-cylindric, the teeth apparently 4; 10th stamen free; pods from upper flowers stalked. 1.5–3 cm. long, flat, oblong, pointed at both ends, 3-seeded; unpetaled flowers small, borne on threadlike creeping branches, self-fertile, the stamens few, free; pods of

PLATE 99
Common Flax (*Linum usitatissimum*)

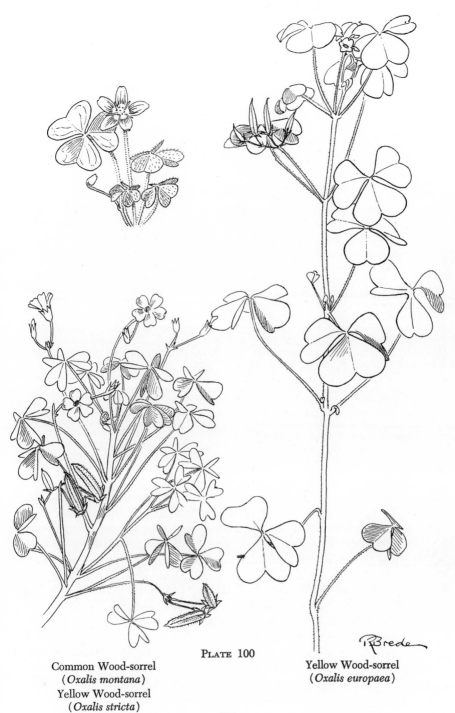

PLATE 100

Common Wood-sorrel
(*Oxalis montana*)
Yellow Wood-sorrel
(*Oxalis stricta*)

Yellow Wood-sorrel
(*Oxalis europaea*)

211

unpetaled flowers often borne underground, fleshy, obovate or pear-shaped, usually with a single large seed. Leaves 3-foliolate, the leaflets broadly ovate, sharply pointed, 2–6 cm. long.

In moist woodlands. Flowering August and September.

The underground seeds are said to be good to eat and to have a flavor somewhat like that of raw peanuts. They are often abundant and generally appear just under the surface of the ground, where they are easily found by hogs—hence the name. Hog-peanuts were highly valued by the Indians. Some tribes obtained considerable quantities by robbing rodents' nests of their stored supplies.

FLAX FAMILY. LINACEAE

This cosmopolitan family of 9 genera includes about 2000 species. Its principal economic importance is flax for linen and the linseed oil produced by some species. A few species are used as ornamentals.

COMMON FLAX

Linum usitatissimum L.   Plate 99

Slender, erect, pale-green annual usually with a single stem up to 1 m. tall. Flowers sky-blue, saucerlike, 2–2.5 cm. broad, borne on very slender, erect pedicels in loose, few-flowered corymbs. Petals 5, separate or barely united at the base, broadly obovate, and flattened or shallowly notched at the apex, soon falling, closing in the evening and in cloudy weather; sepals 5, persistent, in 2 series, the inner ones bearing marginal hairs; stamens 5, the filaments broad, flat, united at the base; pistil 1, the ovary superior, the styles 5, long, slender, spreading, the stigmas linear; capsule globose, 5-celled. Leaves alternate, numerous, linear-lanceolate.

In waste places and fields, along roads and railways. Introduced from Europe. Flowering June to September.

Cultivated since prehistoric times, this species often grows wild here. It is important for the stem fibers, which are used in making linen and for linseed oil derived from the seeds. A similar but perennial species, *L. lewisii* Pursh, is often grown for ornament. It usually has several stems spreading from the crown; the pedicels are arched and spreading, the stigmas capitate, and the sepals without marginal hairs. Five small native species, all with yellow or yellowish flowers, also occur in Michigan.

WOOD-SORREL FAMILY. OXALIDACEAE

This mostly tropical family of 7 genera includes about 1000 species. It is of little economic importance, but a few species of *Oxalis* are grown for ornament.

Our species are easily recognized by their regular flowers with 5 petals and sepals, 10 stamens, the 5-celled, superior ovary, and the shamrocklike leaves.

Oxalis

1. Flowers white to purple; leaves all from base . . . . *O. montana,* Plate 100
1. Flowers yellow; leaves on stem 2
   2. Pedicels of capsules bent down . . . . . *O. stricta,* Plate 100
   2. Pedicels of capsules erect or spreading, not
      bent down . . . . *O. europaea,* Plate 100

COMMON WOOD-SORREL, WOOD SHAMROCK
Oxalis montana Raf.   Plate 100

Low perennial up to 1 dm. tall, creeping by rootstocks. Flowers white with rose or purple veins, solitary, the flowering stalks long-hairy and bearing a pair of small bracts near the middle, the earliest flowering stalks longer than the leaves, the later ones shorter, recurving, and bearing small nonopening flowers. Petals 5, notched at apex, having a small yellow spot near the base; calyx deeply cut, the lobes lanceolate, often bordered with red; stamens 10, barely united at the base, of 2 lengths; pistil compound, deeply 5-lobed, the styles 5, distinct; fruit a capsule. Leaves all from the base, 3-foliolate, the leaflets broadly heart-shaped above, having a pleasant acid taste.

In damp woods. Flowering late May to August.

YELLOW WOOD-SORREL, YELLOW OXALIS
Oxalis stricta L.   Plate 100

Erect, ascending, or partially reclining and matted, grayish-green perennial covered with appressed, whitish hairs, up to 5 dm. tall. Flowers yellow, 1–4 in an umbel. Petals sometimes red at the base; capsules erect on deflexed pedicels. Leaves alternate, the leaflets 1–3 cm. broad; stipules oblong, firm.

In dry, open soil, in woods, and along roadsides. Flowering May to October.

YELLOW WOOD-SORREL, YELLOW OXALIS
Oxalis europaea Jord.   Plate 100

Quite similar to the preceding species, but usually greener, more variable in stature and habit of growth; usually having more than 3 flowers in an umbel; the fruiting pedicels straight, erect or spreading, not deflexed; producing fleshy underground runners; stipules usually lacking.

In cultivated ground, lawns, gardens, fields, and along roadsides. A common weed. Flowering May to October.

This is a variable species for which a number of varieties and forms, based primarily on the presence or absence of hairs on various parts of the plant, have been described.

GERANIUM FAMILY. GERANIACEAE

This is a widely distributed family of 11 genera and about 850 species. It is important primarily for ornamentals, the florist's geranium (*Pelargonium zonale*) being well known. A few species are grown for the aromatic oil in the foliage, and some species of *Geranium* and *Erodium* are cultivated in the garden.

PLATE 101

Storksbill (*Erodium cicutarium*)

Wild Geranium (*Geranium maculatum*)

Herb-Robert (*Geranium robertianum*)

The family is characterized by its regular or nearly regular 5-parted flowers and the beaked fruit which separates elastically to throw out the seeds. The leaves have stipules.

WILD GERANIUM, SPOTTED CRANESBILL

Geranium maculatum L.   Plate 101

Hairy, erect, bushy perennial up to 6 dm. tall. Flowers rose-purple, rose, bluish, or whitish, usually with darker veins, 2.5–4 cm. wide, erect or nodding in loose, few-flowered terminal corymbs, the pedicels and peduncles hairy to long-hairy. Petals 5, separate; sepals 5, separate, lanceolate or narrowly ovate; stamens 10 in 2 circles, the outer stamens maturing first; filaments flattened, woolly at the base, the anthers attached by the middle; ovary deeply 5-lobed, the style compound, the stigma with 5 curved branches; capsule elongate, up to 5 cm. long, tipped with the persistent style, the 5 divisions separating from the base at maturity, arching up and out to throw out the single seed. Leaves deeply 3–5-palmately cut, the segments narrowed at the base, the margin much incised; basal leaves often larger, up to 15 cm. wide, long-petioled.

In rich or moist woods, thickets, and meadows, along roadsides. Mostly in the southern part of the state. Flowering May and June.

This is one of the most satisfactory wildflowers for the garden; it flowers freely and is attractive even when not in bloom. It requires little attention and multiplies readily, sometimes too readily. The Indians used the dried and powdered roots medicinally.

HERB-ROBERT, RED ROBIN

Geranium robertianum L.   Plate 101

Strong-scented, nearly erect, hairy or glandular, many-stemmed and many-branched annual up to 4.5 dm. tall. Flowers rose to reddish-purple, sometimes white, 1–1.5 cm. wide, borne in pairs at the ends of axillary peduncles. Petals 5, veined with a deeper color, the claws very narrow, the blade obovate, indented at the end. Leaves compound with 3–5 bright green, pinnately-cut leaflets, the lobes rounded and abruptly pointed, the terminal leaflet stalked.

In rocky woods, thickets, and ravines and on gravelly shores. Flowering June and July.

In addition to some introduced species, we have another native Geranium, *G. bicknellii* Britt. Its leaves are deeply divided but not compound, the petals are roseate, and only slightly longer than the calyx lobes. It is common on rocky outcrops in the northern part of the state.

STORKSBILL, PIN-CLOVER

Erodium cicutarium (L.) L'Hér.   Plate 101

Rosette-forming winter annual or biennial up to 2.5 dm. tall. Flowers roseate or purple, about 1 cm. wide, borne in several-flowered, long-peduncled umbels in the axils of the leaves. Petals 5, the upper ones slightly smaller than the lower; sepals 5, bristle-tipped; stamens with anthers 5; ovary deeply 5-lobed; ripe fruit long, slender, and pointed, the styles

$1\frac{1}{3}$

РBrede

PLATE 102

Seneca Snakeroot
(*Polygala senega*)

Milkwort
(*Polygala polygama*)

Whorled Milkwort
(*Polygala verticillata*)

Purple Milkwort
(*Polygala sanguinea*)

216

separating below and spirally twisting, bearded on the inner side. Leaves pinnately compound, the leaflets linear, finely pinnately cut, sessile; leaves mostly basal at first but stem leaves produced as the stems elongate.

In fields, along roads, and in waste places. Introduced from Europe. Flowering March to November.

This is a valuable forage plant for small mammals, particularly in the West. Many birds also eat the seeds.

MILKWORT FAMILY. POLYGALACEAE

This widely distributed family has 10 genera and about 700 species. It is of economic importance only for the few species cultivated as ornamentals.

The irregular flowers resemble those of the Pea Family, but their structure is not the same. There are 5 sepals, of which 2 or 3 are small and green and 2 (wings) are larger and petallike. The 3 petals are connected with each other and with the stamen tube; one petal is often keellike and crested with hairs. The filaments of the 8 stamens (6 in one species) are united into a split tube.

Polygala

1. Plants creeping; flowers showy, 1.5–2.5 cm. long, few . . . . *P. paucifolia,* Color Plate 9
1. Plants erect; flowers small (not over 6 mm.), numerous 2
   2. Flowers white; stems several from a tough, thick crown . . . . *P. senega,* Plate 102
   2. Flowers purple, pink, or green 3
3. Racemes headlike, rounded at apex . . . . *P. sanguinea,* Plate 102
3. Racemes elongate 4
   4. Flowers borne in loose racemes, leaves alternate . . . . *P. polygama,* Plate 102
   4. Flowers borne in very compact, spikelike racemes; leaves mostly whorled . . . . *P. verticillata,* Plate 102

FRINGED POLYGALA

Polygala paucifolia Willd.   Color Plate 9

Creeping perennial up to 1 dm. tall. Flowers irregular, of 2 kinds, the showy ones rose-purple to whitish, up to 2.3 cm. long, 1–4 on long pedicels from the end of the stem. Petals 3, united into a tube split along the top, the lower (middle) one keeled and conspicuously fringed at the end; sepals 5, the 2 lower ones small and bractlike, the upper sepal helmet-shaped, the lateral sepals petallike and forming wings; stamens 6, in sets of 3, the filaments united into a split tube connected with the petals; pistil solitary, the style long, the ovary superior, flattened, 2-celled; capsule 2-seeded, flattened. Self-pollinating, non-opening flowers on underground branches, their fruits small, globular. Leaves few, mostly crowded near the top of the flowering stem, ovate, petioled, the lower leaves scattered, small and scalelike.

In light soil in moist woods. Flowering May and early June.

PLATE 103

White Spurge
(*Euphorbia corollata*)

Cypress Spurge
(*Euphorbia cyparissias*)

218

SENECA SNAKEROOT

Polygala senega L. Plate 102

Erect perennial with several simple stems up to 5 dm. tall from a thick crown. Flowers white or whitish, in dense, solitary terminal racemes 6–7 mm. thick. Wings nearly round, 3–3.3 mm. long, equaling or exceeding the petals in length; capsule rounded, persistent. Leaves numerous, alternate, linear-lanceolate to ovate, irregularly toothed, 1.3–7 cm. long, the upper leaves the largest.

In dry or rocky places, chiefly in calcareous areas. Flowering May to July.

The Indians carried roots of this species as a charm to ensure safety and health on their journeys.

PURPLE MILKWORT, PURPLE POLYGALA

Polygala sanguinea L. Plate 102

Annual with solitary, simple or branched, very leafy stems up to 4 dm. tall. Flowers pink to rose-purple, greenish, or white, on short pedicels, overlapping in very dense, thick-cylindric to headlike racemes, which are rounded at the summit, 6–14 mm. thick. Wings broadly rounded above, twice as long as the keel, 9-nerved; fruits soon dropping. Leaves numerous, alternate, linear or narrowly elliptic, 1–4 cm. long, sessile.

In moist acid soil, in fields, meadows, and open woods. Flowering late June to October.

MILKWORT

Polygala polygama Walt. var. *obtusata* Chodat Plate 102

Glabrous, erect, ascending, or partially reclining, many-stemmed perennial up to 4.5 dm. tall. Flowers of 2 kinds. Petaled flowers rose-purple to pink, 3–5 mm. long, borne in loose, somewhat 1-sided, terminal racemes 2–12 cm. long. Petals equal to or shorter than the wings, the keel fringed at the end; sepals 5, the 2 largest forming wings, the upper sepal appressed against the ovary; stamens 8, the filaments united in 2 sets, the anthers free; ovary 1, superior, the stigma 2-lobed; capsule flattened, 2-celled, each cell with a single seed. Self-pollinating, nonopening flowers small, borne in 1-sided racemes on white underground branches, forming plump fruits. Leaves numerous, alternate, the lower ones small and spatulate, the upper ones larger and linear to narrowly oblanceolate, entire, sessile.

In sandy woods and dry open soil. Flowering June to August.

WHORLED MILKWORT

Polygala verticillata L. Plate 102

Slender annual with solitary stems up to 4 dm. tall. Flowers white, greenish, or purplish, borne in slender tapering racemes, the lower branches of the inflorescence opposite or whorled. Wings shorter than or about equaling the capsule in length; keel yellow or yellowish. Leaves, at least those of the lower nodes, in whorls of 3–5, linear to narrowly lanceolate, pointed at apex, 1–2 cm. long.

In sterile open places, in moist to dry, usually sandy, soil, in grasslands and woods. Flowering June to October

219

PLATE 104

Spotted Touch-me-not
(*Impatiens capensis*)

Snow-on-the-mountain
(*Euphorbia marginata*)

SPURGE FAMILY. EUPHORBIACEAE

This cosmopolitan, but predominantly tropical, family has nearly 300 genera and more than 7000 species. Our only economically important members are such ornamentals as Poinsettia, Crown-of-thorns, and Castor Bean. Rubber, tung oil, castor oil, cassava, and tapioca are derived from primarily tropical species.

The members of the family included here are distinguished by the milky juice and the greatly reduced, unisexual flowers. The flowers are borne in a calyxlike, cup-shaped involucre or cyathium. The staminate flowers consist of a single-stalked stamen, the pistillate flowers of a stalked pistil surmounted by 3 curved styles. Several staminate flowers surround a single pistillate flower in the involucre, the whole structure looking like a single flower. In maturity the stalk of the ovary elongates, and the capsule (usually 3-sided) extends beyond the involucre.

Euphorbia

1. Leaves (at least upper ones) having broad, white, petallike margins . . . . *E. marginata*, Plate 104
1. Leaves not bordered with white 2
    2. Leaves oblong-oval to linear . . . . . . *E. corollata*, Plate 103
    2. Leaves narrowly linear to threadlike . . . *E. cyparissias*, Plate 103

SNOW-ON-THE-MOUNTAIN
Euphorbia marginata Pursh   Plate 104

Bright green, glabrous or hairy annual up to 1 m. tall, topped by a usually 3-rayed terminal umbel. Inflorescence like that of the preceding species but the lobes of the bell-shaped involucre finely fringed, the bracts of the inflorescence and the upper leaves with conspicuous, broad, white, petallike margins. Lower leaves broadly oblong to ovate; stipules lanceolate, soon falling.

In dry soil in waste places. Frequently cultivated; spreading readily. Flowering from June to October.

Several additional species of *Euphorbia*, mostly low or prostrate, occur in waste ground in Michigan.

WHITE *or* FLOWERING SPURGE
Euphorbia corollata L.   Plate 103

Bright green, glabrous or somewhat hairy perennial up to 1 m. tall, simple below, many branched above; juice milky. Flowers greatly modified and reduced, the involucre resembling a small white flower with 5 rounded corolla lobes, each with a crescent-shaped, green gland at the base. Leaves numerous (75 or more below the inflorescence), alternate, sessile, firm, glabrous, oblong, oval, or linear, entire, obscurely veined; opposite, bractlike leaves in the inflorescence.

In dry open places, along roads and railways, in fields, clearings, and waste places. Flowering June to October.

CYPRESS SPURGE
Euphorbia cyparissias L.   Plate 103

PLATE 105

Common Mallow
(*Malva neglecta*)

Musk Mallow
(*Malva moschata*)

Erect perennial up to 4 dm. tall, usually growing in large patches from extensively creeping and forking rootstocks; juice milky. Involucres in terminal umbels, yellowish-green, with 4 crescent-shaped glands; capsule stalked, nearly globose, rarely developing. Leaves narrowly linear, numerous above, but few, scattered, and reduced below; leaves in the inflorescence usually in pairs, broadly ovate, yellowish-green, becoming red or purplish.

Along roadsides, in old fields and waste places. Introduced from Europe; now widely distributed. Flowering April to August.

TOUCH-ME-NOT FAMILY. BALSAMINACEAE

This widely distributed family of 2 genera and nearly 500 species is most abundant in the tropics. It includes a few ornamentals, such as Balsam and Touch-me-not.

The Michigan species are characterized by their simple leaves; the showy, horizontal flowers with one of the sepals petallike, sacklike, and spurred; and by the fruit, which opens explosively when ripe. The actual structure of the flowers and the number of floral parts are differently interpreted by different authorities.

SPOTTED TOUCH-ME-NOT, SNAPWEED

Impatiens capensis Meerb.   Plate 104

Succulent, quickly-wilting, many-branched, smooth and sometimes glaucous annual up to 2 m. tall. Flowers few, in axillary racemes, hanging horizontally on slender pedicels, orange, spotted with red (but variable and sometimes unspotted, sometimes pale or nearly cream-color), up to 2.5 cm. long; perianth much modified, irregular, sepals apparently 3, 2 being small, ovate, and green, and one (the lower one) large, forming an inflated sack which is longer than broad, spurred at the base, the spur bent back along the sack; petals seemingly 3, the upper one broader than long, the others 2-lobed and presumably each represent- ing a united pair; stamens 5, the filaments short and flat, each bearing a scale on the inner side, the scales united over the stigma, the anther also united; ovary 5-celled; capsule oblong, opening violently by 5 coiling valves and shooting out the ridged seeds when mature; self-pollinating, nonopening flowers are also frequently produced. Leaves alternate, thin, ovate to elliptic, 3–10 cm. long, bright green above, whitish beneath, the margin with coarse, rounded teeth.

In low wet ground, often in shade, along roads, in thickets, along streams, in springy places. Flowering July to September.

The Indians used the fresh juice to wash nettle stings, for skin rash, and for poison ivy dermatitis. The seeds are eaten by several kinds of birds, and hummingbirds seek the nectar.

Pale Touch-me-not, *I. pallida* Nutt., is very similar, but the flowers are pale yellow and sparingly spotted; the spur is bent at right angles and is less than one-fourth as long as the sack; the sack is broader than long; and the plants tend to be stouter, taller, and more glaucous.

Balsam, *I. balsamina* L., with solitary, purple, rose, or white flowers, is a rather common garden flower that appeals greatly to children because of the explosive capsules.

223

PLATE 106
Rose Mallow (*Hibiscus palustris*)

224

MALLOW FAMILY. MALVACEAE

This family is distributed over much of the earth but is particularly abundant in the American tropics. There are about 82 genera, 1500 species. Economically the most important member is the cotton plant. The seeds produce long fibers which are used for cloth, cottonseed oil is pressed out of the seeds, and a meal is made from the remainder. Okra belongs to this family, and a European species of *Althaea* produces a mucilage which was the original basis for marshmallows. There are several well-known ornamentals: Hollyhock, Rose of Sharon, Poppy Mallow, Hibiscus, and Althaea.

Our members are easily recognized by the numerous stamens which are united around the style by their filaments and resemble a bottle brush in the center of the flower. The flowers are regular and perfect. There are 5 petals and 5 sepals; the ovary is superior and compound. The leaves are alternate and simple, and have stipules.

MALVACEAE

1. Flowers solitary . . . . *Hibiscus palustris*, Plate 106
1. Flowers in clusters 2
  2. Upper leaves deeply divided into 5–7 narrow
    segments . . . . *Malva moschata*, Plate 105
  2. Upper leaves shallowly lobed, nearly round or
    kidney-shaped . . . . *M. neglecta*, Plate 105

Musk Mallow

Malva moschata L.   Plate 105

Erect or somewhat reclining, many-branched, hairy to nearly smooth, faintly musk-scented perennial 3–6 dm. tall. Flowers white, pale pinkish, or rose, about 5 cm. in diameter, slightly fragrant, borne in raceme-like clusters at the ends of branches, each flower subtended by an involucre of 3 small, linear, green bracts just below the calyx. Petals 5, triangular to broadly heart-shaped at apex, 2.4–3 cm. long, attached to the stamen column at the base; calyx deeply 5-lobed, spreading; stamens numerous, the filaments united into a tube around the styles, the anthers pinkish or pale lilac; ovary densely hairy, of 15–30 carpels in a circle; mature fruits rounded on the back, separating readily. Basal and lower stem leaves rounded, shallowly cleft or crenate or with 5 broad lobes; upper stem leaves usually 5–7-parted, the divisions deeply pinnately cut.

Along roads and in waste places. Native of Europe; escaped from cultivation here. Flowering July to September.

Common Mallow, Cheeses

Malva neglecta Wallr.   Plate 105

Low, sprawling, prostrate, or ascending biennial with stems up to 1 m. long. Flowers pale lilac to white, in groups in the leaf axils. Petals heart-shaped at apex, twice as long as the calyx; calyx having a cluster of 3 small leaves at the base; fruits in a ring, usually 12–15. Leaves nearly round or kidney-shaped, often heart-shaped at the base, shallowly 5–9-lobed.

In gardens, waste places, barnyards. A common weed; naturalized from Europe. Flowering April to October.

PLATE 107

Marsh St. John's-wort
(*Hypericum virginicum*)

Common St. John's-wort
(*Hypericum perforatum*)
St. John's-wort
(*Hypericum majus*)

226

ROSE MALLOW, MARSH MALLOW

Hibiscus palustris L.　　　　　　　　　Plate 106

Grayish, hairy perennial up to 2.5 m. tall, having a mouselike odor. Flowers large, showy, solitary, pink to purple or creamy-white. Petals 5, usually red or purplish at base; calyx 5-cleft, subtended by an involucre of numerous small bracts; stamens numerous, united by their filaments; pistils several; ovary and style united, the style 4–5 cm. long, the upper half extending beyond the flower, with 5 densely hairy branches; capsule sub-globose, 2–2.5 cm. long. Leaves alternate, broadly ovate to rounded, usually 3-lobed, those about the middle of the stem 7–18 cm. long and 4.5–11 cm. broad, but sometimes broader than long, dark green and glabrous on upper surface, velvety and grayish-hairy beneath.

In salty, fresh, or brackish marshes. Found in Michigan only in the southern part of the state. Flowering August to October.

ST. JOHN'S-WORT FAMILY.　GUTTIFERAE

This family is composed of about 8 genera and 350 species, according to some authorities, and of about 50 genera and over 1000 species according to others, the discrepancy being due to varying opinion as to whether the species belong to one or two families. The family is of limited economic importance; a few species of St. John's-wort are grown as ornamentals.

The members of this family in Michigan are characterized by pellucid-dotted or black-dotted, opposite leaves and stamens usually united in 3 or more clusters or fascicles.

Hypericum

1. Plants herbaceous 2
1. Plants shrubby . . . . *H. kalmianum*, Plate 108
　2. Flowers pinkish . . . . *H. virginicum*, Plate 107
　2. Flowers yellow 3
3. Styles 3, separate to base; plants of dry places . . *H. perforatum*, Plate 107
3. Styles united into a beak; plants of damp places . . *H. majus*, Plate 107

SHRUBBY ST. JOHN'S-WORT

Hypericum kalmianum L.　　　　　　　　Plate 108

Small, slender, freely branching shrubs up to 6 dm. tall. Flowers bright yellow, 2–3 cm. wide, solitary or in few-flowered, leafy, terminal cymes. Petals 5, separate, spreading, oblique at apex; sepals 5; stamens very numerous, separate, soon falling; pistil 1; styles usually 5, united below; capsule about 5 mm. long. Branches 4-sided, the branchlets flattened and 2-sided; bark papery, whitish. Leaves numerous, opposite, sessile, rather crowded, linear to oblanceolate, entire or somewhat wavy-margined, 3–6 cm. long, finely dotted with translucent spots; veins, except for the midrib, obscure.

In rocky and sandy soil. In Michigan mostly on the shores of the Great Lakes. Flowering July and August.

MARSH ST. JOHN'S-WORT

Hypericum virginicum L. var. *fraseri* (Spach) Fern.　Plate 107

Plate 108

Frostweed
(*Helianthemum canadense*)

Shrubby St. John's-wort
(*Hypericum kalmianum*)

Usually simple but sometimes bushy-branched perennial with 1 to several, often purplish stems up to 8 dm. tall; usually stoloniferous. Flowers relatively few, flesh-color to mauve, large, borne in axillary or terminal clusters. Petals 5; sepals 5, oblong to elliptic, blunt; stamens 9, in 3 clusters which alternate with 3 large, orange glands; capsule often rounded. Leaves opposite, sessile and heart-shaped at base or clasping; oblong to oblong-ovate, entire, 2–7 cm. long, often purplish, dotted with translucent spots; upper leaves smaller.

In open marshes, swamps, bogs, and in wet sand along lakes and in shallow water. Flowering July and August.

It is often hard to find these flowers open, even when the weather appears favorable.

COMMON ST. JOHN'S-WORT

Hypericum perforatum L.   Plate 107

Smooth, many-branched perennial up to 6 dm. tall, having translucent dots and black spots on many parts and frequently producing runners at the base. Flowers numerous, bright yellow, about 2.5–3 cm. broad, borne in leafy terminal cymes. Petals 5, separate, oblique at apex, unequal in size, frequently with black dots along the margin; sepals 5; stamens numerous, united at the base into 3–5 clusters, often with black dots; pistil 1, the ovary superior, ovoid, 3-celled, the styles 3, spreading; capsule 3-celled, many-seeded. Leaves opposite, sessile, narrowly oblong to lanceolate, entire, smooth, having small transparent dots (best seen when held up to the light) and black dots.

In dryish open ground, often in sandy soil, in pastures, along roads and railways. Introduced from Europe; now a common weed. Flowering July to September.

This species produces an interesting photosensitization in unpigmented skin of cattle, sheep, and horses. If a white-skinned animal is exposed to strong sunlight after eating these plants, it suffers a severe skin irritation which may result in blistering of the skin and falling hair.

ST. JOHN'S-WORT

Hypericum majus (Gray) Britt.   Plate 107

Erect perennial with solitary or tufted stems up to 7 dm. tall, often reddish below. Flowers numerous, small, yellow, borne in axillary or terminal cymes. Leaves commonly ascending, opposite, lanceolate, rounded and sessile or clasping at the base, upper ones 3–7-nerved at the base.

On margins of dune ponds, in marshes, on wet sandy or gravelly lake shores, and on river banks. Flowering late June to early September.

Several other small herbaceous species and one very large, tall species, *H. pyramidatum* Ait., also occur in the state.

ROCKROSE FAMILY. CISTACEAE

This small family of about 8 genera and 175 species is especially abundant in the Mediterranean region.

PLATE 109
Canadian White Violet (*Viola canadensis*)

FROSTWEED

Helianthemum canadense (L.) Michx.   Plate 108

Erect perennial 2–5 dm. tall, un-branched at first but branching after the first flowers bloom. Flowers of 2 kinds; petalled flowers showy, yellow, 2.5–3 cm. wide, solitary at the top of the stem, opening in sunshine; petals 5, broadly obovate, soon withering and falling; sepals 5, the 2 outer ones much the smaller; stamens numerous; pistil solitary, the ovary superior, ovoid, the style short; capsule 1-celled, many-seeded; self-pollinating, nonopening flowers small, numerous, lacking petals, producing larger capsules than the petalled flowers. Leaves scattered, elliptic, tapering evenly to both ends, 1–3.5 cm. long, green above, whitish and hairy beneath.

In dry, open, sandy woods, clearings, and barrens. Flowering mid-May to mid-July.

It is said that the name Frostweed was applied because crystals of ice shoot from the cracked bark at the base of the plants in late autumn.

VIOLET FAMILY. VIOLACEAE

This widely distributed family is found on all continents and includes about 16 genera, 850 species. Violets and pansies are well-known ornamental plants. Over 100 species of violet are cultivated.

Our members of this family are low herbs with irregular flowers. There are 5 petals, one of which is spurred, and 5 distinct sepals; the 5 stamens are often slightly united at the base and enclose the ovary; the fruit is a 3-sided capsule.

Viola

1. Flowers white or yellow (sometimes having blue veins) 2
1. Flowers lilac, bluish, or lavender 7
  2. Flowers white 3
  2. Flowers yellow 6
3. Plants with leafy stems . . . . *V. canadensis,* Plate 109
3. Plants stemless 4
  4. Leaves broadly heart-shaped to kidney-shaped 5
  4. Leaves lanceolate . . . . *V. lanceolata,* Plate 110
5. Plants having stolons . . . . *V. pallens,* Plate 110
5. Plants lacking stolons . . . . *V. renifolia,* Plate 110
  6. Plants hairy, usually lacking basal leaves . . *V. pubescens,* Plate 110
  6. Plants soon glabrous; 1–3 basal leaves usually present . . . . *V. pensylvanica,* Plate 110
7. Plants with leafy stems 8
7. Plants stemless 9
  8. Lateral petals beardless, petals with a darker lilac-purple spot near center . . . . . . *V. rostrata,* Plate 111
  8. Lateral petals bearded, petals lacking a darker center spot . . . . *V. conspersa,* Plate 112
9. Leaves cordate-ovate, margin merely toothed . . *V. papilionacea,* Plate 111
9. Leaves deeply cut into narrow segments . . . *V. pedata,* Plate 111

PLATE 110

Lance-leaved White Violet
(*Viola lanceolata*)

(*Viola pubescens*)
Downy Yellow Violet
Smooth Yellow Violet
(*Viola pensylvanica*)

Small White Violet
(*Viola pallens*)
Kidney-leaved White Violet
(*Viola renifolia*)

Canadian White Violet, Tall White Violet
Viola canadensis L.
Plate 109

Smooth perennial with one to many stems up to 5 dm. tall from a thickset subwoody rootstock. Flowers white, veined with purple, and soon violet-tinged on the back, about 2.5 cm. wide, irregular, solitary on slender peduncles from the axils of the leaves. Lateral petals bearded, the spur on the lower petal short and rounded; sepals slender, separate, having basal auricles; stamens flattened, closely sur-rounding the ovary; pistil solitary, the ovary superior, the style capitate; capsule subglobose; seeds numerous, brown. Leaves heart-shaped-ovate, the upper ones narrower; basal leaves long-petioled; stipules narrowly lance-olate, thin, dryish, pointed.

In deciduous woods. Flowering late April to July, infrequently and spo-radically to October.

Lance-leaved White Violet
Viola lanceolata L.
Plate 110

Stemless, freely stoloniferous peren-nial, often growing in dense mats. Flowers white, with purple veins; petals all beardless, the spur on lower petal shorter than the blade. Leaves lanceolate to oblanceolate, gradually tapering to the margined petiole, ob-scurely crenate.

In damp, open ground or in light shade. Flowering May to June.

Small White Violet
Viola pallens (Banks) Brainerd
Plate 110

Small, stemless, stoloniferous peren-nial. Flowers white, veined with pur-ple, borne above the leaves, solitary on peduncles from the base, less than 1 cm. broad, fragrant. Lateral petals beardless, the spur on the lower petal shorter than the blade. Self-pollinat-ing, nonopening flowers on peduncles above the ground, evident at flower-ing time. Leaves all basal, glabrous, heart-shaped-ovate to kidney-shaped, crenate; petioles smooth or with a few short hairs.

In wet or springy woods or thickets, on slopes, and in openings. Flowering early April to July.

V. incognita Brainerd, perhaps our commonest stemless, white-flowered violet, differs in having the lateral petals bearded.

Kidney-leaved White Violet
Viola renifolia Gray
Plate 110

Stemless, nonstoloniferous perennial with threadlike rootstocks. Flowers white, with purple veins, the petals all beardless. Leaves whitened with long silky hairs when young, kidney-shaped to round, heart-shaped at the base.

In cool, mossy woods, and swamps, on calcareous slopes. Flowering May and June.

Downy Yellow Violet
Viola pubescens Ait.
Plate 110

Softly hairy perennial with 1 to a few leafy stems 3–4 dm. tall, leafless at the base or with one leaf. Flowers yellow, with dark purplish or blackish veins, about 1–1.5 cm. wide, solitary on peduncles from the axils of the leaves, borne either above or below the leaves. Lateral petals slightly

PLATE 111

Common Blue Violet
(*Viola papilionacea*)

Long-spurred Violet
(*Viola rostrata*)

Bird-foot Violet
(*Viola pedata*)

234

bearded, the spur on lower petal short; capsule ovoid, white-woolly. Stem leaves few, borne near the summit of the stem, broadly ovate, petioled, densely downy, at least at first, the teeth coarse and shallow, 13–23 on each half; stipules green, semi-ovate.

In rich deciduous woods and thickets. Flowering May and early June.

SMOOTH YELLOW VIOLET

Viola pensylvanica Michx.   Plate 110

Quite similar to the Downy Yellow Violet, but usually with 1–3 small, somewhat kidney-shaped basal leaves, the stem leaves smaller and with fewer teeth (8–15 on each half) and the whole plant becoming quite glabrous.

In damp woods, on cool slopes, in rocky places. Flowering April and May.

LONG-SPURRED VIOLET

Viola rostrata Pursh   Plate 111

Leafy-stemmed perennial up to 12 cm. tall at flowering time. Flowers bluish-lilac, with a darker spot at the center, about 2 cm. wide, solitary on peduncles from the axils of the leaves. Lateral petals beardless, the spur on the lower petal 10–16 mm. long, and upcurved at the tip; style straight, slender, neither capitate nor bearded. Leaves mostly heart-shaped, the lower leaves rounder, crenate; stipules leaf-like, narrowly ovate, with narrow, pointed teeth.

In rich, often calcareous woods. Flowering April to June.

This may be distinguished from our other blue violets by the somewhat flattened appearance of the flower, its more lilac color, and the very noticeable long spurs.

AMERICAN DOG VIOLET

Viola conspersa Reichenb.   Plate 112

Resembling Long-spurred Violet in general appearance and color of the flowers, but there is no darker spot in the center of the flower, the style is bent down at the tip and somewhat hairy, the lateral petals are bearded, and the spur is usually only 4–5 mm. long.

COMMON BLUE VIOLET

Viola papilionacea Pursh   Plate 111

Small, densely tufted, stemless, glabrous perennial. Flowers violet or bluish, with a white center, the earlier flowers borne above the leaves, solitary on peduncles from the base of plant. Style enlarged upward, capitate with a conical beak on the lower side, the stigma inside the tip of the beak; self-pollinating, nonopening flowers borne on prostrate peduncles. Leaves broadly heart-shaped-ovate, long-petioled, crenate, glabrous.

In damp woods, thickets, meadows, and on shady ledges. Flowering late March to early June.

Among the other common Blue Violets, *V. sororia* Willd. is very similar to this species. It also has self-pollinating, nonopening flowers on prostrate peduncles, but the leaves and petioles are downy.

235

PLATE 112
American Dog Violet (*Viola conspersa*)
Prickly Pear (*Opuntia humifusa*)

236

The Hairy Blue Violet, V. *septentrionalis* Greene, is hairy, and the self-pollinating, nonopening flowers are borne on ascending or upright peduncles. Wood Violet, V. *affinis* Le Conte, is smooth, the spurred petal is bearded, the self-pollinating, nonopening flowers are on erect peduncles, and the leaves are narrowly heart-shaped. Marsh Violet, V. *cucullata* Ait., is smooth, the spurred petal has no beard, and there is a dark eye-spot in the center of the flower. It is frequently very difficult to distinguish these and some other species.

BIRD-FOOT *or* CROW-FOOT VIOLET,
PANSY VIOLET (Protected)

Viola pedata L. var. *lineariloba* DC.   Plate 111

Small, glabrous perennial up to 15 cm. tall. Flowers lilac, lavender, or bluish, 2–4 cm. wide, flat and wheel-shaped, borne on peduncles which hold them above the leaves. Petals all beardless, the lower one with a white spot at the base; style club-shaped, beakless, beardless; no cleistogamous, (self-pollinating) flowers produced. Leaves all from the base, fan-shaped, and divided into 3 main parts, the divisions cut nearly to the base into linear or narrowly oblanceolate segments, which may in turn be toothed or cleft near the apex; both early and late leaves less finely cut, smaller and thicker.

Usually in rather sterile soil, in open grassland, sunny woods, and openings, on rocky or sandy slopes. Flowering April and early June.

Unlike most of the violets, this species is difficult to grow in the garden.

CACTUS FAMILY.   CACTACEAE

This primarily American family includes 1200 to 1800 species, in 26 to 150 genera, depending on the authority consulted. The members are important as ornamentals, many species being grown in houses and greenhouses and, in the Southwest, cultivated in the garden. Over 1200 kinds are listed as being cultivated.

PRICKLY PEAR

Opuntia humifusa Raf.   Plate 112

Prostrate perennial often forming mats, the stems composed of pale to deep green fleshy segments up to 2.5 dm. long, the lower segments nearly round and bearing 4–9-mm.-long brown leaves (which soon fall) and numerous persistent clusters of barbed bristles, many of the clusters including stiff spines up to 5 cm. long. Flowers showy, yellow, sometimes with a red star-shaped eye-spot, opening in the sun for 2 days or more, borne along the margins of the newer segments. Petals 8–12; sepals numerous; stamens very numerous, inserted on the tube formed by the union of sepals and petals; ovary inferior; fruit green to dull purple, 2–5 cm. long, pulpy, edible but bearing some bristles around the base.

On sand dunes and open, sandy plains. Infrequent in Michigan. Flowering June and July.

PLATE 113

Water-willow
(*Decodon verticillatus*)

Spiked Loosestrife
(*Lythrum salicaria*)

LOOSESTRIFE FAMILY. LYTHRACEAE

This widely distributed family is most abundant in the American tropics. It includes about 23 genera and nearly 500 species. Several members are used for ornamentals, mostly in the southern part of the country.

The flowers are axillary or whorled. They have a well-developed hypanthium, i.e., a cuplike receptacle on which the calyx, corolla, and stamens appear to be borne. The ovary is superior. The stamens are usually the same number as the petals or twice as many. The style and stamens are often of 2 or 3 lengths.

WATER-WILLOW, WATER-OLEANDER
Decodon verticillatus (L.) Ell.   Plate 113

Herbaceous to slightly shrubby perennial with recurved stems up to 2.5 m. long, the stems 4-sided, the bark of the submersed portion spongy, the arched branches rooting at the tip to form new plants. Flowers magenta, on short pedicels in axillary clusters. Petals 5; calyx with 5–6 erect teeth and a like number of longer, spreading, hornlike processes; stamens 10, of 2 lengths; pistil 1, the styles of 3 lengths; capsule globose, 3–5 celled. Leaves opposite or whorled, lanceolate to narrowly elliptic, nearly sessile, smooth, entire to somewhat wavy.

Along margins of pools and small lakes, in bogs and swamps. Flowering early June to September.

SPIKED LOOSESTRIFE
Lythrum salicaria L.   Plate 113

Somewhat hairy perennial, usually with many erect stems up to 1.5 m. tall. Flowers showy, magenta to purple, cymose in axils of reduced upper leaves, and forming elongate, leafy slender, interrupted spikes. Petals usually 6 (5–7); calyx cylindrical, streaked, 5–7-toothed, having small appendages in the sinuses; stamens twice as many as the petals, of different lengths, inserted low on the throat of the calyx tube; pistil 1; capsule nearly cylindric, 2-celled. Leaves opposite or in 3's, sessile, lanceolate, heart-shaped or rounded to the base, 5–7.5 cm. long; upper leaves reduced.

In wet places, ditches, swamps, on lake shores and low or marshy banks. Introduced from Europe; now common. Flowering mid-June to early September.

This species grows so vigorously that it tends to crowd out some of our native species. Patches several acres in extent make a beautiful display when in bloom.

The native Winged Loosestrife, *Lythrum alatum* Pursh, is much less showy than Spiked Loosestrife. It is somewhat wandlike, simple or branched above, often becoming leafless below, the stems 4-angled and winged. Flowers reddish-purple, solitary and sessile or short-stalked in the axils of the upper leaves.

EVENING-PRIMROSE FAMILY. ONAGRACEAE

This family of about 20 genera and 650 species is worldwide in distribution. A number of species in several genera are cultivated

Plate 114

Common Evening-primrose
(*Oenothera biennis*)

Sundrops
(*Oenothera fruticosa*)

as ornamentals. Evening-primrose, Sundrops, Fuchsia, and Clarkia are familiar examples.

There are 2 or 4 petals and calyx lobes; the stamens are the same number, or twice as many, as the petals. The ovary is inferior, and the calyx tube is attached to it; this may be very slender and is sometimes mistaken for the pedicel. The petals and stamens are attached at the top of the calyx tube.

ONAGRACEAE

1. Petals 4 . . . . **2**
1. Petals 2 . . . . . . *Circaea quadrisulcata* or *alpina*, Plate 116

  2. Flowers usually magenta . . *Epilobium angustifolium*, Color Plate 10
  2. Flowers white or yellow **3**

3. Flowers yellow . . . . . *Oenothera biennis* or *fruticosa*, Plate 114
3. Flowers white, becoming pink . . . . . *Gaura biennis*, Plate 115

FIREWEED, GREAT WILLOW-HERB

Epilobium angustifolium L.   Color Plate 10

Erect perennial with solitary or few very leafy, simple or branched stems up to 3.5 m. tall. Flowers magenta, purplish, or rose-purple, rarely white, borne in an elongate, simple raceme on densely hairy pedicels. Perianth borne at the top of the elongate calyx tube; petals 4, obovate, spreading, slightly unequal, entire; calyx tube cleft to the top of the ovary, the 4 lobes linear, colored about like the petals; stamens 8, curved downward; ovary inferior, elongate; style hairy at the base, longer than the stamens; stigma white, conspicuously 4-lobed; capsule very slender, 5–7 cm. long, the seeds numerous, smooth, bearing a tuft of long whitish hairs at the summit. Leaves alternate, lanceolate, entire or finely toothed, green above, pale beneath, the lateral veins forming conspicuous marginal loops; petioles short.

In dry soil in burned-over land, ravines, and recent clearings, along roads and railways, and in fields. Flowering June to September.

This is a very variable species with a number of varieties and forms. The fresh or moistened dried leaves were used by the Indians as poultices for bruises. The young shoots and leaves may be used as a substitute for asparagus. In spite of its attractive flowers, this species is not desirable in the garden as it tends to grow rank and straggly and to spread too rapidly.

An introduced species, *E. hirsutum* L., is becoming established in the state. This is a more spreading plant with a loose raceme; the flowers are fewer and a little smaller; the petals are notched at the tip; and all parts of the plant are quite hairy. Some much smaller species are quite common. *E. leptophyllum* Raf. usually has white flowers not over 5 mm. wide, and the leaves and stem have tiny, incurved hairs. It grows in bogs, low ground, marshes, and wet meadows. *E. strictum* Muhl. is similar in appearance and habitat but is

PLATE 115
Gaura (*Gaura biennis*)

242

PLATE 116

Enchanter's Nightshade
(*Circaea alpina*)

Enchanter's Nightshade
(**Circaea quadrisulcata**)

more sparingly branched. The flowers are pinkish and the hairs stand out at right angles. The common and variable *E. glandulosum* Lehm. has the leaves and lower part of the stem glabrous or nearly so.

COMMON EVENING-PRIMROSE

Oenothera biennis L.   Plate 114

Stout, erect, sometimes branched biennial up to 2 m. tall, the ridged, often purplish stems produced from the previous year's rosette. Flowers yellow, 2–3 cm. wide, opening in the evening, closing during the day, borne in dense terminal spikes which become greatly elongated, each flower subtended by a leaf. Petals 4 (15–25 mm. long), in age often purplish, broadly ovate, attached with the stamens to the top of the calyx tube; calyx tube slender, greatly elongated beyond the ovary, 4-lobed, the lobes at first closely converging, later reflexed and the tips pointing directly back; stamens 8, equal in length; pistil 1, the ovary inferior; style very long, slender, the stigma with 4 linear lobes; capsule longer than the subtending leaf, oblong-cylindric, narrowed toward the blunt apex. Rosette leaves numerous, compact, elongate; stem leaves lanceolate to narrowly elliptic, 5–15 cm. long, the margin slightly uneven or with a few small teeth; upper leaves sessile, lower leaves petioled.

In dry or sandy soil, in fields, along roads, and in waste ground. Flowering late June to fall.

Common Evening-primrose varies greatly in abundance in a given locality; in some years it may be very abundant, in other years quite rare. Extensive genetical studies have been and still are being made on this and closely related species. Some of these provided the experimental basis for DeVries' theory of evolution by mutation.

Small-flowered Evening-primrose, *O. parviflora* L., has slightly smaller flowers (petals 10–15 mm. long); the tips of the calyx lobes are separate at the base, not forming a tube in bud; and the plants tend to be smaller. Cutleaf Evening-primrose, *O. laciniata* Hill, has fewer, large, yellow or whitish flowers (which become reddish) borne in the axils of the upper leaves and not forming a distinct spike. The leaves are decidedly wavy, toothed, or pinnately cut.

SUNDROPS

Oenothera fruticosa L.   Plate 114

Erect or ascending clustered perennial up to 1 m. tall, usually covered with incurved hairs. Flowers blooming in the daytime, yellow, showy, up to 3.5 cm. broad, borne in the axils of the upper leaves. Calyx tube thread-like, 5–15 mm. long; capsule 4-angled, club-shaped, narrowed at base to a definite stalk. Rosette leaves (mostly lacking when the plant is in flower) ovate to spatulate, petioled; stem leaves alternate, lanceolate to narrowly elliptic or linear, tapered to a short petiole or sessile, hairy, entire or with a few scattered teeth; upper leaves often bearing short branchlets in the axils.

In dry soil, in fields and open woods. Locally common throughout the state. Flowering June and July.

244

O. perennis L. looks quite similar, but the tip of the flowering stem and the buds are nodding; the flowers usually open singly and become erect; and the petals are up to 9 mm. long.

GAURA

Gaura biennis L.   Plate 115

Long-hairy biennial up to 1.5 m. tall from a basal rosette. Flowers numerous, white, becoming pink or red, borne in slender, wandlike spikes. Petals 4, somewhat unequal, oblance-olate, clawed, about 5 mm. long; calyx tube slender, 5–7 mm. long, the 4 lobes reddish, reflexed in pairs; stamens 8, hanging downward, each filament with a small scale at the base; stigma 4-lobed, surrounded by a cup-like border; fruit hard and nutlike, 4-ribbed, hairy, tapered to both ends, sessile. Rosette leaves oblanceolate, 1–3 dm. long; stem leaves alternate, tapering at both ends, sessile, 3–10 cm. long, sparsely toothed.

In dry open ground, sandy or waste soil, or in damp places. In Michigan only in the southern part of the state. Flowering June to October.

ENCHANTER'S NIGHTSHADE

Circaea quadrisulcata (Maxim.) Franch. & Sav. var.
canadensis (L.) Hara   Plate 116

Erect perennial up to 1 m. tall, having threadlike stolons and slender rootstocks. Flowers small, white to roseate, borne in racemes that elongate in fruit. Petals 2, obovate; calyx tube slightly prolonged, the end filled with a cuplike disk, deciduous, the calyx lobes 2, reflexed; stamens 2; style 1; fruit small, burlike, corrugated, covered with strong, hooked bristles, borne on reflexed pedicels. Leaves opposite, oblong-ovate, rounded at the base, shallowly wavy-toothed, firm, dark green above, 4–15 cm. long, usually more than twice as long as broad, petioled.

In rich deciduous woods, in dryish or moist soil. Flowering July and August.

ENCHANTER'S NIGHTSHADE

Circaea alpina L.   Plate 116

Smaller and weaker than the preceding species, up to 3 dm. tall; the leaves ovate, usually less than twice as long as broad, pale green; the disk inconspicuous; the stigma deeply cleft; the fruit not corrugated.

In moist or wet woods and mossy bogs. Flowering June to September.

GINSENG FAMILY. ARALIACEAE

This primarily tropical family includes about 65 genera and more than 800 species. English Ivy (*Hedera*), its variants, and some related species which climb by aerial roots are extensively cultivated evergreen vines, and several species of shrubs and small trees are also cultivated. The pith used in making Chinese rice paper is derived from a member of this family. The medicinal ginseng roots much used by the Chinese are obtained from a Manchurian species

PLATE 117
Wild Sarsaparilla (*Aralia nudicaulis*)

and from *Panax quinquefolius.* Devil's-Club (*Oplopanax horridus*), found in western United States and on Isle Royale, is the bane of hikers because its numerous prickles cause festering sores.

The flowers are borne in umbels, the flower parts are mostly in 5's, the petals are not incurved. The ovary is inferior and is topped by 2 or more styles; the fruit is a berry. The leaves are usually alternate and compound, the petioles are usually adnate to the stipule and are not sheathing at the base.

ARALIACEAE

1. Umbels solitary; leaves once compound, borne in whorls . . . . *Panax trifolius* or *quinquefolius,* Plate 119
1. Umbels 2 or more; leaves 2–3 times compound, alternate or basal . . . . *Aralia,* 2
   2. Plants having sharp bristles on stem, at least at base . . . . *A. hispida,* Plate 118
   2. Stems not bristly 3
3. Leaves and peduncles coming from base; umbels usually 3 . . . . *A. nudicaulis,* Plate 117
3. Leaves borne on stems; umbels usually numerous . *A. racemosa,* Plate 118

BRISTLY SARSAPARILLA

Aralia hispida Vent.   Plate 118

Bristly, strong-scented, erect perennial up to 1 m. tall, the slender spines especially abundant on lower part of the stem. Flowers small, greenish, borne in simple, somewhat globose umbels, the umbels several, usually above the leaves. Berry globose, black.

Leaves pinnately compound or twice compound, the leaflets oblong-ovate, toothed, sessile, smooth or hairy on the veins beneath.

In clearings and in rocky or sandy, open woods. Flowering June to August.

Jelly is sometimes made from the berries of this plant. It has a rather strong flavor.

WILD SARSAPARILLA

Aralia nudicaulis L.   Plate 117

Stemless perennial up to 5 dm. tall, the solitary leaf and peduncle arising from a thick brown rootstock. Flowers whitish, small, borne usually in 3 (2–7) umbels, on a scape which is shorter than the leaf. Petals 5, often tinged with green or purple outside, inserted at the top of the calyx tube, often deflexed but not incurved; calyx teeth 5, small, alternate with the petals; stamens 5, white, inserted on the calyx tube; pistil 1, the ovary 5-

celled, inferior; styles 5, distinct to the base; berry dark bluish-black. Leaf with 3 divisions, each division pinnately 3–5-foliolate, the leaflets oblong-ovate to ovate, up to 15 cm. long, finely and regularly toothed, the upper surface varnished-looking at least when young, the under surface downy.

In moist or dry woods. Flowering late May and June.

The long, horizontal rootstocks are aromatic. The Indians used the

$\frac{1}{3}$

$\frac{2}{3}$

R.Brede

PLATE 118

Spikenard
(*Aralia racemosa*)

Bristly Sarsaparilla
(*Aralia hispida*)

pounded roots for treating nosebleed and to make poultices for infections. The root steeped with other herbs was applied to the chest and legs of horses suffering from exhaustion. The fruits and seeds are eaten by birds and chipmunks.

SPIKENARD
Aralia racemosa L.   Plate 118

Stout, spreading, smooth or slightly hairy perennial up to 2 m. tall from large, thick, spicy-aromatic roots. Flowers small, greenish, borne in numerous umbels which are usually at least partly hidden by the leaves. Styles united; fruits nearly globular, reddish- brown to dark purple. Leaves few, large, widely spreading, the 3 primary divisions pinnately compound, the leaflets ovate, variable in size, up to 15 cm. long, sharply toothed, obliquely heart-shaped at base.

In rich woods and thickets. Flowering June to August.

This species was used medicinally by the Indians, as a poultice and blood purifier and for treating coughs. The roots were also prepared with wild onion, gooseberries, and maple sugar as a food.

DWARF GINSENG, GROUND-NUT
Panax trifolius L.   Plate 119

Small, delicate, smooth, unbranched perennial 1–2 dm. tall from a deep-seated, globose root. Flowers small, white, often unisexual, 15 or more in a single terminal, nearly globose umbel, the peduncle 2–8 cm. long, the pedicels and upper part of the peduncle white. Petals 5, purplish or rose in bud, attached at the top of the ovary; calyx white, tubular, adherent to the ovary, the 5 lobes scarcely noticeable; stamens 5, alternate with the petals; ovary inferior, the styles usually 3; berry small, yellowish, 3-angled. Leaves 3, in a whorl near the summit of the stem, palmately compound, the 3–5 leaflets sessile, narrowly oblong, 4–8 cm. long.

In rich woods and thickets and in clearings, usually in moist soil. Flowering April to June.

GINSENG
Panax quinquefolius L.   Plate 119

Unbranched perennial 2–6 dm. tall, bearing a single long-peduncled umbel. Flowers greenish-white, mostly perfect, the styles usually 3; berry bright red. Leaves usually 3, borne in a whorl, palmately compound, the leaflets usually 5 (3–7), oblong-ovate to ovate, sharply toothed, petioled.

In rich woods. Flowering June and July.

This species was formerly very common. Quantities of the roots were shipped to China for medicinal uses, and it was collected so extensively that it is now quite rare.

PARSLEY FAMILY. UMBELLIFERAE

This is a large, cosmopolitan family of about 125 genera and nearly 3000 species. Nearly 400 species occur in this country. The

PLATE 119

Dwarf Ginseng
(*Panax trifolius*)

Ginseng
(*Panax quinquefolius*)

family is quite important economically. Carrots, parsnips, celery, and parsley are important foods. Anise, caraway, chervil, dill, and fennel are used for flavoring. Blue Laceflower, Angelica, Sea Holly, and Cow-parsnip are grown as ornamentals. Water Hemlock, Fool's Parsley, and Poison Hemlock are very poisonous and several other species slightly so.

The Umbelliferae are characterized by having small flowers usually borne in umbels. The flower parts are in 5's except for the single pistil with its inferior, 2-celled ovary. The petals are usually incurved, and the fruit consists of 2 seedlike, dry carpels which separate from each other when ripe. The foliage is aromatic, and the leaves are usually compound or deeply lobed. The petioles are enlarged to form a sheathing base.

UMBELLIFERAE

1. Ovary and fruit covered with bristles or hooked or barbed prickles . . 12
1. Ovary and fruit lacking bristles or prickles 2
  2. Flowers yellow 3
  2. Flowers white 6
3. Leaflets having entire margins . . . . *Taenidia integerrima,* Plate 126
3. Leaflets with toothed margins 4
  4. Leaves pinnately compound, having 5 or more
    leaflets . . . . *Pastinaca sativa,* Plate 128
  4. Leaves compound or twice compound in 3's 5
5. Central flower of each umbel on a stalk; terminal leaflets
  longer than lateral leaflets . . . . . *Thaspium trifoliatum,* Plate 126
5. Central flower of each umbel not stalked; terminal leaflet
  shorter than lateral leaflets . . . . . . *Zizia aurea,* Plate 123
  6. Leaves 2–3 times compound 7
  6. Leaves once compound, leaflets distinct 10
7. Flowering in early spring; leaves mostly from base
  of plant . . . . *Erigenia bulbosa,* Plate 122
7. Flowering in summer; leaves principally on stem 8
  8. Margin of leaflets merely toothed 9
  8. Margin of leaflets deeply lobed or divided into segments
    to coarsely incised, so that leaf appears to be
    greatly dissected . . . . *Conium maculatum,* Plate 122
9. Umbel densely hairy; blades of upper leaves reduced,
  their sheaths greatly enlarged . . . . *Angelica venenosa,* Plate 127
9. Umbel not hairy; upper leaves having distinct blades, sheaths
  less than 1 cm. wide . . *Cicuta maculata* or *bulbifera,* Plates 124, 125
  10. Leaves pinnately compound, leaflets linear-lanceolate
    (submerged leaves often more than once
    compound) . . . . *Sium suave,* Plate 125
  10. Leaves trifoliolate, leaflets ovate or cordate 11
11. Umbels irregular, few-flowered; plants not hairy; not
  especially robust . . . . . . *Cryptotaenia canadensis,* Plate 125
11. Umbels large, regular; leaflets cordate at base,
  palmately veined; plants robust . . *Heracleum maximum,* Plate 129

Black Snakeroot
(*Sanicula gregaria*)
Black Snakeroot
(*Sanicula canadensis*)

PLATE 120

Black Snakeroot
(*Sanicula marilandica*)

12. Fruit several times longer than
wide . . . . . *Osmorhiza claytoni* or *longistylis*, Plate 121
12. Fruit not several times longer than wide 13
13. Plants pubescent, leaves finely dissected . . . *Daucus carota*, Plate 130
13. Plants smooth, leaves palmately compound with 3–7
leaflets . . . . *Sanicula*, 14
14. Styles longer than bristles of fruit 15
14. Styles shorter than bristles of fruit and hidden
by them . . . . *S. canadensis*, Plate 120
15. Fruits sessile, 5–8 mm. long; sepals of staminate
flowers rigid . . . . *S. marilandica*, Plate 120
15. Fruits on a stalk, less than 5 mm. long; sepals of
staminate flowers soft . . . . *S. gregaria*, Plate 120

BLACK SNAKEROOT

Sanicula canadensis L.   Plate 120

More spreading than the other two species, the branches forking 2 or 3 times, the lower leaves mostly 3-foliolate, the upper leaves greatly reduced, those in the flower clusters very small and usually in pairs; flowers white, anthers white, fruit subglobose.

In dry open woods. Flowering May to July.

BLACK SNAKEROOT

Sanicula marilandica L.   Plate 120

Perennial with strongly ascending branches up to 1.2 m. tall from a thick rootstock. Flowers greenish-white or yellowish, tiny, borne in rather stiff, headlike umbels which have 2 or more stiff, ascending, 3-forked rays and a shorter, unbranched central ray; staminate flowers mixed with the perfect flowers or in separate small umbels. Fruits 3–8, ovoid, 5–8 mm. long, sessile, brownish, 2-celled, not readily separating, covered with stiff, hooked bristles, the styles longer than the bristles, curved and spreading, conspicuous. Basal leaves long-petioled, 5-parted or appearing 7-parted, the leaflets obovate, unequally cut, toothed; stem leaves alternate, similar to the basal or with elliptic leaflets, the upper leaves smaller and sessile; greatly reduced leaves forming the involucre at the base of the umbel.

In thickets and open woods, on ridges, in wet swampy places and marshes. Common. Flowering May to July.

BLACK SNAKEROOT

Sanicula gregaria Bickn.   Plate 120

Quite similar in aspect to the preceding species, but the fruits are globose, 2.5–4 mm. long, and are borne on a stalk. This species tends to be more slender and shorter (up to 8 dm. tall), the leaves mostly smaller, with sharply toothed leaflets; flowers greenish-yellow; anthers bright yellow.

In rich woods and thickets. Flowering late April to July.

SWEET CICELY

Osmorhiza claytoni (Michx.) C. B. Clarke   Plate 121

Slender, downy to long-hairy perennial up to 9 dm. tall. Flowers white, tiny, borne in compound umbels, the umbels usually held above the leaves, subtended by an involucre. Fruit linear to narrowly club-shaped, upright,

PLATE 121

Sweet Cicely
(*Osmorhiza claytoni*)

Anise-root
(*Osmorhiza longistylis*)

blackish, ribbed, the slender ribs covered with stiff, upward-pointing appressed bristles. Leaves thin, basal or alternate, compound, the main divisions in 3's or 5's; lower leaves long-petioled, upper ones sessile, the leaflets ovate to lanceolate, pointed at apex, often cleft and having coarse rounded teeth, 4–7 cm. long, green on upper surface, whitened beneath with stiff hairs.

In low, or rich deciduous woods, on wooded slopes and river banks, in thickets and moist, open fields. Flowering May to June.

The Indians ate the roots and branches as an aid in gaining weight, and used decoctions made from the root in treating sore throat, ulcers, and running sores.

ANISE-ROOT
Osmorhiza longistylis (Torr.) DC.   Plate 121

Coarser than the preceding species, up to 1.2 m. tall, the leaflets larger, the roots sweet and aromatic with an anise odor. The styles are longer than the petals at flowering time and become 3.5–4 mm. long in fruit.

In rich, often alluvial, woods and thickets. Flowering May to June.

These two species of *Osmorhiza* seldom grow together. Two other species also occur in the northern part of the state.

HARBINGER-OF-SPRING, PEPPER-AND-SALT
Erigenia bulbosa (Michx.) Nutt.   Plate 122

Delicate, low perennial not over 4 dm. tall at flowering time, from a deep-seated globose tuber. Flowers white, small, borne in a single, compound, leafy-bracted umbel, the peduncle at first very short so that the flowers often appear to be half buried, later raised a little. Petals flat; anthers blackish-red; seeds flattened, kidney-shaped. Leaves 1–2, 1–3 times compound, the divisions in 3's, the leaf segments linear to oblong.

In deciduous woods. Flowering March (rarely February) and April.

Although not particularly attractive, this species is of interest because of its early flowering. It is also one of the most easily identified species of this rather difficult family. The contrast between the blackish-red anthers and the white petals is the basis for the name Pepper-and-salt.

POISON HEMLOCK
Conium maculatum L.   Plate 122

Smooth, purple-spotted, hollow-stemmed biennial up to 2 m. tall. Flowers white, tiny, in showy umbels, the central or first umbel being quickly overtopped by later ones; involucre of narrow bracts. Fruit ovoid, somewhat flattened, smooth, having prominent wavy ribs, no oil tubes. Leaves alternate, petioled, 2–3 times compound, the leaflets lanceolate, pinnately cut and deeply crenate-dentate, the fresh leaves having a nauseous taste and parsniplike odor when bruised.

In waste places, woodlots, roadsides, around farm buildings. Naturalized from Europe. Flowering late June to September.

255

PLATE 122

Harbinger-of-spring
(*Erigenia bulbosa*)

Poison Hemlock
(*Conium maculatum*)

PLATE 123
Golden Alexanders (*Zizia aurea*)

PLATE 124
Water-hemlock (*Cicuta maculata*)

258

All parts of this species are poisonous and should be avoided. It is said that the poison the Greeks gave to Socrates was derived from this species. One can be poisoned by just blowing a whistle made from the hollow stems. The plant is most poisonous at the time the fruits are ripe.

GOLDEN ALEXANDERS

Zizia aurea (L.) W. D. J. Koch   Plate 123

Erect, often red-tinged, perennial up to 1 m. tall, having a strong parsley odor when crushed. Flowers yellow, tiny, borne in a flattish compound umbel, the central flower of each umbel sessile, the others on pedicels; primary rays of the umbels 10–18, the outer rays of the terminal umbel becoming 3–5 cm. long and stiffly ascending in fruit; involucre lacking. Fruit oblong, glabrous, the ribs threadlike. Leaves membranous; stem leaves mostly 2–3 times compound, the leaflets ovate to lanceolate, sharply toothed, the terminal leaflet no longer than the lateral leaflets; upper leaves merely 3-foliolate.

In fields, along roadsides and shores, in swamps and damp thickets. Flowering April to June.

WATER-HEMLOCK

Cicuta maculata L.   Plate 124

Stout, erect, many-branched perennial up to 2.2 m. tall from a cluster of fleshy, fingerlike roots, the stem often mottled with purple below. Flowers white, tiny, borne in flat-topped terminal or axillary umbels which are usually above the leaves; involucres lacking but the small umbels having several slender, drooping bracts. Fruit ovoid or ellipsoid, having alternate ribs and furrows. Leaves 2–3 times pinnately compound, the lower leaves long-petioled; leaflets linear to lanceolate, bright green, sharply toothed, with conspicuous pinnate veins; upper leaves having distinct blades, the sheaths less than 1 cm. wide.

In marshy places, along streams, in wet meadows and swales. Flowering June to September.

The clustered roots resemble small sweet potatoes. They smell like parsnips and are deadly poisonous.

CUT-LEAVED WATER-HEMLOCK

Cicuta bulbifera L.   Plate 125

This species is characterized by the small clustered bulblets in the axils of the upper leaves; the leaflets are linear or narrowly lanceolate and have only a few teeth.

In swamps and marshes. Flowering July to September.

WILD CHERVIL

Cryptotaenia canadensis (L.) DC.   Plate 125

Smooth perennial up to 1 m. tall. Flowers white, small, in irregular, few-rayed umbels which are not subtended by an involucre. Fruits dark brown, stiffly erect, slenderly ellipsoid, beaked, ribbed, about 5–7 mm. long. Leaves alternate, 3-foliolate (sometimes appearing 5-foliolate), thin, the leaflets large, ovate, often deeply lobed.

In rich woods and thickets, on flood plains, and along roads. Flowering June to September.

R Brede

PLATE 125

Wild Chervil
(*Cryptotaenia canadensis*)

Water-parsnip
(*Sium suave*)

Cut-leaved Water-hemlock
(*Cicuta bulbifera*)

Yellow Pimpernel
Taenidia integerrima (L.) Drude   Plate 126

Smooth, often glaucous perennial up to 8 dm. tall. Flowers tiny, yellow, borne in compound umbels which do not have subtending involucres. Fruit flattened, wingless. Leaves compound or more usually 2–3 times compound, the divisions in 3's, leaflets smooth, sessile or short-stalked, lanceolate to ovate, entire, having a celerylike but somewhat disagreeable odor when crushed.

In dry, rocky or gravelly woods and thickets and along roads. Flowering late May to July.

Water-parsnip
Sium suave Walt.   Plate 125

Erect, branching perennial up to 1.5–2 m. tall, branched mostly above the middle, the stems corrugated or angled. Flowers white, borne in large compound umbels; involucre of narrow bracts. Fruit stalked, prominently corky-ribbed and having 1–3 oil tubes between the ribs. Leaves alternate, petioled, compound, the leaflets 5–17, linear or lanceolate, finely toothed, the earliest submersed rosette leaves very thin, 2–3 times pinnately dissected into linear segments.

In low swampy ground, along streams, on muddy banks, in wet thickets, most commonly in land that is covered with water part of the time. Flowering July to September.

This species is easily distinguished from Poison Hemlock by the once-pinnate leaves and the corrugations of the stems. A different plant of swampy places, Cowbane, *Oxypolis rigidior* (L.) C. & R., is superficially similar to Water Parsnip, but the leaflets are entire or have only a few teeth.

Yellow Meadow-parsnip
Thaspium trifoliatum (L.) Gray var. flavum Blake   Plate 126

Erect, branching perennial up to 1.5 m. tall. Flowers tiny, yellow, all pedicelled, including the central flower in each umbel, the large, compound terminal umbel flattish at first but becoming globular. Fruit ovoid to ellipsoid, slightly flattened, the ribs usually winged. Leaves mostly 3-foliolate or with 5 leaflets, the lateral leaflets sometimes 2–3-lobed; leaflets lanceolate to ovate, sharply toothed; basal leaves simple, and heart-shaped at base, rarely 3-foliolate.

In rich woods and thickets and in marshy places. Flowering May to July.

A quite similar species, *T. barbinode* (Michx.) Nutt., also grows in Michigan. It is slightly smaller, the stems are hairy at the nodes, the stem leaves are twice pinnate, and the flowers are pale yellow. Yellow Meadow-parsnip can be distinguished from Golden Alexanders by its pedicelled flowers and fruit.

Angelica
Angelica venenosa (Greenway) Fern.   Plate 127

Rather slender perennial up to 1.8 m. tall. Flowers white or greenish, borne in large, terminal, densely hairy, compound umbels, the central umbel up to 1.5 dm. broad. Fruit tan, flattened, ribbed, and wing-margined, with sev-

PLATE 126

Yellow Meadow-parsnip
(*Thaspium trifoliatum*)

Yellow Pimpernel
(*Taenidia integerrima*)

PLATE 127
Angelica (*Angelica venenosa*)

PLATE 128
Wild Parsnip (*Pastinaca sativa*)

eral oil tubes between the ribs. Basal and lower leaves compound, with 3 primary divisions, odd-pinnate, the leaflets thick, lanceolate to oblong, toothed, 2–7 cm. long; upper leaves reduced to tubular sheaths with or without small blades; blades, if present, shorter than the sheaths: sheaths greatly dilated, more than 1 cm. wide.

In dry woods, thickets, and openings. Mostly in southern part of Michigan. Flowering July to September.

This species may be distinguished from the closely similar *Cicuta* by the leaf veins which end in the tips of the teeth; in *Cicuta* they terminate in or near the notches, and the sheaths of the upper leaves are usually less than 1 cm. wide. Alexanders, *A. atropurpurea* L., a much more common species, occurs throughout the state. It has a very stout stem which is glabrous or nearly so.

WILD PARSNIP

Pastinaca sativa L.   Plate 128

Smooth, coarse, stout biennial up to 1.5 m. tall. Flowers small, yellow, borne in very broad, flat-topped, compound umbels, the terminal umbels soon overtopped by the others; primary rays 15–25, unequal; involucres lacking. Fruits broadly oval, flattened, ribbed. Leaves pinnately compound, the lower and basal leaves petioled, up to 5 dm. long, thin, the leaflets 5–15, ovate to oblong, 5–10 cm. long, sessile, lobed or cut, sharply toothed; upper leaves similar to lower leaves but smaller.

In old fields, sunny waste places, along roads. Native of Eurasia; long cultivated. Flowering May to October.

According to some authorities two varieties may be distinguished. The edible cultivated form is var. *hortensis* Ehrh.; the weedy, reputedly poisonous form, with a more slender root, is var. *pratensis* Pers.

COW-PARSNIP

Heracleum maximum Bartr.   Plate 129

Very stout perennial up to 3 m. tall, the stems hairy, strongly ridged, up to 5–6 cm. thick at the base. Flowers white, borne in very large, flattish umbels, composed of 15–35 smaller umbels; involucre soon falling. Corolla irregular, largest on the outer flowers; fruit broadly oval or obovate, flattened. Leaves 3-foliolate, up to 6 dm. long, the leaflets broadly ovate, circular, or heart-shaped, deeply lobed and sharply toothed.

In low, moist places, usually in rich soil. Flowering June to August.

The Indians used this species for medicine and food. The young stalks were roasted over hot coals. The leaf stalks were peeled and eaten raw like celery. The young roots when cooked taste like rutabaga.

WILD CARROT, QUEEN ANNE'S LACE

Daucus carota L.   Plate 130

Coarse, stiff, freely branching, bristly-hairy biennial up to 1 m. tall from a deep, fleshy tap root. Flowers very small, white or rarely roseate, borne in compact, compound, many-rayed umbels which usually have a purple

PLATE 129
Cow Parsnip (*Heracleum maximum*)

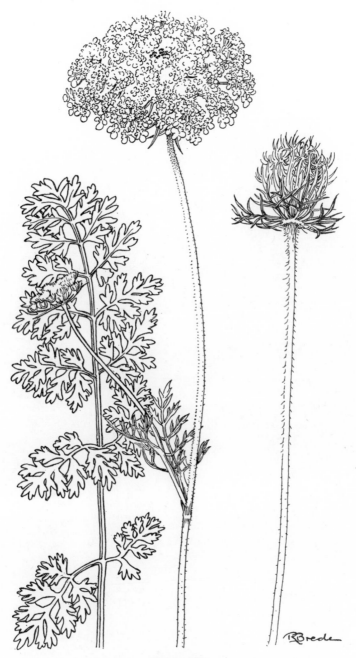

PLATE 130
Wild Carrot (*Daucus carota*)

267

Fruiting   Flowering

PLATE 131

Bunchberry (*Cornus canadensis*)

268

flower or flowers in the center, the umbels flattish at first, but becoming concave, the marginal flowers often enlarged and irregular; fruits flattened, ribbed, armed with barbed prickles; involucre of numerous large, pinnate bracts with long, very narrow, thread-like or linear, pointed lobes. Leaves finely pinnately 2–3 times compound, the segments narrow, lanceolate, tipped with a firm sharp point.

In dry fields and sunny waste places. Introduced from Europe; now a pernicious weed. Flowering June to September.

The cultivated carrot was derived from this wild species. Some people are sensitive to this plant and get a severe skin irritation from handling the foliage.

DOGWOOD FAMILY. CORNACEAE

This widely distributed family includes about 10 genera and 90 species of tropical and temperate plants. Flowering Dogwood, a tree, and several shrubby species of *Cornus* are widely grown as ornamentals. Most members of this family are woody, but a few species are herbaceous.

BUNCHBERRY, DWARF CORNEL
Cornus canadensis L.   Plate 131

Low, usually colonial perennial, the short, erect flowering stems up to 2.5 dm. tall from horizontal, woody, forking rootstocks. Flowers small, numerous, creamy, greenish, or yellow, in a single terminal cluster subtended by 4 large, white, petallike bracts, the whole structure resembling a single 4-petalled flower. Petals 4, borne on the margin of the disk, spreading; calyx tubular, with 4 minute teeth; pistil 1, the ovary inferior, 2-celled; fruit a bright, shining, red drupe. Leaves 2–3 opposite pairs so closely crowded near the top of the stem that they appear whorled, broadly ovate, strongly pinnately veined, entire, 4–7 cm. long; 1–2 opposite pairs of small bracts may be present below on stem.

In moist woods, thickets, and clearings. Mostly in northern part of Michigan. Flowering May to July; fruits ripe late July to October.

The fruits are said to be edible and are eaten by birds. This plant is as pretty in fruit as in flower, but is, unfortunately, difficult to grow in the garden.

WINTERGREEN FAMILY. PYROLACEAE

This is a family of about 10 genera and 32 species growing in temperate and boreal regions. One of the two subfamilies includes plants with normal green leaves; the other includes species which lack chlorophyll and grow saprophytically or parasitically. The family is of no particular economic importance, but a few species of Prince's Pine and Shinleaf are sometimes cultivated.

The members of this family are herbaceous evergreens, have 5 (usually separate) petals, 5 sepals, 8–10 stamens, inverted anthers

PLATE 132

Spotted Wintergreen
(*Chimaphila maculata*)
Prince's Pine
(*Chimaphila umbellata*)

One-flowered Wintergreen
(*Moneses uniflora*)
One-sided Pyrola
(*Pyrola secunda*)

opening by pores, and a solitary pistil developing into a 5-celled capsule. The family differs primarily from the Heath Family (with which some authorities unite it) by being herbaceous and in having the petals usually separate; the heaths are woody and have the petals united, and the anthers are upright and open by terminal pores.

PYROLACEAE

1. Plants not green, lacking true leaves 2
1. Plants having normal, green leaves 3
   2. Corolla urn-shaped, petals united . . . *Pterospora andromedea*, Plate 134
   2. Corolla of separate petals . *Monotropa uniflora* or *hypopithys*, Plate 134
3. Stem leafy; flowers borne in a flattish-topped
   corymb . . . . *Chimaphila umbellata* or *maculata*, Plate 132
3. Leaves basal; flowers solitary or in a raceme 4
   4. Flower solitary . . . . *Moneses uniflora*, Plate 132
   4. Flowers in a raceme . . . . *Pyrola*, 5
5. Flowers borne principally on one side of the raceme; corolla
   longer than broad . . . . *P. secunda*, Plate 132
5. Flowers borne on all sides of the racemes; corolla broader
   than long 6
   6. Leaf blade nearly as long as or longer than the petiole,
      usually 2.5–6 cm. long 7
   6. Leaf blade usually shorter than the petiole, usually
      1–3 cm. long . . . . *P. virens*, Plate 133
7. Leaf blade thin; sepals as broad as long, or
   broader . . . . *P. elliptica*, Plate 133
7. Leaf blade thick, usually lustrous; sepals distinctly
   longer than broad 8
   8. Petals thick, white or creamy . . . . *P. rotundifolia*, Plate 133
   8. Petals thin, pink to pale purple . . . . . *P. asarifolia*, Plate 133

PRINCE'S PINE, PIPSISSEWA (Protected)
Chimaphila umbellata (L.) Bart.
var. *cisatlantica* Blake   Plate 132

Low evergreen perennial with erect, leafy stems up to 2.5 dm. tall from creeping underground rootstocks. Flowers 2–8, roseate, pink or white, nodding in loose, terminal flat-topped corymbs. Petals 5, concave, nearly round, inserted on the calyx; calyx 5-lobed, spreading; stamens 10, rose to rose-violet, inserted with the petals, opening by pores; ovary globose, large, the style nearly lacking, the stigma flattened, sticky; capsule erect, 5-lobed, splitting from the apex downward, many-seeded. Leaves whorled or scattered, green and shining on upper surface, paler beneath, thick, oblanceolate, wedge-shaped at the base, 2–9 cm. long, toothed or nearly entire.

In dry woods, on dune slopes, in upland coniferous forests, and under aspen. Mostly in northern Michigan. Flowering July and August.

SPOTTED WINTERGREEN
Chimaphila maculata (L.) Pursh   Plate 132

Similar to the preceding species, but less common; the flowers 1–5, white, up to 2 cm. broad, very fragrant; leaves lanceolate to ovate-lanceolate,

PLATE 133

Green Pyrola   Pink Pyrola   Round-leaved Pyrola
(*Pyrola virens*)   (*Pyrola asarifolia*)   (*Pyrola rotundifolia*)
Shinleaf. (Leaf only shown.)
(*Pyrola elliptica*)

rounded at the base, the upper surface variegated with white.

In dry woods, on sand dunes, and in shore woods. Flowering June to early August.

ONE-FLOWERED WINTERGREEN, ONE-FLOWERED PYROLA
Moneses uniflora (L.) Gray   Plate 132

Small, low, evergreen perennial, with underground stems giving rise to ascending leafy tips, the flowering stalk up to 1.3 dm. tall. Flowers solitary, nodding, fragrant, white or sometimes pinkish, waxy. Petals 5, spreading, concave; calyx whitish, 5-lobed; stamens 10, the filaments green or white, the anthers opening by pores; pistil 1, the ovary superior, globose, the style slender, the stigma 5-lobed; capsule 5-celled. Leaves short-petioled, nearly round, 1–2 cm. long, the margin with small rounded teeth or nearly entire.

In cool mossy woods. Flowering June to August.

ONE-SIDED PYROLA, ONE-SIDED WINTERGREEN
Pyrola secunda L.   Plate 132

Small evergreen up to 2 dm. tall. Flowers greenish or greenish-yellow, bell-shaped, longer than broad, borne in a 1-sided terminal raceme on a scape bearing 2–5 small green bracts. Filaments and style straight. Leaves in a basal rosette or somewhat scattered on the short stem, somewhat leathery, elliptic to ovate, narrowed to the tip, somewhat toothed, 1.5–4 cm. long, the blade longer than the petiole.

In dry, sometimes in moist, woods. Flowering June to August.

GREEN PYROLA, GREEN SHINLEAF
Pyrola virens Schweigger   Plate 133

Low perennial, the erect scapes up to 3 dm. tall from an evergreen rosette. Flowers pale green or greenish-white, nodding in a simple 2–13-flowered raceme. Flower structure as in the preceding species. Leaves basal, leathery, dark green on upper surface, lighter beneath, nearly round or broadly ovate, usually shorter than the petiole, the teeth slightly rounded.

In rather dry coniferous woods and in thickets. Flowering June and July.

SHINLEAF
Pyrola elliptica Nutt.   Plate 133

Quite similar to the 2 preceding species, the flowers white, the leaf blades thin, usually longer than the petiole, the sepals about as broad as long and the bracts on the scape linear and pointed.

In dry or moist woods. Flowering June to August.

ROUND-LEAVED PYROLA, SHINLEAF
Pyrola rotundifolia L. var. *americana* (Sweet) Fern. Plate 133

Stemless evergreen perennial, the flowering stalk up to 3 dm. tall, 1–7-bracted, more or less 4-angled. Flowers white, creamy white, or tinged with rose, fragrant, nodding in a 5–21-flowered raceme. Petals 5, waxy, concave, separate, thick, and firm, obscurely veined; sepals oblong or ovate-oblong, nearly twice as long as wide, not overlapping at the base; stamens 10, the filaments white, flattened, curved upward, the anthers

273

PLATE 134

Pinesap (*Monotropa hypopithys*)
Indian-pipe (*Monotropa uniflora*)
Pine-drops (*Pterospora andromedea*)

purple, opening by pores; ovary superior, 5-lobed, the style long, bent abruptly down at the base, then arching upward near the apex, the stigma 5-lobed; capsule globose, flattened, 5-lobed, the seeds minute, innumerable. Leaves all basal, leathery, lustrous on upper surface, broadly oblong to nearly round, not heart-shaped, the blade decurrent on the petiole, about the same length as the petiole (2.5–7 cm.), the margin slightly inrolled, with slightly rounded teeth.

In dry woods and clearings, often in sandy soil. Flowering June to August.

PINK PYROLA

Pyrola asarifolia Michx. Plate 133

Extensively creeping evergreen perennial quite similar to the preceding species, but the flowers pink to pale purple, 4–22 in a raceme, the scape with 1–3 ovate, dry bracts, the petals thin, conspicuously veiny at least when dry, the sepals triangular, distinctly longer than broad, slightly overlapping at the base, the leaves kidney-shaped, nearly round, or broadly elliptic, truncate or heart-shaped at base.

In rich woods and thickets, and in bogs, chiefly in calcareous soil. Flowering in July and August.

INDIAN-PIPE

Monotropa uniflora L. Plate 134

Stiffly erect, succulent, usually clustered saprophyte or parasite up to 3 dm. tall, waxy white ("ghostly"), rarely pink or reddish, darkening in age or when bruised, the roots matted, fibrous, brittle, growing on roots of other plants or on decayed vegetable matter. Flowers solitary, white, waxy, nodding, 10–17 mm. long, oblong-bell-shaped. Petals 4–5, separate, firm, somewhat translucent; sepals 2–5, bractlike and soon falling, often lacking; stamens 8 or 10, shorter than the petals, the anthers opening by 2 chinks; pistil 1, the ovary superior, the style short and thick, straight, the stigma broad, funnel-shaped, sticky; capsule ovoid, many-seeded, borne upright owing to the straightening of the stem after flowering. True leaves lacking, the stem clothed with alternate scales or bracts.

In woodland humus. Flowering June to August.

It is said that the Indians made a medicinal tea from this species. Indian-pipe is not suitable for transplanting to the garden because of its parasitic habit.

PINESAP

Monotropa hypopithys L. Plate 134

Resembles Indian-pipe, but with a cluster of flowers, the plants tawny, yellowish or reddish, becoming brown in age or when bruised, the stem up to 4 dm. tall, the flowers drooping in a compact raceme, the terminal flower with parts in 5's, the others with parts in 4's or 3's, the stamens twice as many as the petals.

In woodland humus. Flowering June to September.

PINE-DROPS

Pterospora andromedea Nutt. Plate 134

Slender, leafless, glandular-hairy, reddish, purplish, or brownish perennial up to 15 dm. tall, parasitic on the roots of other seed-bearing plants.

PLATE 135

Bog Laurel
(*Kalmia polifolia*)

Trailing Arbutus
(*Epigaea repens*)

Labrador-tea
(*Ledum groenlandicum*)

Flowers white to reddish, bell-shaped, 6–7 mm. long, drooping in a long, many-flowered raceme. Corolla urn-shaped, constricted at the apex and shallowly 5-lobed; calyx deeply 5-parted; stamens 10, the anthers opening by longitudinal slits and having 2 long slender awns; pistil 1, the ovary superior, 5-celled, the stigma 5-lobed. True leaves lacking, but the stem covered with brownish to reddish lanceolate bracts, particularly toward the base.

In dry woods, chiefly under pine. Flowering June to August.

HEATH FAMILY. ERICACEAE

This is a family of about 70 genera and nearly 2000 species, which grow in acid soil throughout the temperate regions, in the subarctic, and in the mountains of the tropics. Its chief importance is for ornamentals, which include such evergreen shrubs as azaleas, rhododendron, heather, heath, mountain laurel, and leather-leaf. Leaves of salal from the northwest are used a great deal by midwestern florists under the name of lemon-leaf. Cranberries and blueberries, also included in this family, are important fruits.

Many authorities consider the Wintergreen Family to be merely a part of this family. The chief points of difference are given above, under the Wintergreen Family.

ERICACEAE

1. Erect or nearly erect shrubs 2
1. Low, prostrate or creeping shrubs 3

   2. Leaves having a dense rusty wool beneath; flowers
    white . . . . *Ledum groenlandicum,* Plate 135
   2. Leaves whitened beneath; flowers rose
    or pink . . . . *Kalmia polifolia,* Plate 135

3. Corolla having a slender tube enlarged at apex;
leaves round or heart-shaped at base; flowering in
very early spring . . . . *Epigaea repens,* Plate 135
3. Not as in alternate choice 4

   4. Flowers pale rose; corolla deeply
    lobed . . . . . *Vaccinium macrocarpon* or *oxycoccos,* Plate 137
   4. Not as in alternate choice 5

5. Leaves and berries with flavor
of wintergreen . . . . *Gaultheria procumbens* or *hispidula,* Plate 136
5. Not as in alternate choice . . . . *Arctostaphylos uva-ursi,* Plate 137

LABRADOR-TEA

Ledum groenlandicum Oeder   Plate 135

Evergreen shrub up to 1 m. tall. Flowers white, about 1 cm. broad, borne in dense terminal clusters. Petals 5, separate; calyx minute, with rounded lobes; stamens 5–7, spreading, longer than the petals, the filaments threadlike; pistil 1, the ovary superior, green, covered with a sticky mucilaginous substance, the style long; capsule slender, many-seeded, splitting from

PLATE 136
Creeping Snowberry
(*Gaultheria hispidula*)
Creeping Wintergreen
(*Gaultheria procumbens*)

278

the base upward. Leaves alternate, green on the upper surface, the midrib depressed, densely woolly beneath with rusty hairs, linear-oblong or oblong, up to 2.5 cm. long, the margin entire and rolled under; petioles short, stout.

In bogs and damp thickets and along wet shores. Flowering May and June.

Labrador-tea blooms at the same time as Bog Laurel, and the two together make a most attractive sight. It is said that this species is poisonous to sheep. It was used to make a tea by Indians, and by the colonists during the Revolutionary War.

BOG LAUREL, PALE LAUREL
Kalmia polifolia Wang.   Plate 135

Slender, straggling shrub up to 1 m. tall, the branches 2-winged. Flowers showy, deep pink to crimson, 1–2 cm. wide, borne on threadlike pedicels (1–4 cm. long) in terminal corymbs. Corolla shallowly saucer-shaped, with 10 small pouches; calyx 5-parted, free from the ovary; stamens 10, the anthers at first in the pouches of the corolla but soon free as the filaments become straight and erect; ovary superior; capsule globose, many-seeded, persistent. Leaves opposite, green on upper surface, whitened beneath, lanceolate, the margin usually rolled under; veins obscure except for the midrib, which is prominent on lower surface.

In open swamps and bogs, in marshy places, around lakes, and in sphagnum mats. Flowering May and June.

TRAILING ARBUTUS, GROUND LAUREL, MAYFLOWER (Protected)
Epigaea repens L. var. *glabrifolia* Fern.   Plate 135

Prostrate or trailing, somewhat shrubby, freely-rooting evergreen perennial with bristly rusty hairs at least on the stem. Flowers pink or white, having a rich spicy fragrance, borne in terminal or axillary clusters. Corolla salverform, the tube hairy inside, 5-lobed; sepals 5; stamens 10; capsule 5-lobed and 5-celled, many-seeded. Leaves alternate, green on both sides, thick, prominently veined, more or less rusty-hairy when young, becoming smooth in age, oval, oblong or ovate, rounded to somewhat heart-shaped at base; petioles slender, about half as long as the blade, rusty-hairy.

In sandy or rocky woods, frequently under pine or aspen, in upland second growth, and on wooded dunes. Occurring sparingly in southern Michigan, more commonly in the northern part of the Lower Peninsula, and quite commonly in the Upper Peninsula. Flowering mid-April to early June.

This, one of our most charming plants, well deserves to be protected. Picking the flowers usually loosens the roots, causing the plants to die out. The flowers often bloom before the snow is gone and can be readily located under its cover by their fragrance. Contrary to popular belief, this is not always the first wildflower to bloom. In the tip of the Lower Peninsula I have found it still in bud in late April when Dutchman's-breeches, Squirrel-corn, Hepatica, Spring-beauty, and Erythroniums were in full bloom and Trillium was coming into bloom.

PLATE 137
Bearberry
(*Arctostaphylos uva-ursi*)

Small Cranberry
(*Vaccinium oxycoccos*)

American Cranberry
(*Vaccinium macrocarpon*)

CREEPING *or* AROMATIC WINTERGREEN, CHECKERBERRY
Gaultheria procumbens L.   Plate 136

Low-growing evergreen shrub with a wintergreen odor when crushed, the stems somewhat woody, more or less erect, leafy above, 1–2 dm. tall from slender creeping rootstocks. Flowers white, 7–10 mm. long, solitary from the axils of the leaves, drooping on often reddish pedicels which have 2 small fleshy bracts at the base of the flower. Corolla urn-shaped, roughly 5-sided, 5-toothed; stamens 10, attached at the base of the corolla tube; pistil 1, the ovary 5-angled, borne above the glandular disk; fruits red, berrylike, mealy, formed by the fleshy calyx growing out and enclosing the many-seeded capsule, often persistent and in good edible condition when the ensuing year's flowers are in bloom. Leaves alternate, at first light green and tender, soon hard and leathery, sometimes quite brittle, elliptic to narrowly obovate, narrowed to the base or sometimes nearly round, 2–5 cm. long, the margin slightly rolled under and with a few low bristle-tipped teeth; petiole short (2–5 mm. long).

In sterile woods and clearings; frequent under conifers. Flowering July and August.

CREEPING SNOWBERRY
Gaultheria hispidula (L.) Bigel.   Plate 136

Delicate, creeping, matted evergreen perennial with stiffly-hairy, barely woody stems 1–3 dm. long. Flowers white, solitary and nodding on short peduncles in the axils of the leaves. Corolla bell-shaped, deeply 4-cleft; calyx 4-toothed; stamens 8; pistil 1, the ovary 4-celled; berry white, fleshy, juicy, delicately acid and aromatic. Leaves abundant, 2-ranked, firm, dark green on upper surface, bristly-hairy beneath, ovate, 5–10 mm. long, short-petioled.

In mossy, mostly coniferous, woods and in bogs and swamps. Flowering April and May.

BEARBERRY, KINNIKINICK
Arctostaphylos uva-ursi (L.) Spreng.   Plate 137

Trailing evergreen shrub with long grayish to reddish branches. Flowers 5–12 in dense terminal racemes; corolla white, sometimes pink-tipped, or pale pink, 5-cleft into short rounded lobes; stamens 10; anthers with 2 awns as long as the filaments; fruit a dry, red, mealy drupe. Leaves alternate, leathery, shiny on upper surface, obovate, entire, short-petioled.

In rocky and sandy ground. Flowering May to July.

AMERICAN CRANBERRY, LARGE CRANBERRY
Vaccinium macrocarpon Ait.   Plate 137

Trailing evergreen shrub with frequently-branched stems, rooting freely at the nodes, often forming dense mats. Flowers 1–10, pale rose, nodding on slender upright reddish pedicels rising from the end of a stem opposite bracts near the top, the elongate leafy stem continuing to grow and extending beyond the origin of the pedicels. Corolla so deeply 4-cleft that it appears to be composed of long, separate petals, the lobes purplish-red at base, curving abruptly back, inserted on the disk; calyx 4-lobed, adherent to the ovary below; stamens 8; pistil 1, the ovary inferior; berry green

PLATE 138

Bird's-eye Primrose
(*Primula intercedens*)

Bird's-eye Primrose
(*Primula mistassinica*)

at first, becoming red, juicy, tart. Leaves alternate, oblong-elliptic, 6–17 mm. long, green on upper surface, paler beneath, short-petioled.

In boggy meadows, bogs, and swamps and on wet shores. Flowering June and July.

Cranberries are remarkable for their keeping qualities and were especially prized by the early colonists for that reason. In the early days, the entire supply came from wild berries, but they have now been cultivated for over a hundred years. The Indians used the berries as an article of commerce. The plant was originally called "crane berry" because the shape of the flowers suggests the head and neck of a crane.

SMALL CRANBERRY

Vaccinium oxycoccos L.　　　　　　　　　　　　　　Plate 137

Similar in general aspect to the preceding species, but the plants generally smaller, the flowers only 1–4, the pedicels rising from the end of a stem that does not continue to grow, the bracts on the pedicels red, borne at or below the middle, the leaves strongly whitened beneath, ovate, oblong-ovate, or triangular.

In boggy or peaty soil. Flowering June and July; berries ripening August to October.

PRIMROSE FAMILY.　PRIMULACEAE

This family includes about 28 genera and nearly 800 species. It is most abundant in north temperate regions but is widely distributed and occurs on all continents. It is of importance here only for a few ornamentals such as primroses, cyclamens, and Scarlet Pimpernel.

All members of this family are herbaceous. The petals are united, and the calyx is toothed, lobed, or deeply divided. The calyx and corolla lobes are usually 5 but may be 4–9 in some species. The stamens are the same number as the petals and opposite them. The fruit is a many-seeded capsule.

PRIMULACEAE

1. Leaves all basal, forming
   a rosette . 　.　.　.　. *Primula mistassinica* or *intercedens*, Plate 138
1. Leaves borne on stem .　.　.　.　.　.　.　.　.　.　.　.　.　2
   2. Flowers white .　.　.　.　.　.　. *Trientalis borealis*, Plate 141
   2. Flowers yellow .　.　.　.　.　.　.　.　.　.　. *Lysimachia*, 3
3. Plants creeping .　.　.　.　.　.　.　.　. *L. nummularia*, Plate 139
3. Plants erect　.　.　.　.　.　.　.　.　.　.　.　.　.　.　.　4
   4. Flowers all or mostly borne in a terminal
      raceme .　.　.　.　.　.　.　.　.　.　. *L. terrestris*, Plate 140
   4. Flowers borne from axils of leaves .　.　.　.　.　.　.　.　5
5. Flowers borne in dense racemes .　.　.　.　. *L. thyrsiflora*, Plate 139
5. Flowers solitary from axils .　.　.　.　.　.　.　.　.　.　6
   6. Leaves opposite, petioles fringed; corolla lacking
      spots or streaks .　.　.　.　.　.　.　.　. *L. ciliata*, Plate 139
   6. Leaves chiefly whorled, petioles lacking or very short;
      corolla dotted or streaked with black or red .　*L. quadrifolia*, Plate 140

PLATE 139

Tufted Loosestrife
(*Lysimachia thyrsiflora*)

Moneywort
(*Lysimachia nummularia*)

Fringed Loosestrife
(*Lysimachia ciliata*)

284

BIRD'S-EYE PRIMROSE
Primula mistassinica Michx.

Plate 138

Slender perennial with naked flowering stems up to 2.5 dm. tall from a basal rosette. Flowers lilac, pale pink, or white (forma *leucantha* Fern.), with a conspicuous yellow center, borne in terminal umbels, on nearly equal, stiffly ascending pedicels. Corolla salverform, the 5-lobed limb flat, up to 2 cm. broad, the lobes heart-shaped at apex; calyx tubular, 5-cleft; stamens 5; pistil 1; capsule cylindric, longer than the closely appressed calyx, often crowned with the withered corolla; seeds rounded, nearly smooth. Leaves all basal, nearly erect, oblanceolate, long-tapering to the base, irregularly and shallowly toothed, the margin somewhat inrolled.

On wet, calcareous shores and rocks. Chiefly in northern Michigan. Flowering May and early June.

BIRD'S-EYE PRIMROSE
Primula intercedens Fern.

Plate 138

This differs only by very minor characters from the preceding species, and the two are probably better considered to be merely forms of a single species. *P. intercedens* is described as usually having a yellow mealiness on the under side of the leaves and on the calyx; the seeds are somewhat angular and nearly smooth.

On wet lake shores. Flowering in May and early June.

MONEYWORT
Lysimachia nummularia L.

Plate 139

Creeping or trailing perennial rooting freely at the nodes, often forming mats. Flowers bright yellow, showy, about 2 cm. in diameter, solitary on peduncles from the axils of the leaves. Corolla wheel-shaped, dotted with red, so deeply 5-lobed that it appears to be made up of separate broadly ovate petals; calyx deeply 5-parted, red-dotted, spreading in flower but closing around the developing capsule; stamens 5, the filaments united into a tube at the base; ovary superior, red-dotted. Leaves opposite, short-petioled, broadly oval or orbicular, 10–25 mm. long, entire.

Along damp roadsides, in grassy places, and along shores. Introduced from Europe; now often a weed in lawns. Flowering June to August.

SWAMP-CANDLES, YELLOW *or* SWAMP LOOSESTRIFE
Lysimachia terrestris (L.) BSP.

Plate 140

Erect, simple or sparingly branched perennial up to 1 m. tall. Flowers yellow, dotted or streaked with red or purple, about 1 cm. wide, borne in terminal racemes, the pedicels slender, horizontal or ascending. Corolla wheel-shaped, deeply 5-parted; stamens 5, the filaments united at the base, unequal in length. Leaves opposite, nearly sessile, thick, narrow-lanceolate, often black-dotted, entire, obscurely veined, 5–10 cm. long; lower leaves smaller.

Along wet shores and on low wet ground, in thickets, marshes, and swamps. Flowering July and August.

TUFTED LOOSESTRIFE
Lysimachia thyrsiflora L.

Plate 139

PLATE 140

Swamp-candles
(*Lysimachia terrestris*)

Whorled Loosestrife
(*Lysimachia quadrifolia*)

286

Erect, usually unbranched perennial up to 1 m. tall, the stems clustered, red at least below. Flowers yellow, often spotted with red, purplish, or black dots, borne from the axils of the middle leaves in dense, short spikes, the peduncles stout, 2–4 cm. long. Corolla tube very short, the limb deeply lobed, the lobes narrow, much shorter than the stamens; calyx cleft into 6 (5–7) linear segments, light yellowish-green, dotted with red; sta-mens rising from a ring at the base of the ovary; pistil solitary, the ovary green, speckled; capsule about as long as the calyx lobes. Leaves opposite, sessile, lanceolate to elliptic, 5–12 cm. long, and up to 2.5 cm. wide, the lower ones smaller (some merely ovate and scalelike).

In swamps, wet meadows, low woods, springy marshes, and bogs. Flowering May to July.

FRINGED LOOSESTRIFE
Lysimachia ciliata L.   Plate 139

Erect, simple or branched perennial up to 1.2 m. tall, leafless below. Flowers yellow, borne on long, threadlike peduncles in whorls from the upper leaf axils. Corolla unspotted, 1.5–3 cm. broad, the 5 lobes much longer than the stamens, irregularly toothed; calyx 5-toothed, the teeth tipped with a sharp point; stamens 5, separate. Leaves opposite, ovate to ovate-lanceolate, rounded to somewhat heart-shaped at base, 3–15 cm. long; petioles very hairy, appearing fringed.

In moist woods and thickets, on flood plains and in low, wet ground. Flowering July and August.

WHORLED LOOSESTRIFE
Lysimachia quadrifolia L.   Plate 140

Erect, simple, slender perennial up to 8 dm. tall. Flowers yellow, dark-streaked or spotted, borne on thread-like peduncles (2–5 cm. long) from the axils of the whorled leaves. Corolla wheel-shaped, 5-lobed, the lobes lanceolate, entire; calyx deeply 5-parted; stamens 5, united into a ring at the base, the filaments unequal. Leaves usually in whorls of 4 or 5 (the lower ones sometimes opposite), sessile or nearly so, lanceolate to narrowly ovate, 3–9 cm. long, 1–2.5 cm. broad.

In dry or moist, open or partially shaded ground, in woods or along shores. Flowering May to August.

STAR-FLOWER
Trientalis borealis Raf.   Plate 141

Erect, unbranched, fragile perennial up to 2.5 dm. tall from long, creeping rootstocks, spreading by slender, elongate stolons. Flowers white, 8–14 mm. wide, 1–4 on very slender, wiry peduncles from the axils of the leaves at the top of the stem. Corolla flat, star-shaped, cut almost or quite to the base, the lobes usually 7 (5–9), oblong, and pointed; calyx deeply lobed, the lobes usually 7 (5–9), very narrow, pointed, spreading flat; stamens the same number as the petals and opposite them, the filaments white, united into a ring at the base; pistil solitary, the style long and slender, the ovary 1-celled; capsule globular. Leaves mostly alternate and clustered at the top of the stem, sessile, lanceolate or narrowly ovate, 4–10 cm. long, shallowly crenate or nearly entire, the leaves below the whorl few and scale-like.

In moist woodlands and thickets, on peaty slopes, and in bogs. Flowering May to late July.

PLATE 141
Star-flower (*Trientalis borealis*)

PLATE 142

Fringed Gentian (*Gentiana procera*)
Fringed Gentian (*Gentiana crinita*)
Stiff Gentian (*Gentiana quinquefolia*)

PLATE 143

Closed Gentian
(*Gentiana andrewsii*)

Gentian
(*Gentiana puberula*)
Yellowish Gentian
(*Gentiana flavida*)

PLATE 144

Buckbean
(*Menyanthes trifoliata*)

Spurred Gentian
(*Halenia deflexa*)

291

GENTIAN FAMILY. GENTIANACEAE

This family, worldwide in distribution but most abundant in temperate regions, includes about 70 genera and some 100 species. Its only importance to us is for ornamentals: gentians, Buckbean, *Centaurium,* and others.

The family is characterized by opposite, usually sessile leaves without stipules; the corolla is tubular to bell- or wheel-shaped; the stamens are the same number as the corolla lobes and opposite them; the sepals are united; and the single, superior ovary develops into a many-seeded capsule.

GENTIANACEAE

1. Leaves 3-foliolate . . . . . . *Menyanthes trifoliata,* Plate 144
1. Leaves simple 2
   2. Corolla (at least of larger flowers) spurred at base . . . . *Halenia deflexa,* Plate 144
   2. Corolla not spurred at base . . . . *Gentiana,* 3
3. Flowers solitary, corolla 4-lobed, lobes fringed 4
3. Flowers borne in clusters; parts in 5's 5
   4. Upper leaves ovate to broadly lanceolate; ovary and capsule distinctly stalked . . . . . . *G. crinita,* Plate 142
   4. Upper leaves linear to narrowly lanceolate; ovary and capsule sessile or nearly so . . . . . *G. procera,* Plate 142
5. Corolla without folds, teeth, or secondary lobes in sinuses between lobes . . . . . . *G. quinquefolia,* Plate 142
5. Corolla having folds, plaits, or teeth between lobes, these usually different in texture or color 6
   6. Flowers some shade of blue or purplish 7
   6. Flowers yellowish to greenish white . . . . *G. flavida,* Plate 143
7. Corolla nearly closed at top, lobes incurved and shorter than intervening folds . . . . . *G. andrewsii,* Plate 143
7. Corolla open or spreading at top, lobes longer than folds . . . . *G. puberula,* Plate 143

FRINGED GENTIAN (Protected)

Gentiana crinita Froel.   Plate 142

Stiff, erect, simple or branched biennial or annual up to 9 dm. tall, the stems somewhat 4-angled. Flowers showy, violet, blue or rarely white, 4–5.5 cm. long, solitary and upright on stiff, erect peduncles 1–11 cm. long at the ends of the branches. Corolla slenderly bell-shaped, 4-lobed, the lobes wide-spreading in sunshine and closing at night or in cloudy weather, rounded and much-fringed at the summit, slightly fringed on sides; calyx 2.5–4 cm. long, cleft about halfway to the base, the lobes and tube keeled, the 2 inner lobes the shorter; stamens 4, attached to the corolla tube; pistil 1, the ovary superior, long and slender, stalked; seeds numerous, covered with minute projections. Leaves opposite, sessile, the middle and upper ones ovate to ovate-lanceolate, rounded to somewhat heart-shaped at base, parallel-veined.

In wet thickets and low woods, along streams, in damp open meadows and fields. Flowering late August to October.

Fringed Polygala

Color plate 10

Fireweed

Fringed Gentian (Protected)

Gentiana procera Holm
Plate 142

Greatly resembling the preceding species, but the plants slightly smaller, 2–6 dm. tall, the corolla lobes deeply fringed on the sides but having short, thick teeth at the apex, the capsule and ovary sessile or nearly so, the middle and upper leaves narrowly linear-lanceolate, up to 8 mm. wide.

On marly lake shores, in boggy prairies and sandy swamps. Flowering mid-August to October.

Stiff Gentian (Protected)

Gentiana quinquefolia L.
Plate 142

Simple or stiffly branched annual or biennial up to 8 dm. tall, the stems strongly angled and winged. Flowers pale violet-blue, lilac, or sometimes greenish-white, solitary or clustered in the axils of leaves and at the summit of the stems. Corolla funnel-shaped, 1.6–2 cm. long, 5-lobed, the lobes triangular, bristle-tipped; calyx cleft to below the middle; capsule on a slender stalk. Leaves opposite, the middle and upper ones ovate-lance-olate, clasping by rounded bases, up to 8 cm. long; lower leaves oblong-ovate; veins 3–7, parallel.

In dry or moist, shaded ground, in thin woods or thickets, on river banks, and in swamps. Flowering August to mid-October.

Yellowish Gentian (Protected)

Gentiana flavida Gray
Plate 143

Stout, smooth, usually unbranched perennial up to 5.5 dm. tall. Flowers yellowish-white to greenish, 3–4.5 cm. long, crowded in terminal and sometimes axillary clusters. Corolla cylindric to bell-shaped, open at the top, the 5 erect primary lobes much longer than the broad, irregularly toothed secondary lobes; calyx 5-lobed; stamens 5, the anthers united; ovary and capsule stalked. Leaves opposite, sessile, lanceolate to ovate, rounded or heart-shaped at base, 3–5-nerved, the upper leaves the largest, forming an involucre, the lowest leaves reduced to bracts.

In thin woods in wet or dry soil, on rocky shores, and in meadows. Flowering mid-August to mid-October in southern Michigan.

Red-stemmed Gentian, *G. rubricaulis* Schwein., which looks very similar, is common in northern Michigan. It has pale blue flowers, reddish stems, the corolla lobes are longer than the entire or 1-toothed secondary lobes, and the calyx lobes are narrow and glabrous. Growing in wet meadows; flowering in August and September.

Closed Gentian (Protected)

Gentiana andrewsii Griseb.
Plate 143

Smooth, stout, usually many-stemmed, unbranched perennial up to 8 dm. tall. Flowers blue-violet (rarely pinkish or white), sessile, several in a terminal cluster and in some of the upper leaf axils. Corolla 3–4 cm. long, closed or nearly closed at the top, the 5 lobes narrow, truncate, and joined by longer whitish secondary lobes, which are fringed at the summit; calyx 5-lobed, the sinuses rectangular, the lobes linear, spreading, fringed with hairs;

293

PLATE 145
Spreading Dogbane
Indian Hemp   (*Apocynum androsaemifolium*)
(*Apocynum cannabinum*)
294

stamens 5, the broad, flat filaments attached to the corolla tube, the anthers coherent; ovary long, stalked. Leaves sessile, ovate-lanceolate, 3–7-nerved, the 4–6 upper leaves often larger and forming an involucre, the lowest leaves the smallest.

In moist soil in meadows, prairies, and low thickets and on open wooded shores. Flowering August to October.

Another Closed Gentian is the Blind or Bottle Gentian, *G. clausa* Raf., which is usually smaller than the preceding, the incurved primary lobes of the corolla are rounded and equal or exceed the secondary lobes in width, and the calyx lobes are broad and ciliate. This and the following species are found in southern Michigan, but are quite rare.

GENTIAN (Protected)

Gentiana puberula Michx.   Plate 143

Rigid, hairy perennial with 1 to few, often purplish, simple or branched stems up to 5 dm. tall. Flowers showy, 3.5–5 cm. long, blue-purple, crowded at the summit of the stem and in the upper leaf axils. Corolla open-funnel-shaped, 5-lobed, the primary lobes entire, spreading, twice as long as the 2-cleft secondary lobes; stamens 5, anthers free or promptly separating; ovary stalked. Leaves 13–19 pairs below the inflorescence, opposite, sessile, lanceolate, the lower ones the smallest; veins parallel.

In dry soil, on hills and prairies, often in sand, rarely in low open ground. Flowering late August through October.

SPURRED GENTIAN (Protected)

Halenia deflexa (Sm.) Griseb.   Plate 144

Leafy annual or biennial up to 9 dm. tall, simple or branched above. Flowers greenish or bronze, borne in terminal and axillary umbels or sometimes solitary. Corolla nearly tubular, 8–15 mm. long, 4-lobed to below the middle and having 4 basal spreading spurs; calyx 4-parted; stamens 4, inserted on the corolla tube; capsule oblong, flattish. Leaves opposite, the upper leaves sessile, lanceolate to ovate, 3–5-nerved; lower leaves petioled, oblong-spatulate, the lowest often forming a rosette.

In moist or marshy ground, in wet grassy open places, in woods or cedar bogs. Flowering July to September.

BUCKBEAN, BOGBEAN (Protected)

Menyanthes trifoliata L. var. *minor* Raf.   Plate 144

Low-growing smooth perennial with scapes and petioles up to 3 dm. tall from a long rootstock. Flowers white or rose-tinged, borne in short, thick, compact racemes. Corolla with a short tube and 5 densely white-bearded lobes; calyx deeply 5-parted, the lobes shorter than the corolla tube; stamens 5, inserted on and shorter than the corolla tube; ovary 1, superior, the stigma 2-lobed; capsule ovoid, 6–10 mm. long at maturity, bursting irregularly, many-seeded. Leaves smooth, long-petioled, crowded toward the base of the flowering stem, 3-foliolate, the leaflets oval, oblong or obovate, 2.5–7 cm. long, entire to slightly crenate, pinnately veined.

In shallow water, in pond margins, quagmires, bogs, marshes. Flowering late April to mid-July.

DOGBANE FAMILY.   APOCYNACEAE

This primarily tropical family of about 300 genera and 1300 species has only 9 genera and 33 species native to this country. The family is of limited importance here, but includes such ornamentals as Amsonia, Oleander, and Periwinkle.

The members of this family have a milky juice, the leaves are usually opposite, the flower parts are in 5's, the stamens are free from the stigma, the pollen grains are separate, and the 2 superior ovaries have a single style and stigma.

INDIAN HEMP

Apocynum cannabinum L.   Plate 145

Glabrous, erect perennial with milky juice, simple or with ascending to erect, often reddish branches, up to 1.5 m. tall. Flowers small, white or greenish-white, 3–6 mm. long, borne in terminal cymes. Corolla tubular to ovoid, the 5 lobes erect, not veined with red within; calyx 5-lobed, the lobes about as long as the corolla tube; stamens 5, attached to base of the corolla tube, the anthers converging; ovaries 2, readily separating, having a single style; pods 2, elongate, slender, 1–2 dm. long, the seeds with a tuft of silky white hair 2–2.5 cm. long. Leaves opposite, mostly ascending, ovate to lanceolate, 5–25 cm. long, all (except for a few basal leaves) petioled, prominently veined.

In open ground along shores, in thickets, borders of woods, and low places, in damp or dry soil. Flowering June to August.

A quite similar species, *A. sibiricum* Jacq., has leaves of the main stem sessile or nearly so, rounded or heart-shaped at base, the tufts of hair on the seeds 9–12 mm. long, and the pods 5–9 cm. long.

The Indians used fibers from both these species for making rope, twine, and thread. After the stalks of the previous year's growth had become naturally retted the fibers were carded out. They were spun by twining or by rolling the strands on the leg under the palm of the hand. Fabric for diapers was sometimes woven from this thread. A laxative drink was also made from the plant. Horses, cattle, and sheep have been poisoned by eating dried or fresh Indian Hemp; 15–30 grams of the green leaves are said to be fatal to a horse or cow.

SPREADING DOGBANE

Apocynum androsaemifolium L.   Plate 145

More or less inclined, often reddish-stemmed, milky-juiced perennial up to 1.3 m. tall, usually unbranched below but having wide-spreading, arching branches above. Flowers white or pink and white, 6–9 mm. long, fragrant, spreading or nodding in rather loose terminal and axillary cymes. Corolla bell-shaped, the 5 lobes turned back, the tube (at least in young flow-ers) pink-striped within; calyx much shorter than the corolla; pods very slender, hanging down, 7–20 cm. long. Leaves opposite, petioled, ovate to ovate-oblong, tapered to both ends, dark green and smooth on upper surface, paler beneath.

In fields, in thickets, and along the borders of woods. Flowering June to August.

PLATE 146

Swamp Milkweed   Common Milkweed
(*Asclepias incarnata*)   (*Asclepias syriaca*)

Green Milkweed
(*Asclepias viridiflora*)

297

The Indians used the pulverized roots to treat headache, babies' colds, dropsy, and heart palpitations. They also derived a fiber from this species which they made into a very strong cord. This fiber is said to be stronger than that of the related commercial hemp. Fibers from the outer rind of the stem were used for fine sewing.

MILKWEED FAMILY. ASCLEPIADACEAE

This large, primarily tropical family is represented by about 9 genera and 100 species in North America. A few species, including the well-known Butterfly-weed, are grown for ornamentals. Rubber Vine, *Cryptostegia grandiflora*, has been grown commercially for rubber. The down from the seeds of some species was used as a substitute for kapok during World War II.

Michigan members of this family are easily recognized by the peculiar extra whorl (the crown) of parts of the flower, the usually opposite or whorled leaves, and the milky juice. (Butterfly-weed has alternate leaves, at least on the lower part of the stem, and the juice is not milky.) The crown is composed of 5 petallike hoods which stick up between the reflexed corolla and the stamens; this crown is usually more conspicuous than the corolla, and the hoods may or may not have each an incurved horn. The 5 anthers are more or less united to each other and to the stigma, forming a peculiar columnar structure in the center of the flower. The pollen is borne in pear-shaped masses (pollinia). The ovaries and styles are 2, with a single shield-shaped, 5-lobed stigma.

Asclepias

1. Flowers orange; juice not milky . . . . . *A. tuberosa*, Color Plate 11
1. Flowers not orange; juice milky 2
    2. Flowers greenish; no pointed horns present in the hoods; stems trailing or leaning . . . . *A. viridiflora*, Plate 146
    2. Flowers pink, rose, or purplish, sometimes suffused with green; pointed horns present in the hoods; stems erect 3
3. Stem and leaves glabrous or nearly so; leaves thin, tapering to a long, slender apex; flowers pink to rose-purple . *A. incarnata*, Plate 146
3. Stem and leaves finely pubescent; leaves thick, rounded at the apex; flowers dull purple and greenish . . . . . *A. syriaca*, Plate 146

BUTTERFLY-WEED, PLEURISY-ROOT

Asclepias tuberosa L.   Color Plate 11

Rough-hairy, erect or ascending perennial up to 1 m. tall, branching only at the top; juice not milky. Flowers variable from yellow to deep red but usually bright orange, borne in broad terminal umbels or in smaller umbels in the axils of the leaves. Corolla deeply 5-lobed, the lobes bent downward and covering the 5-toothed calyx; the 5 hoods orange, upstanding, each with a slender horn; stamens and pistils united into a column; pods slender, elongate, 8–12 cm. long, erect; seeds with a tuft of white hairs. Leaves alternate (sometimes opposite on the branches), lanceolate to oblong.

In open sunny places and upland woods, especially in sandy soil. Common in southern Michigan; rare to absent northward. Flowering late June to September.

This is the only one of our milkweeds that does not have milky juice. It is a most attractive garden plant but does not stand transplanting well. The deep roots are easily broken and are susceptible to attacks by fungi. The Indians used the young seed pods and the tubers or roots for food; some tribes made a crude sugar from the flowers, and some used the plant medicinally. This species is reputedly poisonous to livestock, but apparently they seldom eat it.

GREEN MILKWEED
Asclepias viridiflora Raf.   Plate 146

Minutely hairy to nearly smooth, prostrate to ascending perennial up to 8 dm. tall; juice milky. Flowers greenish, borne in dense, globose, nearly sessile umbels in the axils of the leaves. Hoods lacking horns; pods slender, 8–11 cm. long. Leaves mostly opposite, very thick, variable in shape, oval, oblong, or linear-lanceolate.

In sandy, open ground, on lake shores and dunes. Flowering mid-June to August.

SWAMP MILKWEED
Asclepias incarnata L.   Plate 146

Glabrous or hairy, up to 1.5 m. tall, branched above, the stems solitary or clustered. Flowers purplish-red to pink, rarely whitish, borne in umbels at the top of the plant. Corolla 6–7 mm. long; the hoods about 3 mm. long, the horns longer; pods 5–10 cm. long, spindle-shaped, erect. Leaves opposite, lanceolate to oblong-lanceolate, the veins prominent.

In swamps, wet meadows, and thickets and on shores. Flowering July and August.

The dried pods are a familiar sight in the fall in marshes and wet places. The Indians made the buds into soup with deer broth; they also dried the pods for winter use. The liquid from the boiled roots was used for a gargle. Twine and thread were made from the fibers of the naturally retted stalks by rolling the fibers on the leg with the palm of the hand.

Tall Milkweed, *A. exaltata* L., has duller, purplish, greenish, or whitish flowers; it grows in moist upland woods.

COMMON MILKWEED, SILKWEED
Asclepias syriaca L.   Plate 146

Stout, finely downy, grayish-green, usually unbranched perennial up to 2 m. tall, spreading rapidly by underground stems; juice copious, milky. Flowers greenish-purple to dull purple, buff, or whitish, often fragrant, borne in globose umbels in the axils of the leaves. Flowers typical of the

299

PLATE 147
Field Bindweed
(*Convolvulus arvensis*)

Low Bindweed
(*Convolvulus spithamaeus*)

Wild Morning-glory
(*Convolvulus sepium*)

family, the horns short and incurved; pods ovoid, usually covered with short, soft warts, splitting along one side; seeds flat, brownish, the hairs long and silky.

In fields and meadows and along roadsides. Flowering June to August.

The young plants make a satisfactory cooked vegetable but are said to require long cooking. The Indians ate the young sprouts, buds, and pods. A crude brown sugar was made from the flowers by some tribes. The silky down of the seeds was used in making pads for babies. It was believed that taking the juice of this plant would increase the milk production of new mothers.

MORNING-GLORY FAMILY. CONVOLVULACEAE

This primarily tropical family includes about 50 genera and more than 1200 species. Its importance comes principally from the sweet potato and the common Morning-glory. The troublesome parasitic dodder also belongs here.

The Michigan leafy, green members are characterized by their twining or trailing habit and the milky juice. The large funnel-shaped flowers are borne in the axils of the leaves. (Dodder is brownish or yellowish, the leaves are reduced to scales, and the flowers are small and clustered.)

Convolvulus

1. Plants twining or trailing, stems forking freely 2
1. Plants partially erect, twining only at the tip; stem
   unbranched or sparsely branched .   .   .   .   . *C. spithamaeus,* Plate 147
   2. Corolla 4–8 cm. long; calyx covered by 2 large, leaflike
      bracts .   .   .   . *C. sepium,* Plate 147
   2. Corolla up to 3 cm. long; bracts small, well below the
      calyx .   .   .   . *C. arvensis,* Plate 147

Low Bindweed

Convolvulus spithamaeus L.   Plate 147

Hairy, grayish-green, partially erect or sometimes prostrate, simple or sparsely branched perennial with stems up to 5 dm. long, the tip twining or not, often elongating and eventually bending downward. Flowers showy, white, sometimes pink, 1–4 on peduncles from the axils of the lower leaves. Corolla funnel-shaped, 4–7 cm. long; calyx completely covered by the 2 large leaflike bracts; stamens 5, borne on the base of the corolla tube; pistil 1, the ovary superior, 2-celled, the style long, 2-cleft at the apex; fruit a globose capsule. Leaves oblong-oval, usually somewhat heart-shaped at base, hairy, prominently veined; lower leaves small.

In poor, sandy or rocky open soil and in thin woods, often under aspens and in old burns. Flowering late May through July.

Wild Morning-glory, Hedge Bindweed

Convolvulus sepium L.   Plate 147

Freely branching, smooth to hairy, creeping or twining vine up to 3 m. long, often climbing on other plants, fences, etc. Flowers showy, white to

301

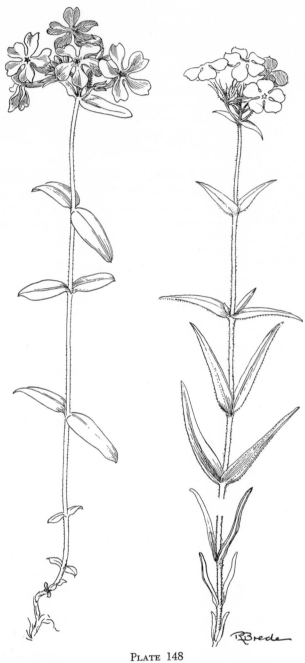

PLATE 148

Wild Blue Phlox
(*Phlox divaricata*)

Downy Phlox
(*Phlox pilosa*)

roseate, borne on peduncles in the axils of the leaves. Corolla 4–8 cm. long and nearly as broad; calyx subtended by and covered by 2 broad, ovate to heart-shaped, leaflike bracts, 1.5–3.5 cm. long, the sepals unequal.

Leaves heart-shaped to triangular and arrow-shaped at base, 5–10 cm. long.

In low or damp ground in the open or in partial shade; often along roads or railways. Flowering mid-May to August.

Several varieties of this species may be distinguished. The plant spreads rapidly and is not desirable in the garden.

FIELD BINDWEED

Convolvulus arvensis L.   Plate 147

Freely branching, trailing or climbing perennial, the stems up to 1 m. long, often forming tangled masses. Flowers showy, white, often tinged with red outside. Corolla 15–20 mm. long; bracts of the peduncle small, pointed, borne below the calyx. Leaves typically ovate with arrow-shaped or

hastate base but quite variable and sometimes linear, oblong, or ovate with a heart-shaped base.

In fields, lawns, along roadsides, and in waste places. Introduced from Europe; now a common weed. Flowering June to September.

This species is persistent and hard to eradicate. Its deep, spreading roots may penetrate to a depth of more than 20 feet. If proper control measures are not taken this weed may so overrun a farm that productivity is seriously impaired.

PHLOX *or* POLEMONIUM FAMILY.
POLEMONIACEAE

This primarily American family includes 13 genera and nearly 300 species, the majority of which are native in western United States. Two genera, with about 8 species, occur fairly commonly in Michigan, and 1 other genus occurs rarely as a weed. The family includes the garden phloxes, Jacob's-ladder, and Gilia. It is valued chiefly for such ornamentals.

The family is characterized by the regular flowers with both petals and sepals 5 and united, the 5 stamens borne on the corolla tube, and the superior, 3-celled ovary with 1 style and 3 stigmas.

WILD BLUE PHLOX

Phlox divaricata L.   Plate 148

Softly hairy perennial up to 5 dm. tall from a partially reclining base, often with prostrate, evergreen rooting basal offshoots. Flowers blue to purplish-blue, rarely white, in terminal or axillary panicles which are at first compact, later becoming loose and

spreading. Corolla salverform, the tube very slender, the 5 lobes notched at the apex; calyx 5-lobed, the lobes slender, pointed, longer than the tube, glandular; stamens 5, inserted at different heights in the corolla tube; pistil solitary, 3-celled, with single

PLATE 149

Jacob's-ladder
(*Polemonium reptans*)

Waterleaf
(*Hydrophyllum canadense*)

304

style and 3 stigmas; capsule ovoid. Leaves few, opposite, lanceolate or narrow-ovate, not sharp-pointed, the lower ones elliptic and evergreen.

In damp to dry open woods or thickets, on rocky slopes and wooded dunes. Flowering April to early June.

This attractive species is often very abundant. It blooms just after the first spring flowers have passed their peak and before the leaves are fully out on the trees. It makes an excellent plant for the garden, where it is attractive with tulips and other early-flowering bulbs.

Moss-pink, *P. subulata* L., which is often cultivated, occurs infrequently in southern Michigan on sand dunes, forming dense evergreen mats. It has small, sharp-pointed, needlelike persistent leaves in tight clusters. In the spring it may be completely covered with white, roseate, pinkish, or lavender flowers. Perennial or Garden Phlox, *P. paniculata* L., is native in the southeast and is often cultivated here.

Downy Phlox

Phlox pilosa L.   Plate 148

Quite similar to Blue Phlox, but the cymes more compact, leafy-bracted, the flowers smaller (1.5–2 cm. wide), usually red-purple, and the lobes of the corolla unnotched; the stems are erect from a crown and if offshoots are produced they are also erect; the leaves are linear to lanceolate and narrowed to a stiff, hard tip.

In dry open woods and thickets, openings, sand dunes, waste places, and on prairies. Flowering May to early June.

This species is quite variable, and several varieties have been described. It is said that it is more susceptible to garden pests, and thus more difficult to cultivate than Blue Phlox. It tends to bloom just after Blue Phlox has passed its prime.

Jacob's-ladder, Greek Valerian

Polemonium reptans L.   Plate 149

Spreading perennial up to 5 dm. tall. Flowers deep blue, open-bell-shaped, borne in few-flowered corymbs. Corolla 10–15 mm. long, divided to below the middle, the lobes rounded, somewhat spreading; calyx bell-shaped, 5-lobed; stamens 5, attached to the corolla tube, the filaments all bent toward one side of the corolla, shorter than the corolla; pistil solitary, the ovary superior, the stigma 3-parted; capsule ovoid. Leaves alternate, pinnately compound, the leaflets lanceolate or narrowly oval, 8–16 pairs plus a terminal one.

In rich woods and bottoms, thickets, and margins of meadows. Flowering mid-April to June.

Some of the numerous western species of this genus have a very disagreeable odor and are known as "skunkweed." In contrast to the phloxes, which are mostly pollinated by butterflies, the species of *Polemonium* are pollinated mainly by bees. Jacob's-ladder is said to be easy to grow.

PLATE 150

Blueweed
(*Echium vulgare*)

Hoary Puccoon
(*Lithospermum canescens*)

WATERLEAF FAMILY. HYDROPHYLLACEAE

This is a small but widely distributed family, particularly abundant in western North America. Only 2 genera occur in Michigan, one of which, *Phacelia,* is rather uncommon.

WATERLEAF
Hydrophyllum canadense L.

Plate 149

Erect, smooth perennial up to 7 dm. tall from scaly, toothed rootstocks. Flowers whitish to pale blue, borne in coiled, somewhat 1-sided clusters in the axils of the leaves. Corolla bell-shaped, 5-lobed, the tube having nectar-bearing grooves opposite the lobes; calyx lobes 5, linear or awllike, having minute teeth in the sinuses; sta-mens 5, extending well beyond the corolla; pistil 1, the ovary superior, the style extending beyond the corolla. Leaves mostly basal, palmately 5–7-lobed (sometimes compound), heart-shaped at base, unequally toothed.

In rich moist woods, borders of woods, and thickets. Flowering June and July.

The Indians ate the roots in times of food scarcity. Two other species of waterleaf are found in Michigan: *H. appendiculatum* Michx. is hairy, the flowers are violet, purple, or whitish, and the calyx has a small reflexed lobe in each sinus; Virginia Waterleaf, *H. virginianum* L., is quite smooth, the flowers are lavender to white, and the leaves are pinnately divided.

BORAGE FAMILY. BORAGINACEAE

This widely distributed family includes about 100 genera and 2000 species. Virginia Bluebells, Heliotrope, Lungwort, Forget-me-not, and a few others are grown as ornamentals.

The members of this family are easily recognized. The plants are usually rough-hairy, the leaves simple and alternate. The flowers are borne in 1-sided coiled racemes which straighten as the flowers open; the flower parts are mostly in 5's, the petals and sepals both united, the stamens borne on the corolla tube, the ovary deeply 4-lobed and with a single style. The flowers often change from pink to blue between bud and maturity.

BORAGINACEAE

1. Corolla slightly irregular . . . . . *Echium vulgare,* Plate 150
1. Corolla regular 2
   2. Flowers yellow to orange
     . . . *Lithospermum croceum* or *canescens,* Color Plate 12; Plate 150
   2. Flowers not yellow or orange 3
3. Flowers reddish purple . . . . . *Cynoglossum officinale,* Plate 151
3. Flowers usually blue, sometimes pink or white 4
   4. Flowers trumpet-shaped, the tube much longer
     than the calyx . . . . *Mertensia virginica,* Plate 153
   4. Flowers flat and circular in outline, the tube scarcely
     if at all longer than the calyx . . *Myosotis scorpioides* or *laxa,* Plate 152

BLUEWEED, VIPER'S BUGLOSS

Echium vulgare L.

Plate 150

Bristly-hairy, erect, stiff biennial becoming freely branched, up to 9 dm. tall. Flower buds pink, the flowers bright blue to violet (sometimes whitish or pink), becoming reddish-purple to purplish-rose in age; flowers numerous, clustered in short, densely hairy, coiled spikes which straighten as the flowers open. Corolla funnel-shaped, unequally 5-lobed, 12–20 mm. long; calyx teeth 5, covered with stiff bristles; stamens 5, borne on the corolla, unequal, the 2 longest extending beyond the corolla tube; pistil 1, the ovary superior, deeply 4-cleft, the style long, slender, extending beyond the corolla tube; nutlets 4, rough, dark brown. Leaves bristly, entire, oblong to linear-lanceolate, those on the stem sessile, the basal leaves long-petioled, up to 15 cm. long.

In poor soil in pastures and old fields, common in waste places in calcareous soil. Introduced from Europe; now a troublesome weed. Flowering June to September.

HAIRY PUCCOON

Lithospermum croceum Fern.

Color Plate 12

Hairy, erect perennial up to 6 dm. tall from deep, purple-staining roots. Flowers bright orange-yellow, 1.5–2 cm. long, borne on short pedicels in compact, leafy 1-sided coiled racemes. Corolla tubular below with a flat spreading limb above, 1.5–2.5 cm. wide, the tube bearded within at base; calyx lobes 9–11 mm. long, strongly keeled. Leaves 33–45 below the inflorescence, alternate, sessile, crowded, linear-lanceolate, up to 5 cm. long and usually 5–6 mm. wide, entire, having long, conspicuous, rather stiff hairs.

On sand dunes, hillsides, and open lake shores, in dry, open oak woods, and in jack-pine plains. Flowering late May to early August.

HOARY PUCCOON

Lithospermum canescens (Michx.) Lehm.

Plate 150

Quite similar to the Hairy Puccoon, but smaller (up to 4 dm. tall), hoary with dense soft down; flowers bright yellow, the limb of the corolla 1–1.5 cm. wide; calyx lobes 3–6 mm. long; leaves 8–30 below the inflorescence, the roots thick, red.

On dry sandy or clayey hillsides, in dry open woods, along roadsides, and on prairies. Flowering May and June.

The Indians used the small, hard nutlets for beads.

COMMON HOUND'S-TONGUE

Cynoglossum officinale L.

Plate 151

Softly hairy biennial, branching only at the inflorescence. Flowers reddish-purple, about 1 cm. wide, borne on 1-sided racemes in a panicle. Corolla with 5 rounded lobes, the tube short, about the same length as the calyx; stamens not extending beyond the corolla; nutlets 4, becoming large and conspicuous, covered with short hooked bristles, overtopped by the style and partially enclosed by the enlarged, flattened calyx. Leaves alternate, softly hairy, close to the stem, lanceolate, the upper ones sessile, the lower petioled.

In pastures, along roads, and in waste places; often abundant. Introduced from Europe; now a noxious weed. Flowering May through July.

Butterfly-weed

Color plate 12

Hairy Puccoon

PLATE 151
Common Hound's-tongue (*Cynoglossum officinale*)

PLATE 152

Forget-me-not
(*Myosotis scorpioides*)

Forget-me-not
(*Myosotis laxa*)

The fruits stick firmly to the fleece of sheep and to clothing. Another, more delicate, species, Northern Wild Comfrey, *C. boreale* Fern., has smaller, attractive blue flowers like Forget-me-nots, in which the delicate style is hidden by the nutlets; the leaves are all below the middle of the stem.

FORGET-ME-NOT

Myosotis scorpioides L.

Plate 152

Slender, weak, appressed hairy perennial with angled stems which are erect at first, partially reclining later and rooting freely at the base. Flowers sky blue with yellow center, borne in coiled terminal racemes, the main branches lacking basal leaves. Corolla 6–9 mm. wide, saucer-shaped with a short tube which is longer than the calyx, the spreading lobes broad, slightly notched at the tip, becoming white toward the center and each bearing a conspicuous yellow crest; calyx tubular, the 5 lobes hairy, shorter than the tube; stamens 5, attached to the corolla tube, not extending beyond it; pistil 1, the ovary deeply 4-lobed, the style overtopping the 4 nutlets. Leaves alternate, sessile, oblong to oblanceolate, narrowed to the base, 2.5–7 cm. long.

Along margins of brooks, in quiet water in marshes, or in very moist woods. Introduced from Europe. Flowering May to September.

FORGET-ME-NOT

Myosotis laxa Lehm.

Plate 152

Similar to the preceding species, but the flowers smaller (3–6 mm. broad) and often paler, the corolla tube about as long as the calyx, the style shorter than the nutlets and the calyx tube; the main branches of the inflorescence usually with 1 or 2 leaves near the base.

In wet, open or partially shaded ground, tamarack swamps, shallow water. Flowering May to September.

LUNGWORT, VIRGINIA COWSLIP, BLUEBELLS

Mertensia virginica (L.) Pers.

Plate 153

Smooth, often glaucous, fleshy, erect, simple or branched perennial up to 7 dm. tall. Flowers showy, blue (becoming purple or pinkish-purple), or rarely white, borne in short racemes in a terminal panicle. Corolla trumpet-shaped (the cylindric tube enlarged and bell-shaped at the end), 18–25 mm. long; calyx short, the 5 lobes pointed; stamens 5, borne on the corolla tube; pistil solitary, the ovary superior, 4-cleft; nutlets 4, ovoid, roughened. Leaves alternate, the upper ones oblong or lanceolate and sessile or clasping at the base, the lower ones oblong to obovate, narrowed to margined petioles.

In rich woods and thickets, in low meadows and along streams. Sometimes seen outside of cultivation in Michigan. Flowering April to June.

This species is native in southern Michigan. It is often planted in the garden and naturalized in woods. A hairy species, *M. paniculata* (Ait.) G. Don, with smaller flowers 10–15 mm. long, is conspicuous in the Porcupine Mountains and is found occasionally elsewhere in the Lake Superior region.

PLATE 153
Lungwort (*Mertensia virginica*)

312

VERVAIN FAMILY. VERBENACEAE

This predominantly tropical family has nearly 100 genera and over 2500 species. Economically the family is most important for teak-wood from the East Indies. Verbena and, to a lesser extent, Callicarpa and Lantana are cultivated for ornamentals.

The slightly irregular flowers, each subtended by a bract, are borne in dense spikes; the 5 petals are united, and the 4 stamens are borne on the corolla tube; the ovary is somewhat 4-lobed and produces 4 nutlets; the stem is usually square; and the leaves are opposite.

Verbena

1. Plants stiffly erect; leaves with regular teeth 2
1. Plants low, prostrate with branches radiating from base, leaves cut or lobed . . . . *V. bracteata*, Plate 155
   2. Spikes numerous, stalked; plants of moist places . . . . *V. hastata*, Plate 154
   2. Spikes solitary or few, sessile; plants of dry places . . . . *V. stricta*, Plate 155

BRACTED VERBENA

Verbena bracteata Lag. & Rodr.   Plate 155

Prostrate perennial with numerous partially reclining or ascending hairy branches radiating from the base. Flowers small, purple to bluish, borne in elongate, thick, terminal, sessile spikes with conspicuous divergent bracts. Leaves opposite, hairy, pinnately cut or 3-lobed, narrowed at the base, 1–6 cm. long.

In dry sunny places, in fields, on prairies. Flowering June to September.

BLUE VERVAIN

Verbena hastata L.   Plate 154

Stiff, erect, rough-hairy perennial up to 1.5 dm. tall, freely branched above, the stems angled. Flowers small, violet-blue or blue, in numerous slender, erect, very compact spikes on fairly long peduncles. Corolla tubular, with 5 spreading lobes and a dense ring of hairs at the top of the tube; calyx tubular, hairy, 5-toothed; stamens 4, inserted on the corolla tube and not extending beyond it; pistil 1, the ovary superior, the style slender, terminal, the stigma 2-lobed; nutlets 4, readily separating. Leaves opposite, lanceolate to narrowly elliptic or ovate-lanceolate, coarsely sharp-toothed, 4–18 cm. long, sometimes having 2 basal lobes.

In damp thickets, swales, and moist meadows, along streams, in swamps and wet fields. Flowering June to October.

This species is readily grown in a moist garden. The Indians made a tea from the leaves and also used the plant for treating nosebleed.

HOARY VERBENA

Verbena stricta Vent.   Plate 155

PLATE 154
Blue Vervain (*Verbena hastata*)

PLATE 155

Hoary Verbena
(*Verbena stricta*)

Bracted Verbena
(*Verbena bracteata*)

315

PLATE 156

Common Skullcap
(*Scutellaria epilobiifolia*)

Mad-dog Skullcap
(*Scutellaria lateriflora*)

Wood Sage
(*Teucrium canadense*)

Coarser than Blue Vervain, the flowers larger (8–10 mm. wide) and more irregular, and the color more roseate; the spikes larger, solitary or few, sessile; the entire plant covered with long, soft, white hairs; leaves nearly round, oval, or oblong-ovate, strongly veined, coarsely toothed.

In dry soil, open sandy ground, on prairies, in barren fields, and along roads. Flowering July and August.

The root system of this species extends down more than a yard. The plants show remarkable resistance to drought. The foliage is so bitter that cattle will not eat it even when forage is scarce.

MINT FAMILY. LABIATAE

A large family of some 200 genera and 3200 species, and cosmopolitan in distribution. It is centered in the Mediterranean region, where it often forms a dominant part of the vegetation. Among the volatile aromatic oils derived from this family are spearmint, peppermint, lavender, and rosemary. Hyssop, pennyroyal, thyme, sage, marjoram, savory, and basil, the last sacred to the Hindus, are among the important culinary herbs. Hoarhound is used in medicines. Salvia, Dragonhead, False Dragonhead, Monarda, Skullcap, Coleus, Deadnettle, and many others are grown for ornament.

Most of our representatives of this family can be easily recognized. They have square stems, opposite, simple leaves, and an aromatic odor, especially when crushed. The flowers are borne in pairs or whorls in the axils of the leaves. They are irregular to nearly regular, the petals are united, and the 2 or 4 stamens are borne on the corolla tube. The ovary is usually deeply 4-lobed and the single style is attached at the base of the ovary. The usually 4 nutlets are attached at the base.

The Verbena family is quite similar to it in many respects, but the foliage is not aromatic; the ovary is merely slightly lobed, with the style borne at the top and the nutlets attached at the side.

LABIATAE

1. Corolla split on upper side, appearing to have a single 5-lobed lip (the lower), the stamens protruding through the split; ovary only slightly lobed . . . . *Teucrium canadense*, Plate 156
1. Corolla not split; ovary deeply 4-parted 2
  2. Calyx having a small knoblike projection on the upper side near the base; flowers blue . . . *Scutellaria epilobiifolia* or *lateriflora*, Plate 156
  2. Calyx without a projection on upper side; flowers blue or not 3
3. Stamens with anthers 4 4
3. Stamens with anthers 2 12
  4. Corolla strongly 2-lipped, the upper lip concave 5
  4. Corolla regular to weakly 2-lipped, the upper lip flat or nearly so 10

WOOD SAGE, AMERICAN GERMANDER

Teucrium canadense L.   Plate 156

Erect, hairy, very aromatic perennial up to 1 m. tall. Flowers rose-purple to cream, the separate whorls of about 6 flowers forming slender, elongate spikes. Corolla tube short, the limb irregularly 5-lobed, split at the top so that the 4 small, nearly equal upper lobes and the larger lower lobe appear to form a single lip; calyx bell-shaped, with a dense, feltlike covering, 5-toothed; stamens 4, in 2 unequal pairs, protruding through the split in the corolla; ovary 4-lobed only at the apex, the style 2-lobed, protruding with the stamens; fruit consisting of 4 nutlets. Leaves opposite, short-petioled, light grayish-green, often tinged with purplish-red, soft-hairy, ovate to lance-oblong.

In moist, usually open, soil, sometimes in open woods, common on mud flats. Flowering July and August.

Another genus of mint which appears to have a single lip, Bugleweed (*Ajuga reptans* L. and *Ajuga genevensis* L.), is low-growing and mat-forming, with stems up to 3 dm. tall. The blue flowers are borne 4–6 in a cluster in the axils of the leaves, and have a very short (but not split) upper lip. This widely cultivated genus, introduced from Europe, is a common escape.

PLATE 157

Heal-all (*Prunella vulgaris*)

Catnip (*Nepeta cataria*)

Ground-ivy (*Glechoma hederacea*)

319

COMMON SKULLCAP
Scutellaria epilobiifolia A. Hamilton
Plate 156

More or less erect, nonaromatic perennial up to 7 dm tall, often freely branched, hairy on the ridges of the square stems. Flowers violet-blue, 15–25 mm. long, ascending, solitary on very short pedicels from the axils of the leaves. Corolla tubular, 2-lipped, the throat enlarged, the upper lip hooded, the lower lip broader and spreading, notched; calyx bell-shaped, 2-lipped, with a small but distinct protuberance on the upper side near the base, splitting to the base in fruit; stamens 4, in 2 pairs, the anthers bearded; nutlets 4. Leaves sessile or nearly so, having fine recurved hairs beneath, oblong-lanceolate, crenate, prominently veined.

On rocky, sandy, or gravelly shores; in swamps, bogs, and wet thickets; along streams. Flowering June to September.

This is a rather variable species, which, like so many other blue-flowered plants, sometimes has white or pink flowers.

MAD-DOG SKULLCAP
Scutellaria lateriflora L.
Plate 156

Quite similar to the preceding species, but the flowers smaller (5–9 mm. long) and borne in slender, compact, 2–24-flowered, 1-sided axillary racemes, the leaves petioled.

In low, wet places, swampy woods and thickets, in meadows, along streams, frequently in a dense tangle of other vegetation. Flowering July to September.

CATNIP
Nepeta cataria L.
Plate 157

Stout, erect, branched, downy, grayish, strongly aromatic perennial up to 1 m. tall. Flowers small, white, striped or dotted with rose-purple, crowded in many-flowered whorls in rather dense terminal inflorescences. Corolla tubular, dilated in the throat, strongly 2-lipped, the upper lip erect, large, and spreading, 2-lobed, the lower lip smaller, 3-cleft; calyx tubular, with 5 long narrow lobes, downy; stamens 4, the anthers lying on or close to the lower lip; ovary deeply 4-cleft; nutlets 4. Leaves opposite, soft-hairy, ovate to oblong, coarsely toothed.

In yards, roadsides, and waste places. Introduced from Europe; now a common weed. Flowering June to September.

The leaves are sometimes used for making tea. This plant is well known as a favorite of cats and is often used in stuffing toys for them.

GROUND-IVY, GILL-OVER-THE-GROUND
Glechoma hederacea L.
Plate 157

Smoothish to somewhat hairy, extensively creeping perennial. Flowers blue or purplish-blue, 1.6–2.2 cm. long, usually 3 in each axil. Corolla 2-lipped, the tube elongate; calyx tubular, slightly oblique. Leaves round to kidney-shaped, crenate.

In yards, along roads, in moist woods. Introduced from Europe. Flowering April to July.

HEAL-ALL, SELF-HEAL
Prunella vulgaris L.
Plate 157

Hairy to nearly smooth, simple or sparsely-branched perennial with at least the tips of the square stems erect. Flowers violet, lavender, bluish, pinkish, or whitish, borne in 3-flowered clusters subtended by a leafy bract, the clusters forming dense terminal heads which elongate and may be 5–10 cm. long in fruit. Corolla ascending, 10–16 mm. long, strongly 2-lipped, the upper lip erect, entire, arching over the stamens, the lower lip spreading or drooping, 3-lobed, the middle lobe the largest, rounded and finely toothed on the margin; stamens 4, the filaments forked at the top. Leaves opposite, oblong, ovate, or lanceolate, entire or somewhat toothed.

In fields, woods, waste places. Introduced from Europe; now a common weed. Flowering May to October.

FALSE DRAGONHEAD
Physostegia virginiana (L.) Benth.   Plate 158

Smooth perennial, simple or branched at the summit, up to 1.5 m. tall. Flowers purple to roseate, rarely white, 2.5–3 cm. long, borne singly in the axils of small bracts and forming elongate, terminal, wandlike spikes. Corolla funnel-shaped with an inflated throat, 2-lipped, the upper lip erect, nearly entire, the lower lip spreading, 3-lobed, with middle lobe notched; calyx sticky-glandular, short-tubular, with short, sharp-tipped teeth, slightly inflated in fruit. Leaves opposite, lanceolate, sharply toothed, the upper ones reduced.

In damp thickets, on river banks and shores. Flowering June to September.

COMMON MOTHERWORT
Leonurus cardiaca L.   Plate 159

Coarse, erect, weedy perennial up to 1.5 m. tall, usually many branched above, hairy on the 4 angles of the stem and on the nodes. Flowers pale purple, borne in whorls in the axils of the upper leaves. Corolla 2-lipped, the upper lip oblong and entire, somewhat arched, densely bearded, the lower lip spreading, 3-lobed; calyx teeth nearly equal, spiny; stamens 4, the upper pair the shortest. Leaves opposite, long-petioled; lower leaves broadly rounded at base and palmately lobed, the margin toothed; upper leaves smaller, wedge-shaped at base, more or less 3-lobed, the margin toothed or entire.

In farmyards, along railways and roads, in dry open ground, and in moist shaded places. Introduced from Europe; now a common weed. Flowering June to August.

WOUNDWORT
Stachys palustris L.   Plate 160

Rank-smelling, simple or sometimes loosely branched perennial up to 1 m. tall, having underground stolons which terminate in whitish tubers. Flowers rose-purple, mottled, borne in usually 6-flowered whorls in leafy terminal spikes which grow up to 2.5 dm. long. Corolla 1.2–1.5 cm. long, the lower lip 3-lobed, much longer than the nearly entire upper lip; calyx bell-shaped, hairy, the lobes about as long as the tube; stamens 4, ascending under the upper lip, the anthers in pairs, the upper pair shorter than the lower pair. Leaves opposite, lanceolate to narrowly ovate, pale green, firm and obscurely veined, hairy on both surfaces, slightly toothed; sessile or nearly so, rarely with elongate petioles.

In damp ground in waste places, on shores, in fields and meadows. A variable, wide-ranging, circumpolar species. Flowering late June to September.

PLATE 158
False Dragonhead (*Physostegia virginiana*)

322

PLATE 159
Common Motherwort (*Leonurus cardiaca*)

323

PLATE 160

American Pennyroyal
(*Hedeoma pulegioides*)
Woodmint
(*Blephilia hirsuta*)

Woundwort
(*Stachys palustris*)

324

The extensively creeping *S. tenuifolia* Willd. also occurs in Michigan. It has thin, conspicuously veined leaves which are dark green and glabrous above, and the marginal teeth are prominent. The flowers are pale rose and the calyx is glabrous, but sometimes has stiff hairs along the veins. Another Hedge-nettle, *S. hyssopifolia* Michx., is a delicate, linear-leaved Coastal Plain species which also occurs in the southwestern part of the Lower Peninsula.

WILD BERGAMOT

Monarda fistulosa L.   Plate 161

Erect, many-stemmed, gray-green, hairy to smooth, very aromatic perennial up to 1.2 m. tall. Flowers lavender, borne in solitary, compact, headlike clusters which are terminal or arise from the upper axils, and are subtended by numerous green or lavender-tinged leaflike bracts. Corolla 2–3 cm. long, tubular, inflated above, 2-lipped, the upper lip erect, the lower spreading, 3-lobed; calyx tubular, nearly regular, having a ring of hairs at the throat; stamens 2, extending beyond the corolla. Leaves gray-green, very strongly scented, strongly pinnately veined, lanceolate, toothed.

Along roadsides, in clearings and dry thickets, on open hillsides, and in borders of woods. Flowering June to August.

The leaves of this species are sometimes made into tea. The Indians boiled the plant with Sweetflag and bone-marrow to make a perfumed hair dressing.

A similar species, Oswego Tea or Bee-balm, *M. didyma* L., is often cultivated and grows wild in Michigan, both natively and as an escape from cultivation. It has bright red flowers 3–4.5 cm. long.

DOTTED MONARDA, HORSEMINT

Monarda punctata L. var. *villicaulis* Pennell   Plate 161

Simple to branching, grayish-green, long-hairy, odorous perennial up to 1 m. tall. Flowers cream-color to yellowish, with purple spots, borne in leafy, interrupted spikes, the leaflike bracts conspicuous, recurved, lilac to whitish. Corolla tube elongate, with a slightly inflated throat, the upper lip longer than the stamens. Leaves grayish (especially beneath) with fine hairs, lanceolate, coarsely and shallowly toothed.

Along roads and railways, in sandy open ground, on low dune ridges, and on sandy plains. Mostly in southern Michigan. Flowering mid-July to mid-September.

Lemon-mint, *M. citriodora* Cerv., somewhat resembles Dotted Monarda but is an annual and has a strong lemon odor. It does not grow wild in Michigan.

WOODMINT

Blephilia hirsuta (Pursh) Benth.   Plate 160

Hairy perennial up to 1 m. tall. Flowers white to pale bluish, purple-spotted, borne in dense globose, axillary and terminal clusters. Corolla inflated in the throat, hairy, the 2 lips nearly equal, the upper lip erect, entire, the

325

PLATE 161

Wild Bergamot
(*Monarda fistulosa*)

Dotted Monarda
(*Monarda punctata*)

326

lower lip spreading, 3-cleft; calyx 2-lipped, the 3 upper teeth tipped with awns; stamens 2, extending beyond the corolla. Leaves long-petioled, ovate, round or heart-shaped at the base, strongly toothed.

In moist or shady places. Flowering early June to September.

B. ciliata (L.) Benth., a less hairy species with nearly sessile leaves, also occurs in dry woods in Michigan.

AMERICAN PENNYROYAL, MOCK PENNYROYAL

Hedeoma pulegioides (L.) Pers.   Plate 160

Erect, freely branching, hairy, odorous annual 1–4 dm. tall. Flowers bluish, borne in few-flowered whorls in the axils of the leaves. Corolla scarcely longer than the calyx, weakly 2-lipped, the upper lip flat, erect, notched, the lower lip 3-lobed; calyx tubular, 2-lipped; stamens 2. Leaves opposite, small, the larger ones petioled, lance-olate to oblong-ovate, usually toothed.

In moist or dry upland woods. Flowering July to September.

Horse-balm, *Collinsonia canadensis* L., also with 2 stamens, has a spreading panicle of yellowish flowers with a distinct lemon odor. The elongated corolla has 4 nearly equal lobes and a lower, much larger, lobe which is fringed around the margin. The leaves are numerous, large, and ovate. The species grows in rich moist woods.

LOW CALAMINT

Satureja arkansana (Nutt.) Briq.   Plate 162

Essentially glabrous, erect, simple or branching perennial up to 4 dm. tall, with a Pennyroyal-like odor. Flowers rose-purple to lavender, one to a few on slender pedicels in the axils of the leaves. Corolla tubular, somewhat inflated above, 8–15 mm. long, 2-lipped; calyx tubular, with 5 sharp-pointed teeth; stamens 4. Leaves opposite, often reddish, linear-oblong to linear-oblanceolate, entire, up to 2.5 cm. long and less than 6 mm. wide.

On calcareous shores, banks, and barrens, and on rock. Flowering June to October.

Summer Savory, *S. hortensis* L., long cultivated as a culinary herb, sometimes escapes from cultivation and persists. It resembles Low Calamint, but the internodes are hairy, the flowers nearly sessile, smaller (5–7 mm. long), and pale pinkish-purple to white.

WILD BASIL, DOGMINT

Satureja vulgaris (L.) Fritsch   Plate 162

Erect, hairy, usually simple, slightly aromatic perennial up to 6 dm. tall from a creeping base, often growing in large patches. Flowers usually rose-purple but at times purple, pink, or white, borne in dense, headlike, axillary and terminal clusters about 2.5 cm. in diameter. Corolla tubular, slightly inflated, 2-lipped; calyx tubular, hairy, 2-lipped, the upper lip cleft; stamens 4, ascending under the upper lip of the corolla, of 2 unequal lengths; style cleft into 2 unequal lobes. Leaves opposite, elliptic-ovate, bright green on upper surface, pale and hairy beneath, short-petioled, the margin entire, wavy, or crenate.

In open woods or thickets, along roads and in rocky or alluvial soil. Flowering June to September.

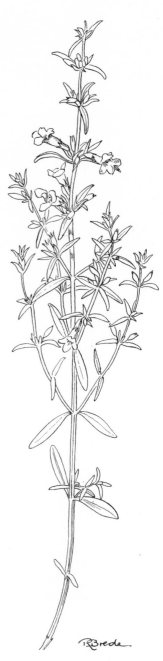

PLATE 162

Wild Basil
(*Satureja vulgaris*)

Low Calamint
(*Satureja arkansana*)

Mountain Mint

Pycnanthemum virginianum (L.) Durand & Jackson　　Plate 163

Pungent perennial up to 1 m. tall, freely branching above the middle, finely hairy on the angles of the stems, smooth on the 4 sides. Flowers small, whitish or purplish, the lips dotted with purple, borne at ends of branches or in the axils of the leaves in dense crowded whorls which usually form heads. Corolla short, slightly irregular, 2-lipped, the upper lip straight, nearly flat; calyx tubular, nearly regular, the teeth all about the same length; stamens 4. Leaves numerous, crowded, sessile, smooth on the upper surface, often hairy on the veins beneath, linear-lanceolate, entire.

In thickets, upland woods, and meadows, and on gravelly shores. Flowering July to September.

Water-horehound, Bugleweed

Lycopus americanus Muhl.　　Plate 163

Simple or branching, erect, glabrous to slightly hairy, nonaromatic, stoloniferous perennial up to 1 m. tall. Flowers white, small, borne in dense clusters in the axils of the leaves. Corolla nearly regular, bell-shaped, 4-lobed, with one lobe larger than the others; calyx bell-shaped, the teeth tapered to a long sharp point; stamens 2. Leaves opposite, ovate-lanceolate, the lower ones pinnately cut and often falling when the fruit is mature, the upper leaves merely toothed.

In low wet ground, in swampy areas around lakes, along streams and wet shores. Flowering July to September.

Medicinal horehound is not derived from this but from a European species. Several other species also occur in Michigan.

Peppermint

Mentha piperita L.　　Plate 164

Smooth, usually branched perennial up to 1 m. tall, with a strong peppermint odor. Flowers purplish, small, borne in crowded, compact, ovoid, terminal spikes which elongate and become loose, the lower flower clusters becoming widely separated. Corolla nearly regular, the tube short, 4-lobed; calyx tubular, the 5 teeth nearly equal; stamens 4, all the same

American Wild Mint

Mentha arvensis L.　　Plate 164

Erect, usually simple, aromatic perennial 1.5–8 dm. tall, spreading by stolons, hairy on the angles of the stem. Flowers lilac, pinkish, or purplish, rarely white, small, borne in dense, subglobose clusters in the axils of the leaves. Corolla regular, short-tubular, with 4 spreading lobes, one of which is notched and often larger than the others; calyx 5-toothed, densely glandular; stamens 4, longer than the corolla. Leaves opposite, short-petioled, strongly veined, ovate to lanceolate, sharply toothed.

In damp, open soil, along shores and streams, in marshes and swamps. Flowering July to September.

This is our only native true mint. The Indians used the leaves in treating fevers and pleurisy.

PLATE 163

Water-horehound
(*Lycopus americanus*)

Mountain Mint
(*Pycnanthemum virginianum*)

330

length. Leaves opposite, lance-oblong to ovate-oblong, toothed, definitely petioled, the petioles of the principal leaves 4–15 mm. long.

In damp open ground, in pastures, along roadside ditches and streams. Introduced from Europe, often cultivated and now wild over a large area. Flowering late July to late September.

Oil of peppermint and peppermint extract are derived from this species. Spearmint, *M. spicata* L., also a frequent and persistent escape from cultivation, has more slender, elongate spikes, and the leaves are sessile or have petioles only 3 mm. long, or less.

NIGHTSHADE FAMILY. SOLANACEAE

This large family of about 85 genera and over 2000 species is most abundant in tropical America. It includes food and drug plants, as well as ornamentals. Potato, tomato, eggplant, and green and red peppers are among the best-known foods. Belladonna, atropine, stramonium and henbane are important drugs. Petunia, Salpiglossis, *Datura*, *Solanum*, and others are grown for ornament. Tobacco also belongs to this family.

The foliage is rank-scented and often narcotic. The fruits are narcotic in some species, deadly in some, edible in others. The leaves are alternate; the regular corolla is often plaited (folded lengthwise), and consists of 5 united petals; the 5 sepals are united; the 5 equal stamens are borne on the corolla; the 2-celled superior ovary produces a capsule or berry.

NIGHTSHADE

Solanum dulcamara L.   Plate 165

Somewhat woody perennial vine, all parts of which are poisonous. Flowers violet or purple (rarely white) borne in several-flowered, loose cymes which arise between the nodes or opposite the leaves. Corolla wheel-shaped, about 1 cm. wide, deeply 5-cleft; calyx 5-cleft; stamens 5, extending beyond the corolla, the anthers converging around the style, opening at the tip by pores; ovary superior, 2-celled; fruit an ovoid or ellipsoid bright red berry. Leaves ovate, with or without 1 or 2 basal lobes.

In moist thickets and clearings. Naturalized from Europe. Flowering mid-May to September.

Jerusalem Cherry, *S. pseudo-capsicum* L., is often grown indoors. It has white flowers and globose scarlet to yellow berries. Black Nightshade (*S. americanum* Mill. and *S. nigrum* L.), is a common, erect, widely branching annual with white or very pale flowers and shiny black berries. The berries are poisonous at first, but it is said that they are nontoxic when fully ripe, and they are then sometimes used in cooking.

LARGE WHITE-FLOWERED GROUND-CHERRY

Chamaesaracha grandiflora (Hook.) Fern.   Plate 165

Erect, slightly hairy annual 1.5–9 dm. tall. Flowers white, yellow-centered, 3–5 cm. broad, 2–4 in the upper axils. Corolla wheel-shaped, nearly flat, 5-

PLATE 164

American Wild Mint
(*Mentha arvensis*)

Peppermint
(*Mentha piperita*)

PLATE 165
Large White-flowered Ground-cherry
(*Chamaesaracha grandiflora*)
Nightshade
(*Solanum dulcamara*)

333

$\frac{2}{3}$

$\frac{1}{3}$

PLATE 166
Jimsonweed
(*Datura stramonium*)
Ground-cherry
(*Physalis heterophylla*)
334

angled with a 5-lobed hairy spot in the center; calyx 5-lobed, becoming greatly inflated in fruit; stamens 5; fruit a globose berry which is enclosed by the calyx. Leaves glandular-hairy, sticky to the touch, wing-petioled, lance-ovate, the margin wavy or entire.

In recent clearings, along roadsides, in open woods, and on sandy and rocky shores. Flowering June to August.

GROUND-CHERRY

Physalis heterophylla Nees   Plate 166

Sticky-hairy, freely branching perennial with deeply buried thick rootstocks. Flowers yellow with a dark center, 1.5–2.5 cm. broad, solitary, drooping. Corolla tube very short, the limb between wheel-shaped and bell-shaped, shallowly 5-lobed; calyx small, 5-lobed, becoming greatly inflated in fruit; stamens 5, erect, the anthers separate; fruit a small yellow globose berry enclosed by the inflated calyx. Leaves alternate, hairy, ovate, usually coarsely and irregularly toothed.

In dry, open woods and orchards, along roads and railways, at the foot of sand dunes, in gardens and waste places. Flowering June to September.

The related low, weak Ground-cherry, *P. pubescens* L., is an annual that is often cultivated. It has larger, sweetish, edible berries which are used in preserves, pies, or sauce. The Indians ate the berries raw or cooked, and used the roots medicinally. The attractive Chinese Lantern-plant, *P. alkekengi* L., native to Asia, has been introduced as an ornamental. It has a large, bright red to scarlet fruiting calyx about 5 cm. long and is used extensively in winter bouquets.

JIMSONWEED

Datura stramonium L.   Plate 166

Glabrous, stout, ill-scented, poisonous annual up to 1.5 m. tall. Flowers showy, white to pale violet, solitary and erect at the forks of the stem, each subtended by a leaf and 2 young branches. Corolla funnel-shaped, 5-lobed, 7–10 cm. long; calyx about half as long as the corolla, 5-toothed; stamens 5, erect; capsule globular to ovoid, 3–5 cm. long, many-seeded, usually prickly.

In fields, barnyards, and waste ground. Introduced from Asia. Flowering July to October.

FIGWORT FAMILY. SCROPHULARIACEAE

This large cosmopolitan family includes about 200 genera and 3000 species. The drug digitalis, used in treating heart ailments, is derived from Foxglove. Snapdragon, Beard-tongue, Monkeyflower, and Speedwell are often grown in the garden; *Calceolaria*, or Slipperplant, in the greenhouse.

The family is characterized by simple leaves without stipules; the flowers are not terminal; the corolla is of united petals and is usually irregular 2-lipped and 5-lobed (sometimes nearly regular,

335

PLATE 167

Moth Mullein
(*Verbascum blattaria*)

Common Mullein
(*Verbascum thapsus*)

sometimes apparently 4-lobed); stamens usually 4 (in 2 unequal pairs) or 2 (5 in *Verbascum*), inserted near the base of the corolla tube and alternate with the lobes; ovary superior, 2-celled; fruit a globose to ovoid capsule.

SCROPHULARIACEAE

1. Anther-bearing stamens 5; corolla wheel-shaped,
   5-lobed . . . . . . *Verbascum thapsus* or *blattaria*, Plate 167
1. Anther-bearing stamens 2 or 4; corolla not wheel-shaped 2
   2. Corolla having a spur at base . . . . . *Linaria vulgaris*, Plate 168
   2. Corolla not having a spur at base 3
3. Stamens with anthers 2 4
3. Stamens with anthers 4 5
   4. Leaves mostly in whorls of 3–6;
      plants erect . . . . . . *Veronicastrum virginicum*, Plate 172
   4. Leaves mostly opposite; plants
      sprawling . . . . *Veronica americana*, Plate 172
5. Leaves alternate or basal, usually lobed or
   pinnately dissected 6
5. Leaves opposite, not deeply cut 7
   6. Leaves sessile, 3–5 lobed; bracts surrounding
      flowers scarlet . . . . . . *Castilleja coccinea*, Color Plate 13
   6. Leaves mostly petioled, finely dissected; floral
      bracts not scarlet . . . . . . *Pedicularis canadensis*, Plate 174
7. Flowers solitary in axils of normal leaves 8
7. Flowers in clusters 9
   8. Flowers white to cream . . . . . *Melampyrum lineare*, Plate 174
   8. Flowers yellow or blue . . . *Mimulus ringens* or *glabratus*, Plate 171
9. Flowers brown to greenish purple; stems
   square . . . . *Scrophularia lanceolata*, Plate 169
9. Not as in alternate choice 10
   10. Flowers pink to rose-purple . *Gerardia paupercula* or *tenuifolia*, Plate 173
   10. Not as in alternate choice 11
11. Flowers blue and white, the corolla cut
    nearly to base . . . . *Collinsia verna*, Plate 168
11. Not as in alternate choice 12
    12. Flowers sessile or nearly so, borne in a rather compact
        cluster, corolla nearly closed at tip . . *Chelone glabra*, Plate 170
    12. Not as in alternate choice;
        sterile stamen bearded . . . . *Penstemon hirsutus*, Plate 171

COMMON MULLEIN, FLANNEL-PLANT

Verbascum thapsus L.   Plate 167

Robust, stiffly erect, unbranched, yellowish or grayish, densely woolly biennial up to 2.3 m. tall, producing a rosette of leaves the first year, from which the stout strongly-winged, flowering stem rises the second year. Flowers pale yellow, borne in a stiff, elongate, compact terminal spike. Corolla open-bell-shaped to wheel-shaped, the 5 rounded lobes only slightly unequal; calyx regular, deeply 5-lobed; stamens 5, all fertile, attached to the co-

337

PLATE 168

Butter-and-eggs
(*Linaria vulgaris*)

Blue-eyed Mary
(*Collinsia verna*)

rolla tube, the 3 upper filaments densely white-bearded; ovary superior, with 5 spreading styles; capsule longer than the calyx, many-seeded. Leaves felted on both sides with many branched hairs, thick, oblong blade long-decurrent on the stem, entire or somewhat crenate, lower leaves having winged petioles.

In fields, along roadsides, and in waste places, sometimes in open forests. Introduced from Europe. Flowering July to September.

MOTH MULLEIN

Verbascum blattaria L. Plate 167

Slender, green, smooth or slightly hairy, simple or branched biennial. Flowers yellow (white in one form), borne on pedicels 1–1.5 cm. long in elongate, loose, terminal racemes; corolla 1.5–2.5 cm. wide, the filaments all violet-bearded. Leaves alternate, not decurrent on stem, variable, narrowly triangular, oblong, lanceolate or oblanceolate, sometimes pinnately cut or lyrate, toothed to nearly entire; upper leaves sessile, clasping, lower ones petioled.

In open pastures and old fields. Introduced from Europe. Flowering late June through September.

BUTTER-AND-EGGS

Linaria vulgaris Hill Plate 168

Erect perennial usually with many stems, up to 1.3 m. tall from creeping rootstocks. Flowers yellow, in compact terminal racemes. Corolla tubular, 2-lipped, closed, strongly spurred; calyx 5-parted, the lobes overlapping; stamens 4, in 2 pairs of unequal length, attached to the base of the corolla tube; ovary 1, superior. Leaves very numerous, alternate, thickish, the midrib prominent, linear, tapering to both ends.

In dry fields and waste places, along roadsides. Introduced from Europe. Flowering May to October.

Aberrant forms with white flowers, with regular corollas or with 3, 5, or no spurs also occur.

A much coarser species, *L. dalmatica* (L.) Mill., is less common. It may be up to 1 m. tall, simple or branched. The corolla is yellow, and the flowers are 3.5–4 cm. long. The leaves are ovate, ovate-lanceolate or oblong, clasping at the base. It grows locally along roadsides and in fields.

BLUE-EYED MARY

Collinsia verna Nutt. Plate 168

Weak, simple to many-branched, slightly hairy annual or biennial 1–6 dm. tall. Flowers blue and white, in whorls of 4–6 or solitary in the upper axils. Corolla tubular, the tube swollen on the upper side near the base, 2-lipped, the upper lip erect, white, the middle lobe of the blue lower lip folded together forming a pouch which encloses the stamens; calyx bell-shaped, deeply 5-lobed; normal stamens 4, the filaments bearded, sterile stamen short, glandlike. Lower leaves ovate to nearly round, long-petioled, the upper leaves opposite or whorled, sessile or clasping by a heart-shaped base, ovate to lanceolate or linear, toothed or entire.

In rich woods and thickets. Flowering May to June.

339

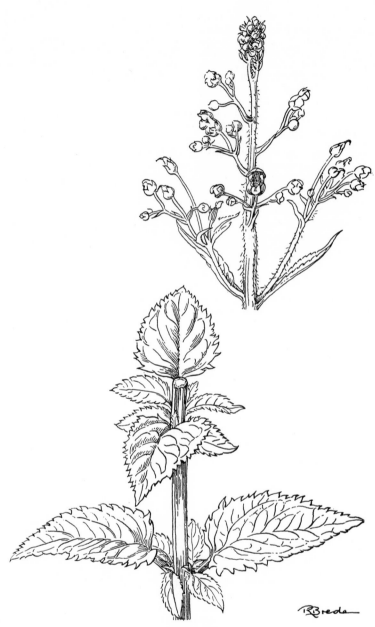

PLATE 169
Figwort (*Scrophularia lanceolata*)

Scrophularia lanceolata Pursh
Plate 169

Coarse, erect, strong-smelling, many-stemmed perennial up to 2 m. tall, smooth or finely hairy, the stems square, the sides flat or shallowly grooved. Flowers numerous, small, 7–11 mm. long, dull reddish brown except for the yellowish-green lower lobe, borne in large, loose, cylindric panicles, 1–5 dm. long. Corolla lustrous, short, the tube wide, 2-lipped, the middle lobe of the lower lip drooping or turned back; calyx regular, deeply saucer-shaped, 5-lobed; normal stamens 4, the sterile filament yellowish green, usually wider than long; capsule ovoid, dull brown. Leaves opposite, lanceolate to ovate, wedge-shaped, tapering or subtruncate at the base, coarsely toothed, the petioles wing-margined.

In open woods, thickets, along roads, and in open fields. Common and often conspicuous in northern Michigan. Flowering in June and July.

TURTLEHEAD, BALMONY
Chelone glabra L.
Plate 170

Stout, erect, leafy perennial up to 2 m. tall, simple or with a few ascending branches, highly variable in shape of leaves and color of flowers. Flowers creamy-white to slightly pinkish, nearly sessile in compact terminal spikes. Corolla tubular, irregular, 2-lipped, the lips nearly closed, the upper lip arched, at first covering the bearded lower lip; calyx very deeply 5-parted; fertile stamens 4, the sterile stamen much shorter, slender, greenish; pistil 1, the ovary superior; capsule ovoid, splitting. Leaves opposite, sessile or with short, winged petioles, linear-lanceolate to ovate-lanceolate, sharply toothed.

In low wet ground, along streams, in swales and swamps. Flowering late July to October.

HAIRY BEARD-TONGUE
Penstemon hirsutus (L.) Willd.
Plate 171

Stiffly erect, glandular-hairy perennial up to 1 m. tall, with 1 to several stems which are usually purple, at least at the base. Flowers pale violet to dull purplish with white lobes, borne in stiff terminal racemes. Corolla tubular, flattened, the throat somewhat swollen, 2-lipped, closed, the upper lip 2-lobed, covering the lower one in bud; calyx deeply 5-lobed; fertile stamens 4 in 2 unequal pairs, not extending beyond the corolla tube, the sterile stamen flattened, densely yellow-bearded, longer than the fertile stamens; pistil 1, the ovary superior; fruit a capsule. Leaves many, opposite, sessile, somewhat clasping, sharply toothed, hairy at first, becoming smooth, the stem leaves lanceolate, the basal leaves lanceolate, oblanceolate, oblong, or elliptic.

On grassy, sunny banks, along roads, and in dry or rocky ground. Flowering June and July.

The name Beard-tongue refers to the 5th, sterile, bearded stamen, which is found in all members of this genus.

Three species of White Beard-tongue are also found in Michigan: *Penstemon digitalis* Nutt., a glabrous, erect perennial up to 1.5 m. tall, with white or faintly purple-tinged flowers, tubular corolla, the anthers bearded. *P. calycosus* Small is quite similar, but the corolla is purplish outside, white inside, and the anthers are smooth. *P. pallidus* Small is smaller, the flowers are white outside (but may have purple

PLATE 170
Turtlehead (*Chelone glabra*)

PLATE 171

Hairy Beard-tongue
(*Penstemon hirsutus*)

Blue Monkey-flower
(*Mimulus ringens*)

Yellow Monkey-flower
(*Mimulus glabratus*)

343

PLATE 172

Culver's-root
(*Veronicastrum virginicum*)

Speedwell
(*Veronica americana*)

344

lines at base inside), the corolla is 1.7–2.2 cm. long, flattened and strongly ridged within, the lower lip is longer than the upper, and the sterile stamen is densely bearded.

BLUE MONKEY-FLOWER
Mimulus ringens L. Plate 171

Glabrous, erect perennial with square stems up to 1 m. tall. Flowers blue-violet, pinkish, or rarely white, solitary on long pedicels from the leaf axils. Corolla tubular, 2–4 cm. long, 2-lipped, the throat nearly closed; calyx 5-angled and 5-toothed; stamens 4; ovary superior; capsule covered by the calyx in fruit. Leaves opposite, sessile or clasping, lanceolate, narrowly oblong or oblanceolate, crenate.

Along shores, in wet meadows and swamps. Flowering July to September.

M. alatus Ait. is similar, but the leaves are somewhat broader and petioled and the angles of the stems are somewhat winged.

YELLOW MONKEY-FLOWER
Mimulus glabratus HBK. Plate 171

Weak, prostrate or ascending, smooth to finely hairy perennial, rooting freely at the nodes. Flowers similar to the preceding species but the corolla yellow, 9–12 mm. long; calyx irregular, becoming inflated and loosely enclosing the capsule, the leaves ovate or nearly round, wavy-toothed to nearly entire, the lower leaves petioled, the upper ones sessile or nearly so, palmately veined.

In cool wet sand or soil, along lakes and streams, and in springy places. Flowering June to September.

Muskflower, *M. moschatus* Dougl., has a scent of musk and is sticky and hairy; the ovate leaves are pinnately veined; the calyx is nearly regular and does not become inflated.

CULVER'S-ROOT
Veronicastrum virginicum (L.) Farw. Plate 172

Tall, slender, erect, smoothish, many-stemmed perennial up to 2 m. tall, branching only at the inflorescence. Flowers small, blue, purplish, or rarely white, borne in dense terminal spikes 5–25 cm. long. Corolla tubular, nearly regular, the tube short, 4-lobed; calyx saucer-shaped, lobed; stamens 2, attached low on the corolla tube; ovary superior, 2-celled; capsule ovoid. Leaves short-petioled, sharply toothed, in whorls of 3–7, lanceolate to lance-ovate.

In rich dry or moist woods and thickets, in meadows and on prairies. Flowering late June to September.

SPEEDWELL, AMERICAN BROOKLIME
Veronica americana (Raf.) Schwein. Plate 172

Glabrous, somewhat fleshy, prostrate or sprawling perennial rooting at the lower nodes. Flowers blue to violet, in several lax racemes from the upper axils. Corolla wheel-shaped, the 4 lobes spreading; calyx 4-lobed; stamens 2, attached to the corolla tube; pistil 1, the ovary superior; capsule borne on threadlike pedicel 6–11 mm. long. Leaves opposite, petioled, lanceolate, widest just above the base, pointed at the tip, sharply toothed.

In shallow water, wet places; frequent along streams and around springs. Flowering June to September.

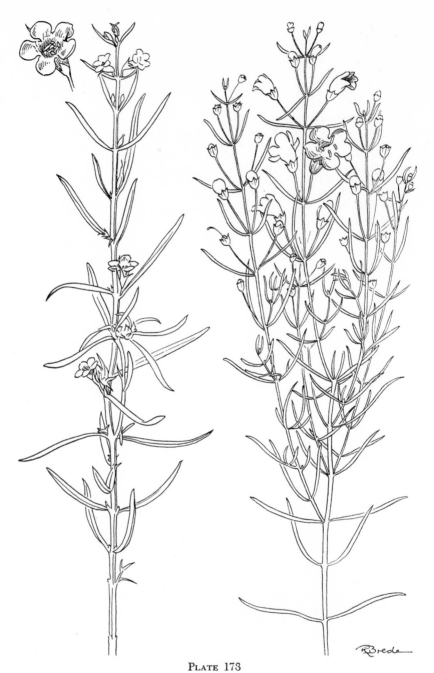

PLATE 173

Purple Gerardia
(*Gerardia paupercula*)

Gerardia
(*Gerardia tenuifolia*)

346

The closely similar European Brooklime, *V. beccabunga* L., differs in having elliptic to ovate, crenate leaves which are widest near or above the middle and rounded at the tip. The fruiting pedicels are thicker and shorter (4–5 mm. long). This species is now naturalized in America. Several other species of *Veronica* also occur in the state.

PURPLE GERARDIA

Gerardia paupercula (Gray) Britt.   Plate 173

Erect, nearly smooth annual, simple or with ascending branches, up to 8 dm. tall, the stem 4-angled. Flowers pink, rose-purple, or (rarely) white, borne in elongate, very loose terminal racemes, the pedicels shorter than the calyx and rising from the upper axils. Corolla inflated-tubular, open, with 5 spreading lobes, the upper lobes the smaller, the throat hairy inside, with darker spots and 2 yellow lines; calyx regular, 5–toothed; stamens 4, hairy; ovary superior. Leaves opposite, often with clusters of smaller leaves in the axils, linear, the upper leaves reduced to bracts subtending the pedicels, becoming blackish on drying.

Along marshy lake shores and pond margins, in bogs, on damp open ground, and in grassy ditches. Flowering August and September.

GERARDIA

Gerardia tenuifolia Vahl   Plate 173

Quite similar to the preceding species in general aspect, but the leaves are narrower, the upper lobes of the corolla are longer than the lower, the corolla tube is smooth inside, and the pedicels are mostly longer than the flowers.

In dry woods, thickets, and fields. Flowering August to October.

Downy False Foxglove, *G. virginica* (L.) BSP., has large yellow flowers, 3–4.5 cm. long; the lower leaves are ovate-lanceolate and usually have 2 pairs of large lobes below the middle, and the capsule is hairy. Two other species with conspicuous yellow flowers are *G. flava* L., with stem and capsule glabrous, and *G. pedicularis* L., a glandular-hairy annual.

INDIAN PAINTBRUSH, PAINTED CUP

Castilleja coccinea (L.) Spreng.   Color Plate 13

Stiffly erect, hairy annual or biennial with unbranched, usually solitary stems up to 6 dm. tall from a basal rosette. Flowers yellowish or greenish, enclosed by conspicuous scarlet-tipped 3-lobed bracts, and borne in dense terminal spikes which become elongate in age. Corolla flattened laterally, 2-lipped, the upper lip (the larger) arching and forming a hood over the lower lip; calyx tubular, split along the lower and sometimes along the upper side, hairy, often tipped with scarlet or yellow; stamens 4, attached to the corolla tube; style curved, protruding from the corolla; capsule many-seeded. Basal leaves forming a rosette, hairy, linear to narrowly obovate or oblong, usually entire; stem leaves sessile, alternate, varying from

347

PLATE 174

Wood-betony
(*Pedicularis canadensis*)

Cow-wheat
(*Melampyrum lineare*)

348

entire (rarely) to 3–5-cleft, the segments narrow, the terminal one the longest.

In damp sands and gravels, in peaty meadows, moist prairies, grassy thickets, and margins of woods. Flowering May and June to September.

COW-WHEAT

Melampyrum lineare Desr.   Plate 174

Simple or, more commonly, densely bushy-branched annual up to 5 dm. tall, the stems somewhat 4-angled. Flowers white, small, borne in the axils of the leaves. Corolla tubular, 2-lipped, the lips closed by a yellow projection on the lower lip which is sometimes purplish-tipped; calyx bell-shaped, 5-cleft; stamens 4, ascending under the upper lip; ovary superior, flattish, the capsule flat. Leaves opposite, linear to elliptic-ovate, pointed, the lower ones entire, those in the inflorescence entire or with 2–6 bristle-tipped teeth.

In dry, open, sandy woods and thickets, in bogs and damp peaty or rocky barrens. Flowering July and August.

WOOD-BETONY, COMMON LOUSEWORT

Pedicularis canadensis L.   Plate 174

Low, coarse, clustered, densely hairy perennial up to 5 dm. tall. Flowers yellowish to dull purplish-red or maroon, borne in short, dense, leafy, terminal spikes which become elongate in fruit. Corolla irregular, 2-lipped, 2–2.5 cm. long, the upper lip hooded, flattened, longer than the lower, toothed; calyx oblique, entire except for a split along the front; stamens 4; pistil solitary, the ovary superior; capsule flattened, oblique. Leaves thick, mostly basal, oblong-lanceolate, pinnately cut almost to the midrib (the segments incised or sharply toothed), petioled, the stem leaves smaller, scattered, sessile.

In dry woods and thickets and in clearings. Flowering April to June.

P. lanceolata Michx., with stem glabrous above and leaves opposite or nearly so, occurs in moist ground, bogs, and shores.

The common name Lousewort refers to the old belief that the presence of this species in fields caused lice in sheep.

BROOM-RAPE FAMILY. OROBANCHACEAE

This is a small family of about 13 genera and 140 species, none of which are now economically important, although some were formerly used medicinally.

The plants in this family have no chlorophyll and are parasitic or saprophytic on the roots of green plants. The stems are usually yellowish, brownish, purplish, or whitish, and the leaves are reduced to scales. The flowers have a tubular, 2-lipped corolla, and the 4 stamens are borne on the corolla tube; the ovary is superior and becomes a many-seeded capsule.

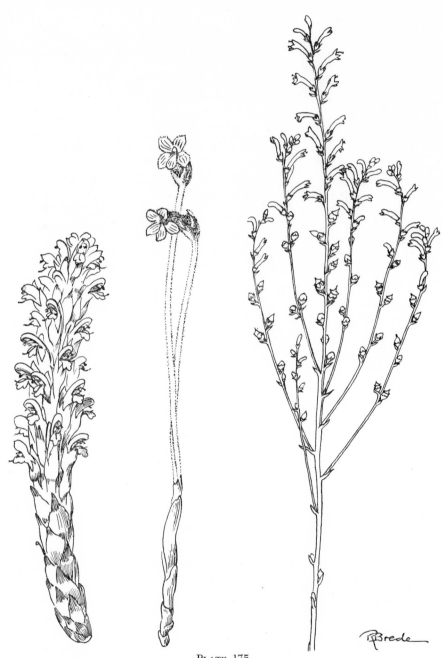

PLATE 175

Squaw-root (*Conopholis americana*)
One-flowered Cancer-root (*Orobanche uniflora*)
Beech-drops (*Epifagus virginiana*)

OROBANCHACEAE

1. Stems freely branched; flowers of 2 kinds, only upper
   ones having a well-developed corolla . . . *Epifagus virginiana,* Plate 175
1. Stems usually unbranched; flowers all alike 2
   2. Flowers numerous, in thick, compact spikes somewhat
      resembling cones of the White Pine . . *Conopholis americana,* Plate 175
   2. Flowers solitary, borne on slender
      pedicels . . . . *Orobanche uniflora,* Plate 175

BEECH-DROPS, CANCER-ROOT
Epifagus virginiana (L.) Bart.   Plate 175

Low, slender, purplish to yellowish-brown, many-branched herbs up to 4.5 dm. tall, the stems striped or flushed with brown or madder. Flowers nearly sessile, in elongate spikes which may form large panicles, the flowers of two kinds. Corolla of upper flowers tubular, somewhat 2-lipped, whitish and brown or madder, that of the lower flowers caplike, not opening; calyx cup-shaped, 5-toothed; stamens 4, borne on corolla tube; ovary superior, forming a many-seeded capsule.

Saprophytic or parasitic on roots of beech. Flowering August and September.

SQUAW-ROOT, CANCER-ROOT
Conopholis americana (L.) Wallr.   Plate 175

Short, thick, fleshy, usually unbranched, often clustered parasite up to 3 dm. tall from large rounded knobs on tree roots, yellowish to pale brown, changing to brown when bruised, in general aspect somewhat resembling slender elongate cones of White Pine. Flowers sessile or nearly so, each subtended by a basal bract or scale, borne in a dense spike. Corolla tubular, swollen at the base, curved, 2-lipped; calyx tubular, split down the upper side, irregularly toothed; stamens 4, attached to the corolla tube and extending beyond it; pistil 1, the ovary ovoid, superior, the stigma a flat disk. Scales fleshy at first, becoming dry and hard, persisting, the upper ones subtending the flowers.

In rich woods, mostly under oaks. Flowering April to July.

ONE-FLOWERED CANCER-ROOT
Orobanche uniflora L.   Plate 175

Whitish, pale purplish, or brownish parasite up to 3 dm. tall. Flowers white, solitary on 1–4 hairy pedicels 6–20 cm. long from the short, mostly underground stem. Corolla tubular, long, curved, 5-lobed; calyx bell-shaped, 5-lobed; stamens 4, borne on the corolla; pistil 1, the ovary superior, enlarged, and causing a swelling at the base of the corolla; capsule many-seeded, usually capped by the withered corolla. Scales smooth, oblong-ovate, blunt or pointed.

In rich damp woods and thickets, growing on roots of various trees. Flowering April to June.

Broom-rape, *Orobanche fasciculata* Nutt., is somewhat similar, but the 3–10 pedicels are shorter (2–6 cm. long); the stems are above ground and are 5–15 cm. long; the scales are ovate-lanceolate and, at least the upper ones, sharply pointed. In Michigan, it is parasitic on Wormwood (*Artemisia caudata* Michx.), grows on dunes and other sandy ground, and flowers April to August.

351

PLATE 176

Common Bladderwort
(*Utricularia vulgaris*)

Horned Bladderwort
(*Utricularia cornuta*)

Intermediate Bladderwort
(*Utricularia intermedia*)

Butterwort
(*Pinguicula vulgaris*)

352

BLADDERWORT FAMILY. LENTIBULARIACEAE

This small but widely distributed family includes 15 genera, 2 of which occur in Michigan. Its members are important elements of marsh and aquatic vegetation.

The flowers superficially resemble those of the Figwort family, but the plants are insectivorous and grow in water or wet places. The bladderworts have small, inflated bladders with a lid which traps insects. Butterwort catches insects on the sticky leaves. The spurred corolla and the calyx are 2-lipped; there are 2 stamens, and the fruit is a capsule.

LENTIBULARIACEAE

1. Flowers lilac to purple, solitary; leaves broad and
   simple . . . . *Pinguicula vulgaris,* Plate 176
1. Flowers yellow, 2 or more on a stalk; leaves tiny or finely
   dissected . . . . *Utricularia,* 2
   2. Plants terrestrial, the minute leaves and bladders
      hidden in the mud . . . . *U. cornuta,* Plate 176
   2. Plants growing in water, having noticeable, finely
      dissected leaves 3
3. Plants coarse, free-floating, the bladders borne on leafy
   branches . . . . *U. vulgaris,* Plate 176
3. Plants slender, creeping, the bladders borne on separate
   leafless branches . . . . *U. intermedia,* Plate 176

HORNED BLADDERWORT
Utricularia cornuta Michx.   Plate 176

Terrestrial plant of wet places, the erect, wiry scapes up to 3.5 dm. tall, the branches and leaves few, delicate, hidden in the substratum. Flowers fragrant, bright yellow, usually 1–3 in a terminal raceme but sometimes up to 9, the freshly opened lower flower overlapping the buds above. Corolla strongly 2-lipped, the upper lip erect, the lower larger and spurred; calyx 2-lipped; stamens 2; pistil 1, the ovary superior; capsule covered by the beaked calyx, yellowish, persistent, upright. Leaves simple, threadlike, not readily seen, the minute bladders borne along the margin.

On wet peaty, sandy, or muddy shores, in marly flats or bogs. Flowering July to September.

This species often grows in great profusion, and may turn an area several hundred meters long into a golden sea. When growing in such profusion, as it does in spots along the Lake Michigan shore of the Upper Peninsula, it perfumes the air with an odor suggestive of locust trees or Scotch Broom.

COMMON BLADDERWORT
Utricularia vulgaris L.   Plate 176

Aquatic perennial with prolonged stems bearing plumose branches of foliage 2–11 cm. in diameter, floating just below the surface of the water. Flowers 6–20, bright yellow, borne above the water on long, coarse scapes.

PLATE 177
Lopseed (*Phryma leptostachya*)

354

Corolla lips about the same size, the spur longer than the lips. Leaves mostly alternate, sessile or short-petioled, ellipitic to ovate in outline, very finely cut, the bladders, scattered among the leaves, relatively large and easily seen with the naked eye.

In quiet waters. Flowering May to September.

INTERMEDIATE BLADDERWORT
Utricularia intermedia Hayne

Plate 176

Plants usually creeping on the bottom in shallow water and sending up rather stout, erect, bracted scapes up to 30 cm. tall. Flowers yellow, 2–5 in a terminal raceme. Lower lip of the corolla about twice as long as the upper lip; leaves numerous, fan-shaped in outline, usually forked 3 times into very slender segments; bladders borne on separate leafless branches.

Creeping at the bottom of shallow pools, on shores, and in quagmires, rarely free-floating. Flowering May to September.

BUTTERWORT
Pinguicula vulgaris L.

Plate 176

Ground-hugging, rosette-forming perennial up to 20 cm. tall. Flowers pale violet to reddish-purple, white in the throat, solitary on long peduncles. Corolla 2-lipped, the lips unequal, the tube short, the spur long and slender; calyx small, 2-lipped; stamens 2; ovary superior; capsule subglobose, splitting at the apex. Leaves all in a basal rosette, fleshy, yellowish-green, greasy in appearance and slimy to the touch, spatulate, elliptic, or oblong, the margin entire and usually inrolled.

In bogs, on wet rocks or shores, chiefly in calcareous regions. Flowering June and early July.

It is claimed that small insects caught on the slimy leaf surfaces are digested by the plant.

LOPSEED FAMILY. PHRYMACEAE

This family is composed of a single genus which was until recently thought to have but a single species, but 2 other species have recently been described from Asia.

LOPSEED
Phryma leptostachya L.

Plate 177

Slender perennial, simple or with a few divergent branches, up to 9 dm. tall. Flowers purplish to rose or white, opposite, horizontal in slender, elongate terminal spikes (or from the upper axils). Corolla tubular, 2-lipped, the upper lip notched, the lower lip much larger, 3-lobed; calyx cylindrical, 2-lipped, the upper lip of 3 bristly teeth, the lower of 2 shorter, broader teeth, closing in fruit and becoming up to 1 cm. long; stamens 4, borne on the corolla tube; pistil 1; ovary superior, forming a small 1-seeded nutlet reflexed against the stem. Leaves opposite, bright green, the lower leaves long-petioled, the upper leaves sessile or nearly so, ovate, coarsely toothed.

In moist or wet woods. In Michigan mostly in the Southern Peninsula. Flowering July and August.

PLATE 178
Sweet-scented Bedstraw (*Galium triflorum*)
Wild Licorice (*Galium lanceolatum*)
Northern Bedstraw (*Galium boreale*)

356

MADDER FAMILY. RUBIACEAE

This large, mainly tropical and subtropical family has nearly 5000 species. About 14 genera occur in the United States. The family is important as the source of coffee, ipecac, and quinine. *Gardenia* and other genera are grown as ornamentals.

The leaves are in whorls or are opposite and have stipules (which may be very small) between the petioles. The corolla is regular and 4-lobed; the calyx is adherent to the inferior ovary, and the 4 stamens are borne on the corolla tube.

Galium

1. Principal stem leaves in whorls of 6; plants prostrate . . . . *G. triflorum,* Plate 178
1. Principal stem leaves in whorls of 4; plants erect 2
   2. Flowers numerous, white, in dense clusters . . *G. boreale,* Plate 178
   2. Flowers few, yellowish at first, becoming maroon . . . . *G. lanceolatum,* Plate 178

SWEET-SCENTED BEDSTRAW

Galium triflorum Michx.   Plate 178

Smooth, weak perennial with simple or forked stems up to 10 dm. long (sometimes longer), often sweet-scented in drying. Flowers tiny, greenish-white, borne on 3-flowered or 3-forked peduncles in the axils of the leaves; fruits densely bristly. Leaves mostly in whorls of 6, elliptic-lanceolate to linear, some greatly reduced.

In woods and thickets. Flowering mid-May to September.

NORTHERN BEDSTRAW

Galium boreale L.   Plate 178

Rather stiff, erect perennial up to 8 dm. tall, with hollow 4-angled stems covered with short stiff hairs and enlarged at the nodes. Flowers with heavy sweet fragrance, tiny, numerous, white, borne in conspicuous, dense, terminal panicles. Corolla saucer-shaped, 4-lobed; calyx very small, not lobed, adherent to the ovary; stamens 4, inserted on the corolla; pistil 1, the ovary inferior, 2-celled; fruit separating into 2 seed-like bristly parts. Leaves in whorls of 4, sessile, linear-lanceolate, strongly 3-nerved, hairy, and inrolled on the margin.

Along roadsides, in rocky soil, on shores and gravelly banks, along streams. Introduced from Europe. Flowering June to August.

The Indians used roots of this species and of *G. tinctorium* L. to make a red dye. *G. tinctorium* is a weak, matted, many-branched perennial with 3-flowered inflorescences, the principal leaves in whorls of 5 or 6, the corolla 3-lobed, and the fruit smooth.

Another species of Bedstraw, *G. aparine* L., also called Goosegrass or Cleavers, is a weak or reclining many-stemmed annual, with a clinging or sticky feel owing to the backward-pointing bristly hairs.

PLATE 179
Buttonbush (*Cephalanthus occidentalis*)

The fruit is densely bristly; the leaves are mostly in whorls of 8 and are margined with curved bristles. This is often abundant in deciduous woods in the Lower Peninsula.

The cultivated Scotch-mist or Baby's-breath, *G. sylvaticum* L., has the lower leaves in whorls of 8, the upper leaves mostly in 4's and 6's; the numerous stems are erect or nearly so; the small white flowers are borne on threadlike ascending pedicels in loose, leafy racemes; and the fruit is smooth.

Another interesting introduced species is Yellow Bedstraw, *G. verum* L., which has bright yellow flowers, the leaves in 8's or 6's. According to early Christian tradition, this is the bedstraw that filled the Manger in Bethlehem. Several additional native species also occur in Michigan.

WILD LICORICE

Galium lanceolatum Torr.   Plate 178

Nearly smooth, erect perennial with slender 4-angled stems up to 6 cm. tall. Flowers yellowish, becoming dull maroon with lines of cream-color, mostly sessile on 3-flowered forking peduncles in the axils of the leaves. Corolla spreading, about 4 mm. wide; fruit bristly. Leaves in whorls of 4, lance-ovate to lanceolate, the largest ones about the middle of the stem.

In rich dry woodlands, often under beech and maple; on sandy bluffs and in rocky or gravelly soil. Flowering June and early July.

BUTTONBUSH

Cephalanthus occidentalis L.   Plate 179

Smooth, spreading shrub 1–3 m. tall. Flowers small, white, borne in dense, globose, peduncled heads 2–2.5 dm. in diameter. Corolla tubular, regular; calyx tubular, 4-toothed; stamens 4, attached to the corolla tube; the threadlike styles with their knobby stigmas protruding well beyond the corollas and forming a halo around the heads; fruits small, dry. Leaves opposite or in whorls of 3 or 4, petioled, oblong-ovate or elliptic.

In wet places, often in water, in wooded swamps and flood plains; also in drier habitats such as jack-pine plains and the sandy beds of receding lakes. Flowering July and early August.

PARTRIDGE-BERRY, TWO-EYED-BERRY

Mitchella repens L.   Plate 180

Low, mat-forming evergreen herb, the slender, trailing stems freely branching and rooting at the nodes. Flowers somewhat fragrant, twin, united at the base, white, often tinged with rose-purple or scarlet. Corolla funnel-shaped, with 4 short, spreading lobes, densely long-hairy within; stamens 4, alternate with the lobes, attached to the corolla tube; pistil 1, the ovary inferior, the style long, with 4 stigmas; fruit a double, edible, scarlet berry crowned with the calyx teeth of the twin flowers (the "eyes"), persisting through the winter and often still present when the ensuing year's flowers are blooming. Leaves dark green, opposite, and with minute stipules between the opposite petioles, nearly round or broadly ovate, blunt

PLATE 180

Houstonia
(*Houstonia longifolia*)

Twinflower
(*Linnaea borealis*)

Partridge-berry
(*Mitchella repens*)

at apex, often heart-shaped at base, entire, the veins often white, prominent on upper surface.

In woods, on dry or moist knolls; particularly common in pine forests. Flowering June and July.

The bright red berries make a nice contrast against the deep green leaves, and these plants are often grown in terraria. The berries have a pleasant, slightly aromatic flavor and are eaten by birds. The Indians ate the berries and made a medicinal infusion from the plants.

HOUSTONIA

Houstonia longifolia Gaertn.
Plate 180

Smooth to hairy perennial with numerous stems, up to 2.5 dm. tall. Flowers pale purple to lilac or white, borne in terminal or axillary cymes. Corolla funnel-shaped, with 4 equal lobes; calyx short, 4-lobed, the tube adherent to the ovary; stamens attached to the corolla tube; ovary inferior, 2-celled; capsule projecting beyond the calyx tube. Stem leaves usually 2–4 pairs below the branches, sessile, opposite, linear to narrow-oblong, 1-nerved, the stipules connecting the bases of opposite pairs; rosette leaves narrowly oblanceolate.

In open, sandy or rocky fields and jack-pine plains, on sandy banks and exposed ledges. Flowering mid-May to mid-July.

HONEYSUCKLE FAMILY.   CAPRIFOLIACEAE

This family of about 18 genera and nearly 300 species occurs mostly in the northern hemisphere. It includes many of our well-known ornamentals. Over 100 species in 13 genera are offered for sale in this country. These include Honeysuckle, Snowberry, and Coralberry, Elderberry, Beauty-bush, Twinflower, Viburnums, and Weigelias. Wine and jelly are made from some of the elderberries.

The members of this family have opposite leaves without stipules. The corolla is 4–5-lobed, the calyx tube is attached to the inferior ovary, the stamens are borne on the corolla tube and do not exceed the lobes in number.

TWINFLOWER

Linnaea borealis L. var. *americana* (Forbes) Rehd.
Plate 180

Slender, creeping, somewhat woody evergreen perennial with long, prostrate stems which give rise to numerous, erect, leafy branches up to 10 cm. tall. Flowers delicate, fragrant, nodding in pairs at the top of the erect, threadlike peduncles, white tinged with pink, rose, or rose-purple (sometimes almost entirely rose). Corolla bell-shaped, spreading, 5-lobed, 10–15 mm. long, attached to the top of the ovary; calyx tube adherent to the densely hairy, glandular ovary; stamens 4, in 2 unequal pairs; ovary 1, inferior, the style long, slender, extending beyond the corolla tube; capsule 3-celled but one-seeded. Leaves opposite, hairy, short-petioled, nearly round, oval, or broadly elliptic, often somewhat 3-lobed or crenate at apex, sometimes entire.

In cold, moist or dry woods and peaty bogs. Flowering June to August, occasionally again late in the fall.

PLATE 181

Swamp Valerian
(*Valeriana uliginosa*)

Tinker's-weed
(*Triosteum perfoliatum*)

This circumpolar species is one of our most attractive plants and often occurs in large patches. It is quite common in some areas in the northern part of the state. It was named for the great Swedish botanist, Linnaeus, the father of our system of classifying plants.

TINKER'S-WEED

Triosteum perfoliatum L.   Plate 181

Coarse, hairy perennial up to 1.2 m. tall, glandular above and leafy to the top. Flowers yellowish or greenish to dull purple, sessile, erect, 3 or 4 in the leaf axils. Corolla tubular to bell-shaped, 5-lobed, scarcely longer than the calyx; calyx 5-lobed, the lobes linear-lanceolate; stamens 5, borne on the corolla tube and nearly equaling it; pistil 1; fruit a dry, dull orange-yellow, globose drupe superficially re-sembling a small, hard tomato, 3-seeded, the calyx tube persistent. Leaves opposite, sessile or united at the base, downy, soft to the touch beneath, oblong-ovate to ovate, the middle ones violin-shaped.

In thin or rocky soil in or at the edges of woods and thickets. In Michigan mostly in the southern part of the state. Flowering mid-May to mid-June.

VALERIAN FAMILY.   VALERIANACEAE

This primarily north-temperate family includes about 10 genera and nearly 400 species. It includes a few ornamentals. The thick, strong-scented roots of some species are used as antispasmodics.

SWAMP VALERIAN

Valeriana uliginosa (T. & G.) Rydb.   Plate 181

Smooth, coarse, many-stemmed perennial 4–12 dm. tall from a basal rosette. Flowers white, small (about 5 mm. wide) in clustered headlike terminal cymes which are very compact at first. Corolla tubular, with a small swelling on one side at the base, the limb regular and 5-lobed; calyx tube adherent to the ovary, the limb composed of about 10 elongate plumose bristles which are inrolled at flowering time but which unroll and spread as the fruit matures; stamens 3, borne on the corolla tube; pistil 1, the ovary inferior; fruit an achene. Basal leaves simple or cleft (if pinnately cut, the terminal leaflet the largest); stem leaves opposite, smooth, pinnately cut, with 3–11 divisions or leaflets.

In wet woods and meadows, in bogs and calcareous swamps; often associated with larch and arbor vitae. Flowering late May to July.

The familiar Garden Heliotrope, *V. officinalis* L., which often persists as an escape, is quite similar, but the flowers are pinkish, all of the leaves are pinnate, the divisions being nearly equal, and at least the lower leaves are hairy beneath.

TEASEL FAMILY.   DIPSACACEAE

This Old World family includes 9 genera and about 160 species, none of which are native to this country. A few species are grown

PLATE 182
Wild Teasel (*Dipsacus sylvestris*)

364

for ornament, of which Scabiosa is probably the best known. Wild Teasel is a troublesome weed, but one species, *Dipsacus fullonum* L., was formerly grown commercially because the ripe inflorescences were used by textile mills for raising the nap on cloth.

WILD TEASEL

Dipsacus sylvestris Huds.   Plate 182

Stout, coarse biennial with ridged prickly stems up to 2 m. tall. Flowers small, white, shorter than the long-pointed bracts, borne in large, dense, ovoid-ellipsoid heads surrounded by an involucre of linear prickly leaves. Corolla nearly regular, 4-lobed; calyx small; stamens 4, distinct; pistil 1, the ovary inferior. Leaves opposite, sessile, and partly clasping, lance-oblong, often prickly on margin and on veins beneath.

Along roadsides, in pastures, old fields, and waste places. Introduced from Europe; now a common weed. Flowering July to October.

The stalks and heads are persistent and can be found for a considerable time after flowering. They are sometimes used in winter bouquets, either in their natural state or painted.

GOURD FAMILY.   CUCURBITACEAE

This mainly tropical and subtropical family, comprising about 100 genera and 850 species, is important both for food and for ornament. Pumpkins and squash, cucumber, gherkins, muskmelons, watermelons, and citron, as well as gourds, belong here.

The members of this family are easily recognized by the succulent, usually weak, tendril-bearing stems, and the unisexual flower with inferior ovary which develops into a special type of fleshy or membranous fruit.

WILD *or* PRICKLY CUCUMBER, BALSAM-APPLE

Echinocystis lobata (Michx.) T. & G.   Plate 183

High-climbing, herbaceous annual vine with angular, grooved, nearly smooth stems often several meters long, bearing single leaves and 3-forked tendrils at the nodes. Flowers greenish-white, glandular-hairy, unisexual, the staminate flowers numerous, in many-flowered compound racemes borne singly in the leaf axils, the pistillate flowers short-stalked, one or a few from the same axils as the staminate racemes. Corolla wheel-shaped, 6-parted nearly to the base, the lobes linear, spread-ing, usually twisted; calyx small, 6-lobed; stamens united; pistil 1, the ovary inferior, prickly, 2-celled; fruit ovoid, 3–5 cm. long, fleshy, becoming dry, covered with weak prickles. Leaves thin, alternate, bright green, rough on both sides, roundish in general outline (but deeply palmately 5-lobed), sharply toothed.

In rich moist soil, in thickets or woods or along streams. Flowering July to September.

PLATE 183
Wild Cucumber (*Echinocystis lobata*)

BLUEBELL FAMILY.   CAMPANULACEAE

This family of about 60 genera and 1500 species, largely temperate and subtropical, is important for a large number of ornamentals. Over 100 species of bellflower and about 20 of *Lobelia* are cultivated, as are smaller numbers of several other genera.

The family is characterized by the milky juice (often scanty), alternate simple leaves, corolla of united petals, 5 stamens, the single pistil with an inferior ovary, and the fruit a capsule. Two distinct subfamilies are recognized; some authorities consider them two separate families.

CAMPANULACEAE

1. Corolla regular; anthers separate (subfamily
   CAMPANULOIDEAE) . . . . *Campanula,* 2
1. Corolla irregular; anthers united into a tube around the
   style (subfamily LOBELIODEAE) . . . . *Lobelia,* 4

   2. Stem leaves narrowly ovate to heart-shaped ovate; corolla
       wheel-shaped . . . . . . *Campanula americana,* Plate 185
   2. Stem leaves linear or nearly so; corolla bell-shaped 3

3. Erect, smooth plants; corolla about 1–2 cm.
   long . . . . *C. rotundifolia,* Plate 184
3. Weak, usually reclining, rough-stemmed plants; corolla usually
   smaller . . . . *C. aparinoides,* Plate 184

   4. Flowers bright red . . . . . *Lobelia cardinalis,* Color Plate 14
   4. Flowers blue, violet, or whitish 5

5. Flowers 1.5–3.5 cm. long, bright blue; corolla tube having
   openings along the side . . . . . . *L. siphilitica,* Plate 186
5. Flowers up to 1.6 cm. long, light blue to whitish; corolla tube
   lacking openings on the side 6

   6. Leaves linear or narrowly lanceolate; bracts on the pedicels
       at about the middle; lower lip of corolla glabrous
       within . . . . *L. kalmii,* Plate 186
   6. Some or all the leaves more than 1 cm. wide;
       bracts near the base of the pedicels; lower lip
       of corolla hairy within . . . . *L. spicata,* Plate 186

TALL BELLFLOWER

Campanula americana L.   Plate 185

Erect, usually unbranched annual, up to 2 m. tall. Flowers light blue, solitary or clustered in the axils of the upper leaves. Corolla wheel-shaped, 2–2.5 cm. broad, the 5 lobes long and spreading; calyx 5-lobed; style long, declined, then curved upward, extending beyond the corolla; capsule opening by terminal pores. Leaves alternate, petioled, narrowly ovate to elliptic, coarsely toothed.

In moist rich soil, usually in woods. Flowering mid-July to mid-September.

HAREBELL, BLUEBELL

Campanula rotundifolia L.   Plate 184

PLATE 184

Harebell
(*Campanula rotundifolia*)

Marsh Bluebell
(*Campanula aparinoides*)

368

Extremely variable, erect, usually many-stemmed, smooth perennial up to 5 dm. tall with scant milky juice. Flowers 1–15, blue, pale lavender, or whitish, somewhat nodding on slender pedicels from the axils of the upper leaves. Corolla bell-shaped with broad, spreading lobes; calyx tube united to the ovary, the lobes very slender; stamens 5, united only at the base; pistil 1, the ovary inferior, the style not extending beyond the corolla; capsule nodding, many-seeded,

opening by pores at the base. Leaves numerous, alternate, sessile, linear to narrowly lanceolate, becoming much smaller upward; basal leaves (usually lacking at flowering time), broadly ovate to somewhat heart-shaped, long-petioled, usually toothed.

In a variety of habitats: grassy fields, marshy flats, mossy banks, open woods, rock crevices, sandy shores. Common and widespread. Flowering early June through September.

This is the well-known Bluebell of Scotland and northern England. It is extremely variable in almost all respects, but the variations are said to be readily produced by changes in environment and are of no particular taxonomic significance. In meadows the plants are tall and many-flowered, with thin, elongate stem leaves. In drier, more exposed places they are shorter, the foliage is firmer and thicker, and the upper leaves are smaller. In mountains or the far north the plant seldom exceeds 2 dm. in height and may have only a single flower.

Marsh Bluebell

Campanula aparinoides Pursh   Plate 184

Slender, weak, branching perennial, usually reclining on other plants, the stems rough, 3-angled, somewhat zig-zag, 3–10 dm. long, with scant milky juice. Flowers pale blue with darker lines, or pale lavender, or whitish and fading to lavender or bluish, solitary on slender peduncles. Corolla bell-shaped, 4–5 mm. long; capsule sub-

globose, erect, opening near the base. Leaves alternate, linear, entire or slightly toothed, hairy on margin and midrib, the principal ones 2–5 cm. long and not over 6 mm. wide.

In swales, wet meadows, boggy lake margins, open grassy marshes, marly flats on lake shores. Flowering late June into September.

A second species of Marsh Bluebell, *C. uliginosa* Rydb., is recognized by some authorities, but others consider that the differences are not sufficient to justify a different species.

Cardinal-flower

Lobelia cardinalis L.   Color Plate 14

Coarse, stiffly erect, usually unbranched perennial up to 1-8 m. tall, the juice acrid and milky, usually growing in patches from numerous short basal offshoots. Flowers very showy, deep rich red, 3–4 cm. long, borne in a somewhat 1-sided terminal raceme 1–5 dm. long, on pedicels which are

shorter than the subtending bract. Corolla tube straight, split down the middle on the upper side and having openings along the sides, 2-lipped, the upper lip of 2 usually erect lobes, the lower lip spreading and 3-lobed; stamens 5, united into a tube which encloses the slender style and pro-

PLATE 185
Tall Bellflower (*Campanula americana*)

PLATE 186

Great Blue Lobelia (*Lobelia siphilitica*)

Pale Spike Lobelia (*Lobelia spicata*)

Brook Lobelia (*Lobelia kalmii*)

371

trudes through the cleft corolla; ovary inferior, capsule 2-celled, many-seeded, opening at the top. Leaves alternate, the upper ones sessile, the lower ones petioled, oblong-lanceolate to lanceolate.

In low wet places, in meadows, along streams, swamp borders, and shores. Flowering July and August.

This beautiful species can be grown on wet soil in the garden, but it is said that it tends to die out after flowering. The Indians made a cough medicine and a love charm from it.

GREAT BLUE LOBELIA

Lobelia siphilitica L.   Plate 186

Smooth or sparsely hairy, coarse, erect, unbranched perennial up to 1.5 m. tall, with milky juice, the stems ridged, leafy to the top, often with short offshoots at the base. Flowers purplish-blue, with some white on the lower lip or throat (rarely all white), 2.3–3.3 cm. long, borne in dense terminal leafy racemes. Flower structure similar to that of the preceding species. Leaves lanceolate, sharply and irregularly toothed, becoming progressively smaller above.

Along streams and shores, in swamps and low rich woods. Flowering August to October.

BROOK LOBELIA, KALM'S LOBELIA

Lobelia kalmii L.   Plate 186

Slender, erect or reclining, simple to diffusely branched perennial up to 5 dm. tall, with scant, acrid juice. Flowers violet to blue, with a conspicuous white eye-spot, borne on threadlike pedicels which have small bracts at about the middle. Flowers quite similar to those of the two preceding species but smaller (7–16 mm. long) and lacking the openings along the sides of the corolla tube. Leaves sessile or the basal ones tapering to a petiole, linear to narrowly oblanceolate, entire or sparingly toothed, 1–4 cm. long, less than 1 cm. wide.

In damp soil, usually in calcareous regions, in meadows, sedge mats, bogs, ditches, along shores. Flowering July to September.

PALE SPIKE LOBELIA

Lobelia spicata Lam.   Plate 186

Quite similar to the preceding species, but often tall, usually unbranched, the flowers 9–12 mm. long, the pedicels with a pair of small bracts at or near the base; leaves ascending, obovate to oblanceolate, 5–10 cm. long, some or all more than 1 cm. wide.

In rich moist or dry soil, in meadows, fields, and thickets, and around lakes. Flowering June to August.

This species is quite variable, and several varieties have been described. It is fairly common, often a weed.

COMPOSITE FAMILY (SUNFLOWER FAMILY)
COMPOSITAE

This, the largest family of flowering plants, includes about 950 genera and over 20,000 species. A number of our most common species, including dandelions and burdock, have been naturalized from Europe and South America. The family is important for both food and ornamentals. Lettuce and endive, salsify and chicory are important foods. Some 200 genera used for ornamentals include *Aster, Coreopsis, Cosmos, Dahlia, Cineraria,* Marigold, Shasta Daisy, and *Zinnia.* The insecticide pyrethrum is derived from a species of *Chrysanthemum,* and sunflower seeds are used for chicken and bird feed. Among the many noxious weeds in the family are hawkweed, yarrow, sow-thistle, fleabane, everlasting, and ragweed. The pollen of ragweed is one of the principal causes of hay fever.

Members of this family are easily recognized. Several to many sessile flowers in a head, itself resembling a flower, are borne on a common receptacle; each head is surrounded by an involucre of many bracts (sometimes called phyllaries) which functions as a calyx in relation to the head. The five petals are united into a tube at least at the base and the five stamens are inserted on the corolla tube and their anthers are united into a tube. There is a single pistil, the style is usually 2-cleft at the apex in fertile flowers and entire in sterile flowers, the ovary is inferior, united with the calyx tube, and usually has a crown of scales, awns, and teeth, called a pappus, and the fruit is seedlike (an achene). The flowers may be unisexual or bisexual. In addition to the flowers, the receptacle may bear bracts or scales called chaff. When there is no chaff the receptacle is said to be naked.

The corolla of Michigan species of the Compositae may be either of two types, tubular or ligulate. Flowers which have a tube-shaped or trumpet-shaped corolla are said to be tubular, and heads composed solely of this type of flower are said to be discoid. The second type of corolla is tubular only at the base; above this it is flat and straplike, and is usually toothed or lobed at the apex. This type of corolla is referred to as ligulate. A head composed solely of this type of flowers, called ray flowers, is also said to be ligulate. A head in which the center (disk) is occupied by tubular flowers and the edge is provided with ray flowers (sometimes mistakenly called "petals," as in sunflowers and daisies) is said to be radiate. Some discoid heads have flowers of two lengths, the shorter ones being in the center; these are said to be falsely radiate (e.g., knapweed).

In order to identify the composites one must determine whether or not the plant has a milky juice; the type or types of flowers present; and the nature of the pappus (the "crown" of the ovary). The pappus is best seen in fruit, but if none is available the oldest flowers should be studied.

COMPOSITAE

1. Some or all of flowers having tubular corollas; juice
watery . . . . TUBULIFLORAE, 2
1. Flowers all having straplike corollas; juice of plant (at least
in older stems or roots) milky . . . . LIGULIFLORAE, Key C

2. Heads discoid, having only tubular flowers . . . . . Key A
2. Heads radiate, having both tubular and ray flowers . . . Key B

Key A. Tubuliflorae (Heads Discoid)

1. Leaves prickly . . . . *Cirsium,* p. 429
1. Leaves not prickly 2
  2. Fruit a spiny bur 3
  2. Fruit not a spiny bur 4
3. Flowers greenish; heads of 2 kinds . . . *Xanthium italicum,* Plate 202
3. Flowers lavender; heads alike . . . . . . *Arctium minus,* Plate 221
  4. Flowers some shade of purple or lavender 5
  4. Flowers not purple or lavender 8
5. Leaves deeply pinnately cut into narrow
  segments . . . . *Centaurea maculosa,* Plate 224
5. Leaves entire or somewhat toothed 6
  6. Leaves mostly in whorls . . . *Eupatorium purpureum,* Plate 188
  6. Leaves alternate 7
7. Leaf margins entire . . . . *Liatris,* p. 381
7. Leaf margins toothed . . . . . . *Vernonia altissima,* Plate 187
  8. Flowers yellow 9
  8. Flowers not yellow 11
9. Plants grayish, leaves deeply cut and
  dissected . . . . *Artemisia caudata,* Plate 219
9. Plants green 10
  10. Heads fairly large and conspicuous; leaves deeply cut
    or lobed; aromatic . . *Tanacetum vulgare* or *huronense,* Plate 218
  10. Heads small, borne in large clusters,
    leaves merely toothed or entire . . . . . *Solidago,* p. 385
11. Flowers green or greenish 12
11. Flowers white, whitish, sordid, or very pale dirty yellow . . . 14
  12. Plants having a distinct pineapple odor when
    crushed . . . . . . *Matricaria matricarioides,* Plate 217
  12. Plants not having a pineapple odor 13
13. Leaves entire or toothed . . . . *Erigeron canadensis,* Plate 199
13. Leaves deeply pinnately cut . . . *Ambrosia artemisiifolia,* Plate 202
  14. Heads wilting on drying 15
  14. Heads not wilting on drying, retaining virtually their
    original appearance (everlastings) 17
15. Leaves deeply pinnately cut . . . . *Centaurea diffusa,* Plate 224
15. Leaves toothed or shallowly lobed 16
  16. Leaves alternate, lower leaves largest . *Cacalia atriplicifolia,* Plate 219
  16. Leaves opposite, lower leaves
    smallest . . *Eupatorium perfoliatum* or *rugosum,* Plates 189, 190
17. Plants usually having a basal rosette of well-developed leaves,
  stem leaves small, bractlike . . . . *Antennaria fallax,* Plate 200
17. Plants usually lacking a basal rosette, stem leaves well developed . . 18
  18. Heads pearly white; plants white-woolly,
    essentially odorless . . . . *Anaphalis margaritacea,* Plate 200
  18. Heads sordid white to yellowish; plants often
    sticky to touch, spicy-fragrant when
    crushed . . . *Gnaphalium macounii* or *obtusifolium,* Plate 200

KEY B. TUBULIFLORAE (Heads Radiate)

1. Ray and disk flowers same or nearly same color 2
1. Ray and disk flowers different colors 13
  2. Heads white . . . . *Achillea millefolium*, Plate 216
  2. Heads yellow 3
3. Involucre very sticky . . . . . *Grindelia squarrosa*, Plate 193
3. Involucre not sticky 4
  4. Plants having a very strong odor when crushed;
    leaves deeply pinnately cut; rays very
    small . . . . *Tanacetum vulgare* or *huronense*, Plate 218
  4. Not entirely as in alternate choice 5
5. Heads small, numerous, borne in compact clusters; pappus
   of bristles; stem leaves sessile or nearly so . . . . *Solidago*, p. 385
5. Not as in alternate choice 6
  6. Disk globose or conic 7
  6. Disk flat to slightly convex 8
7. Leaves ovate with short petioles . . *Heliopsis helianthoides*, Plate 205
7. Leaves narrowly lanceolate, sessile or decurrent
   at the base . . . . *Helenium autumnale* or *nudiflorum*, Plate 215
  8. Leaf margin entire (may be lobed but not
    toothed) . . . . . . *Coreopsis lanceolata* or *tripteris*, Plate 213
  8. Leaf margin toothed or wavy 9
9. Fruits with sharp, barbed, awllike
   teeth . . . . *Bidens coronata* or *cernua*, Plate 214
9. Fruits lacking awllike teeth 10
  10. Heads rather small, disk not over 1.2 cm. wide; pappus
    of soft, threadlike bristles . . *Senecio aureus* or *pauperculus*, Plate 220
  10. Heads generally larger; if pappus is of bristles,
    disk is 3–5 cm. wide 11
11. Disk flowers fertile, styles split 12
11. Disk flowers sterile, style not split
  . . . . *Silphium perfoliatum* or *terebinthinaceum*, Plates 203, 204
  12. Receptacle bearing chaff . . . . . . *Helianthus*, p. 407
  12. Receptacle not bearing chaff . . . . *Inula helenium*, Plate 201
13. Ray flowers yellow 14
13. Ray flowers not yellow 16
  14. Disk flat to broadly rounded . . . . . . *Helianthus*, p. 407
  14. Disk conic, columnar, or ellipsoid 15
15. Ray flowers having bracts at base . . . *Ratibida pinnata*, Plate 207
15. Ray flowers lacking bracts at base . . . . . *Rudbeckia*, p. 405
  16. Heads mostly solitary, relatively large and showy, flat
    or nearly flat, rays white, disk yellow; leaves with
    prominent lobes or finely dissected 17
  16. Heads smaller, mostly clustered; leaf margins entire or
    merely toothed 18
17. Leaves finely dissected, heads 1.5–3 cm.
   broad . . . . *Anthemis cotula*, Plate 217
17. Leaves pinnately lobed, heads 2–5 cm.
   broad . . . . *Chrysanthemum leucanthemum*, Plate 217
  18. Heads clustered on leafy branches; bracts of involucre
    of unequal length, successively shorter and overlapping . *Aster*, p. 391

PLATE 187
Tall Ironweed (*Vernonia altissima*)

18. Heads solitary or in clusters on mostly leafless branches;
bracts of involucre nearly equal in length or with one
long series surrounded by a short basal series; rays usually
narrower and more numerous than in alternate
choice .   .   .   . *Erigeron canadensis* or *philadelphicus*, Plate 199

Key C. Liguliflorae

1. Leaves grasslike with parallel veins .   .   .   .   .   . *Tragopogon*, 2
1. Not as in alternate choice 4
　2. Heads yellow 3
　2. Heads purple .   .   .   . *T. porrifolius*, Plate 227
3. Bracts of involucre longer than flowers; peduncles enlarged
upward .   .   .   . *T. major*, Plate 227
3. Not as in alternate choice .   .   .   . *T. pratensis*, Plate 227
　4. Heads bright blue (rarely white) .   .   . *Cichorium intybus*, Plate 225
　4. Not as in alternate choice 5
5. Leaves all or principally at base of plant 6
5. Leaves borne along stem 10
　6. Heads solitary on hollow, unbranched scapes; leaves usually
　deeply pinnately cut or lobed; achenes having a ring of
　bristles attached to end of a long
　beak .   .   .   . *Taraxacum officinale* or *erythrospermum*, Plate 228
　6. Not as in alternate choice 7
7. Leaf margins entire; heads usually several in a cluster; achenes
topped by bristles .   .   .   . *Hieracium*, 8
7. At least the later leaves toothed on margin; heads solitary or
few; achenes topped with a row of scales and a row of
bristles .   .   .   . *Krigia virginica*, Plate 226
　8. Heads deep orange to orange-red .   .   . *H. aurantiacum*, Color Plate 16
　8. Heads yellow 9
9. Leaves narrowly oblanceolate, pale green .   .   . *H. florentinum*, Plate 231
9. Leaves elliptic-oblong, marked with reddish-purple along the
veins .   .   .   . *H. venosum*, Plate 231
　10. Heads white or whitish, often tinged with rose or
　green .   .   .   . *Prenanthes alba* or *altissima*, Plate 230
　10. Heads yellow 11
11. Heads 3–5 cm. broad, becoming swollen at base, including 50 or
more flowers .   .   .   . *Sonchus arvensis*, Plate 229
11. Heads smaller, not becoming swollen at base, including 12–20
flowers .   .   .   . *Lactuca canadensis*, Plate 229

Tall Ironweed

Vernonia altissima Nutt.   Plate 187

Hairy, leafy-stemmed perennial up to 2 m. tall. Heads 13–30-flowered, usually purple, rarely white, numerous, borne in loose cymes 1–5 dm. wide. Flowers perfect, longer than the involucre; achenes cylindrical, ribbed, the ribs bearing minute hairs; pappus purple, double, with an outer series of minute scalelike bristles and inner series of copious hairlike bristles. Leaves alternate, spreading or loosely ascending, lanceolate to narrowly ovate or lance-oblong, sharply and finely toothed, 3–8 cm. broad, hairy beneath.

In rich damp soil. Flowering August to October.

PLATE 188
Joe-Pye Weed (*Eupatorium purpureum*)

Missouri Ironweed, *Vernonia missurica* Raf., is very similar to Tall Ironweed, but the heads are 34–55-flowered; the lower surface of the leaves is finely and densely woolly; and the pappus is typically tawny. It is found in rich low ground and on prairies; it flowers July to September. These two species of Ironweed frequently hybridize, so that intermediate forms are common.

JOE-PYE WEED

Eupatorium purpureum L.   Plate 188

Erect perennial up to 2 m. tall, the stems slightly glaucous, usually green (purple at the nodes), the drying foliage having a sweet vanilla odor when bruised or crushed. Heads numerous, small, usually 4–7-flowered, pale pink to pinkish-purple, in an open, somewhat domed, corymb. Flowers all tubular and perfect, 4.5–7.5 mm. long; involucre cylindric, the bracts closely overlapping; pappus of slender bristles in single row. Leaves mostly in whorls of 3 or 4, lanceolate, ovate, or elliptic, narrowed to the short petiole, sharply and coarsely toothed, 8–30 cm. long, up to 15 cm. wide.

In rich, dry or dryish, usually calcareous soil in thickets and open woods. Flowering July to mid-September.

Spotted Joe-Pye Weed, *Eupatorium maculatum* L., is quite similar, but the stem is deep purple or purple-spotted, not glaucous; the inflorescence flat-topped; the flowers mostly 9–22 in a head and usually more deeply colored.

In low wet places, swamps, and meadows, along streams and shores, usually in rich or calcareous soil. Flowering mid-July to early September.

The Indians used a decoction made from this species to bathe weak or paralyzed children, believing that it strengthened the legs and feet. This species is suitable for a large garden of wildflowers.

THOROUGHWORT, BONESET

Eupatorium perfoliatum L.   Plate 189

Coarse, erect, long-hairy perennial up to 1.5 m. tall, branched above. Heads small, dull white, 10–16-flowered, crowded in a flattish-topped terminal corymb; involucre bell-shaped to cylindric, green, the hairy lanceolate bracts in 2 or 3 overlapping series; pappus a row of whitish bristles. Leaves opposite, usually united by their bases and completely encircling the stem, tough, wrinkled, veiny, lanceolate, crenate, the larger blades 7–20 cm. long and 1.5–4.5 cm. wide.

In low woods or thickets, in swamps, on wet shores, along streams, and in swales. Flowering late July to October.

This is one of our best-known medicinal plants. It was used by the Indians, early settlers, and southern Negroes as a general tonic and for treating influenza, rheumatism, and fevers. The Indians made a cathartic from the steeped foliage, and dressings for snake bites were made by chewing any part of the plant. Used with milkweed, the root fibers were supposed to act as a charm when applied to a whistle for calling deer.

PLATE 189
Thoroughwort (*Eupatorium perfoliatum*)

380

I have seen two explanations for the name boneset. According to one, this species was used for the treatment of breakbone fever; according to the other, it was believed by the doctrine of signatures that the union of the leaves at the base signified that the plant would promote the knitting of bones.

WHITE SNAKEROOT
Eupatorium rugosum Houtt.   Plate 190

Erect, glabrous to hairy perennial with solitary or clustered stems up to 1.5 m. tall. Heads white, 15–30-flowered, borne in loose corymbs from the upper axils (corymbs rather compact and terminal in the smaller plants). Leaves opposite, petioled, ovate, coarsely and often sharply toothed, 2–8 cm. long.

In rich woods, thickets, and clearings. Flowering late July to October.

This species is responsible for trembles in cattle and milk sickness in human beings. The poison, tremulol, is soluble in milk fat and may be transferred to other animals or human beings through milk. Dried plants in hay are less dangerous than fresh plants.

Liatris

1. Heads solitary or few; bristles of pappus having fine,
   elongate hairs . . . . *L. cylindracea,* Plate 191
1. Heads numerous; bristles of pappus covered with fine barbs 2
   2. Heads sessile or nearly so, having 7–9 flowers . . *L. spicata,* Plate 192
   2. Heads borne on peduncles or nearly sessile, having
      16–80 flowers 3
3. Heads containing 16–35 flowers . . . . . . *L. aspera,* Plate 192
3. Heads containing 30–80 flowers . . . . *L. novae-angliae,* Plate 191

BLAZING STAR
Liatris cylindracea Michx.   Plate 191

Slender, stiffly erect, smooth to sparsely hairy, leafy, unbranched perennial, up to 7 dm. tall from a bulblike base. Heads 30–60-flowered, rose-purple to light purple, few or solitary on short peduncles from the upper axils, or sessile. Flowers all tubular, perfect; corolla slender; stigmas 2, colored, extending beyond the corolla tube, giving the heads a ragged appearance; involucre of leathery, closely overlapping bracts; pappus of bristles covered with elongate fine hairs; receptacle naked. Leaves alternately sessile, linear and grasslike in appearance, rigid, punctate, entire, becoming progressively smaller above, parallel-veined.

In dry open soil, on gravelly banks, pine plains. Flowering July to September.

SPIKED BLAZING STAR
Liatris spicata (L.) Willd.   Plate 192

Stiffly erect, smooth or rarely hairy perennial up to 20 dm. tall, often with a strong turpentine like odor when crushed. Heads 10–18-flowered, cylindric-bell-shaped, purplish-pink, in a dense spike 1–7 dm. long, the upper heads overtopping the bractlike leaves, the lower heads usually shorter than the leaves, mostly sessile. Flowers 7–9 (sometimes up to 18); involucre 8–10

PLATE 190
White Snakeroot (*Eupatorium rugosum*)

382

PLATE 191

Blazing Star
(*Liatris novae-angliae*)

Blazing Star
(*Liatris cylindracea*)

PLATE 192

Blazing Star
(*Liatris aspera*)

Spiked Blazing Star
(*Liatris spicata*)

mm. long and about half as thick, the bracts green, or purple-tinged. Leaves numerous, linear to lanceolate or the lower ones oblanceolate, tapering to long, narrow-winged petioles, upper leaves smaller.

In meadows, damp slopes, marshes, and other moist open places. Flowering July to September.

BLAZING STAR

Liatris aspera Michx.   Plate 192

Distinguishable from the preceding species only with difficulty. It may have more leaves below the inflorescence, fewer flowers in a head (16–35), and generally shorter peduncles.

The involucre is usually glabrous, and the middle involucral bracts have broad, dry, and papery slashed borders.

In dry, often sandy, soil. Flowering August and September.

BLAZING STAR

Liatris novae-angliae (Lunell) Shinners var. *nieuwlandii* (Lunell) Shinners   Plate 191

Smooth or hairy perennial up to 10 dm. tall. Heads 30–80-flowered, pinkish-purple, 6–50 on peduncles 5–50 mm. long. Corolla lobes long and slender, the stigmas extending beyond them; pappus of bristles covered with small barbs (scarcely visible to the naked eye); receptacle naked; involucre 12–17 mm. high; achenes slender, tapering to the base, ribbed.

Leaves crowded, linear-elliptic, parallel-veined, 25–60 below the inflorescence, the upper leaves small and sessile, the lowest petioled and 2–5 cm. wide.

In dry or sandy soil, often along railways and roads. Flowering August and September.

(In Gray's Manual treated as a hybrid, $\times$ *L. nieuwlandii*.)

STICKY-HEADS, CURLYCUP GUMWEED

Grindelia squarrosa (Pursh) Dunal   Plate 193

Stout, erect, smooth biennial or perennial up to 1 m. tall. Heads several to many, yellow, 3–4 cm. wide, terminal on leafy branches, having both tubular and ray flowers. Rays up to 1 cm. long or sometimes lacking, narrowly oblong, entire at apex, pistillate; disk flowers perfect; achenes flattened, those of the ray flowers the largest; pappus of 2–8 awns; involucre hemispheric, sticky, the bracts in several rows, linear and with strongly recurving pointed tips. Leaves clasping, thickish, alternate, narrowly oblong to oblanceolate or ovate, 3–7 cm. long, abundantly punctate, finely serrate, entire, or coarsely toothed, obscurely veined.

In open or waste places, usually in dry soil. Flowering July to September.

Several varieties of this species have been described. It is native on the prairies and plains but is now found locally in dry soil as far east as the Atlantic states. The Indians used the species medicinally. They ground the seeds to make a flavoring and used the resin to hold women's hair in place.

Solidago

1. Flower clusters flattish on top; leaves fairly uniform in size, linear to linear-lanceolate . . . . . . *S. graminifolia*, Plate 194
1. Flower clusters not flat-topped; leaves variable in size 2

PLATE 193
Sticky-heads (*Grindelia squarrosa*)

2. Flower cluster long and slender; heads spirally
arranged on branches 3
2. Flower cluster pyramidal; heads borne mostly on
upper side of branches 4

3. Leaves hairy to bristly . . . . *S. hispida,* Plate 195
3. Leaves glabrous to minutely hairy . . . . *S. racemosa,* Plate 195

4. Lower leaves much larger than upper; basal rosettes
usually formed 5
4. Basal leaves mostly smaller than upper leaves;
basal rosettes rarely formed . . . . . *S. canadensis,* Plate 196

5. Flower cluster slender, usually arched or leaning, and
somewhat one-sided; stems and leaves covered with minute
grayish hairs . . . . *S. nemoralis,* Plate 195
5. Flower cluster as broad as tall, or broader; plants not hairy
except for margins of leaves . . . . *S. juncea,* Plate 196

GRASS-LEAVED GOLDENROD
Solidago graminifolia (L.) Salisb.   Plate 194

Smooth, hairy, or minutely hairy perennial 2.5–6 dm. tall, branched only above. Heads small, yellow, 12–45-flowered, borne in a flat-topped many-branched corymb up to 3 dm. broad; ray flowers pistillate, disk flowers perfect; achenes round, ribbed involucre cylindric. Leaves linear to lanceolate, sessile, grasslike, with 2 or 4 lateral veins parallel to the midrib.

On lake shores, beaches, and rocky places, in thickets. Flowering August and September.

This is a variable and very common species. It has several recognized varieties.

HAIRY GOLDENROD
Solidago hispida Muhl.   Plate 195

Downy perennial up to 1 m. tall, unbranched or with a few ascending branches. Heads yellow, borne in a simple or branched, slender, cylindric, wandlike inflorescence and in small clusters in the axils of the leaves. Basal leaves rather thick, oblanceolate to narrowly obovate, crenate to serrate, somewhat downy, at least beneath, the stem leaves becoming much smaller upward, velvety to the touch.

In dry to moist rocky places, often in calcareous soil (one variety in peaty soil). Flowering July to October.

GOLDENROD
Solidago racemosa Greene   Plate 195

Sticky, glabrous to slightly hairy perennial up to 1 m. tall; stolons lacking at the base. Heads yellow (white in one form), borne on upright pedicels mostly 5–15 mm. long and forming a slender, loose terminal raceme or panicle of upright racemes; rays about 10; involucres slenderly bell-shaped, 5–8 mm. high. Leaves numerous, the basal and lower leaves mostly oblanceolate, entire or toothed, the midrib slender; stem leaves decreasing in size upward, oblanceolate to linear, often subtending a cluster of heads.

On dry ledges or rocky banks, on shores, in gravels and sands, or on dunes along the Great Lakes. Flowering June to October.

387

PLATE 194
Grass-leaved Goldenrod (*Solidago graminifolia*)

388

Indian Paintbrush

Cardinal-flower

CANADIAN GOLDENROD

Solidago canadensis L.   Plate 196

Perennial with solitary or clustered stems up to 11 dm. tall, glabrous below, becoming hairy above. Heads yellow, borne in a broad, pyramidal panicle 5–40 cm. high, the dense, 1-sided divergent racemes recurved at the tip. Leaves numerous, crowded, lanceolate, long-tapering to the tip, mostly sharply toothed, 3-nerved, the basal and lower leaves mostly smaller than the middle and upper.

In open woods, thickets, and clearings and along dry roadsides. Flowering mid-July to September.

Both the flowers and roots of this species were used medicinally by the Indians. The flowers of various species of goldenrod were boiled to make a yellow dye.

Nearly two dozen species of goldenrod occur in Michigan, several of them distinguishable only with difficulty. Only a few of the species are described and illustrated here.

DWARF GOLDENROD

Solidago nemoralis Ait.   Plate 195

Grayish-green, finely downy perennial with solitary or tufted, usually somewhat arching stems 1.5–6 dm. tall. Heads yellow, crowded, mostly on one side of the spreading or recurved branches of the terminal panicle; rays 5–9, disk flowers 3–6. Rosette and basal leaves mostly tufted, oblanceolate to obovate, petioled, round-toothed, stem leaves thick, rough, decreasing in size upward, at least the upper ones entire, mostly subtending small tufts of reduced leaves.

In dry, sterile, often sandy or clayey soil in open places or in thin woods. Flowering August and September.

SMOOTH GOLDENROD

Solidago juncea Ait.   Plate 196

Mostly smooth, stiffly erect perennial up to 13 dm. tall. Heads yellow, borne in a dense panicle as broad as long or broader, the racemes strongly 1-sided. Basal leaves tufted and persistent, narrowly elliptic, tapering to long, winged petioles, sharply toothed, 15–40 cm. long; upward on the stem the leaves become sessile, smaller, and less toothed; margins of leaves and petioles hairy.

In dry open places and in open woods. Flowering June to October.

This is one of the earliest goldenrods to bloom.

Aster

1. Rays purple to violet or blue-violet 2
1. Rays white, heads borne on one-sided racemes . . . A. ericoides, Plate 197

   2. Leaves sessile, usually clasping at base 3
   2. Leaves petioled, heart-shaped at base . . . . A. macrophyllus, Plate 198

3. Involucre covered with glandular hairs and sticky to touch;
   stem hairy . . . . A. novae-angliae, Plate 197
3. Involucre not sticky; stem glabrous . . . . . . A. laevis, Plate 198

PLATE 195

Goldenrod (*Solidago racemosa*)

Dwarf Goldenrod (*Solidago nemoralis*)

Hairy Goldenrod (*Solidago hispida*)

PLATE 196

Canadian Goldenrod
(*Solidago canadensis*)

Smooth Goldenrod
(*Solidago juncea*)

391

PLATE 197

New England Aster
(*Aster novae-angliae*)

White Aster
(*Aster ericoides*)

392

PLATE 198

Large-leaved Aster
(*Aster macrophyllus*)

Smooth Aster
(*Aster laevis*)

WHITE ASTER

Aster ericoides L.

Plate 197

Stiffly erect to partially prostrate perennial up to 2 m. tall, densely covered with curved or divergent hairs. Heads small, about 1 cm. wide, borne in slender panicles of elongate, mostly one-sided racemes (or solitary and terminal on the branches); rays 8–20, narrow, usually white but sometimes blue, violet, or roseate, 3–5 mm. long; disk yellow; involucral bracts with spreading tips. Leaves numerous and crowded, somewhat rigid, linear, scarcely narrowing to the sessile base, the uppermost leaves much reduced.

In dry open soil in fields, along roads, and in thickets. Flowering July to October.

The arrangement of the small heads on one side of the stems, rather like that in most goldenrods, makes this white aster fairly easy to recognize. The Calico Aster, *A. lateriflorus* (L.) Britt., has 9–15 white (rarely pinkish) rays 4.5–7.5 mm. long; the disk corollas are purplish; the stems usually have arching or wide-spreading branches from the middle or below, and the thin, lanceolate leaves taper to apex and base. *A. simplex* Willd. has larger heads, with 20–40 white rays 4.5–12 mm. long.

LARGE-LEAVED ASTER

Aster macrophyllus L.

Plate 198

Coarse perennial frequently occurring in colonies of many clusters of leaves, the flowering stems when present up to 1.5 m. tall, sticky at least in the inflorescence. Heads numerous, borne in broad, irregular, somewhat flat-topped corymbs; rays about 16, violet or pale blue, about 1 cm. long; disk becoming reddish-brown in age; involucre slender, bell-shaped, of 3 or 4 series of greenish bracts, the inner ones often with roseate margins. Basal leaves large, thick, firm, heart-shaped, coarsely toothed, rough to touch, 4–20 cm. long, petioled; stem leaves smaller and narrower, the upper ones ovate or oblong, and sessile.

In dry to moist shady places, open woods, and thickets. Flowering August and September.

Another species, *A. cordifolius* L., has heart-shaped basal leaves, but it does not usually occur in colonies. It has a more elongate inflorescence, with smaller heads; the leaves are relatively thin and up to 12 cm. long.

NEW ENGLAND ASTER

Aster novae-angliae L.

Plate 197

Stout, long-hairy, many-stemmed, corymbosely branched perennial up to 2.6 m. tall. Heads numerous, showy, about 3 cm. wide, borne on short peduncles in leafy corymbs; rays violet-purple, sometimes roseate or white, 40–50 in a single series; disk flowers orange at first; achenes more or less flattened, the pappus a single series of bristles; receptacle flat. Involucre broadly hemispheric, 8–10 mm. high, of thin, long-tapering, often purple-tinged, recurving bracts which are sticky owing to glandular hairs. Leaves numerous, crowded, usually hairy on both surfaces, lanceolate, cordate-auriculate and clasping at the base, entire, the principal ones 5–10 cm. long.

In damp thickets, meadows, open woods, and on shores. Flowering August to October.

More than 2 dozen species of asters occur in Michigan. Since it is often difficult to identify species, only a few of the more distinctive kinds are treated here.

Various forms of the New England Aster are cultivated under the name Michaelmas Daisy.

Smooth Aster

Aster laevis L.   Plate 198

Smooth and usually glaucous, erect, simple or branched perennial up to 1.3 m. tall. Heads numerous, borne in stiff panicles which have greatly reduced, bractlike leaves; rays 15–20, blue, lavender, violet, or rarely white, 8–15 mm. long; disk yellow at first, becoming dark; involucre bell-shaped, the bracts obtuse to acute, rigid, green, appressed in several rows. Leaves thick, obscurely veined, the basal leaves tapered to winged petioles, the upper and middle leaves narrowly lanceolate, oblanceolate, or elliptic, sessile and more or less clasping, usually entire.

In dry open habitats, in thin woods, borders of woods, and in thickets. Flowering August to October.

Red-stemmed Aster, *A. puniceus* L., also usually has blue rays. It is somewhat taller (up to 2.5 m.); the stems are reddish and usually pubescent; there are 30–60 rays, which are 7–18 mm. long; and the involucral bracts are loose and spreading.

Common Fleabane, Daisy Fleabane

Erigeron philadelphicus L.   Plate 199

Soft-stemmed, softly downy, short-lived perennial up to 1 m. tall. Heads fairly numerous, (about 2.5 cm. wide,) nodding in bud but becoming upright; rays more than 100, very narrow, pale pink, pinkish-lavender, or whitish; disk yellow; achenes flattened, covered with scattered stiff hairs; pappus a single row of bristles with smaller bristles between the long ones; involucre saucer-shaped, the bracts narrow, equal, greenish, the receptacle slightly rounded, naked. Leaves long-hairy, the basal and lower stem leaves obovate or spatulate, toothed, 2–7 cm. long, narrowed to short petioles, the upper leaves smaller, oblong to lanceolate, heart-shaped below and clasping.

In fields and rich thickets, on shores and springy places. Flowering May to August.

Robin's-plantain, *E. pulchellus* Michx., is quite similar to Common Fleabane, but the heads are fewer and larger (2–3.5 cm. broad) and have about 50 rather broad rays. Several species of *Erigeron* with white rays are commonly known as White-top, or as Daisy Fleabane. They may be distinguished from the White Aster by their earlier blooming (chiefly in spring and early summer), the typically narrower and more numerous rays, and the heads borne on essentially leafless stems.

PLATE 199

Common Fleabane
(*Erigeron philadelphicus*)

Horse-weed
(*Erigeron canadensis*)

396

HORSE-WEED, BUTTER-WEED

Erigeron canadensis L. Plate 199

Erect, hairy or downy annual up to 2 m. tall, simple below, branched into very slender panicles above. Heads usually very numerous, small, few-flowered, and inconspicuous; rays white, usually shorter than the diameter of the disk or lacking; involucre narrowly bell-shaped at first, spreading in fruit, often persisting. Leaves numerous, oblanceolate to linear, toothed to entire.

In waste places, along roadsides, in cultivated fields. Flowering July to November.

This is an unattractive but common, semi-cosmopolitan weed. It is easily recognized, even from a distance, by its narrow, small-headed panicles.

PUSSY'S-TOES

Antennaria fallax Greene Plate 200

Densely white-woolly, stoloniferous, mat-forming, dioecious perennial, the pistillate plants up to 5 dm. tall, the staminate less frequent and about half as tall. Heads small, whitish, several in a compact cyme at the top of the flowering stalk. Flowers tiny, tubular, the corolla threadlike; styles yellowish or brown; receptacle naked; involucre of several series of dry, white-tipped bracts. Stem leaves alternate, the lower ones oblong lanceolate, sessile, the upper ones narrower; rosette leaves petioled, ovate, obovate, or nearly round, the larger 2–8 cm. long, having 4 prominent veins, often woolly, sometimes becoming glabrous.

In dry ground, open woods, and clearings. Flowering April to June.

The various species of *Antennaria* are easily recognized as everlastings. They are frequently used in winter bouquets. They may be grown in a dry rock garden where a soil cover is more important than the beauty of the flower.

Several to numerous species are recognized in this genus. They are extremely difficult to distinguish, and botanists are not agreed upon them. The plant illustrated is typical of the group of species with broad basal leaves, exemplified by *A. fallax*.

CLAMMY EVERLASTING, CUDWEED

Gnaphalium macounii Greene Plate 200

Strongly fragrant, white-woolly, somewhat viscid biennial up to 1.5 m. tall. Heads numerous, many-flowered, dirty-yellowish, densely clustered in corymbs; flowers all tubular, the outer ones very slender, pistillate, the central flowers perfect; pappus a single row of entirely distinct, rough bristles; involucre yellowish-white, woolly only at the base, the bracts dry, overlapping in several rows. Stem leaves alternate, linear-lanceolate, tapering to apex, clasping at the base and having decurrent wings extending down the stem, greenish on upper surface, densely white-woolly with a feltlike covering beneath, the margin entire, somewhat inrolled; rosette leaves oblanceolate.

In clearings, along roadsides, in pastures, waste places, and the borders of woods. Flowering July to October.

397

PLATE 200

Clammy Everlasting
(*Gnaphalium macounii*)
Pussy's-toes
(*Antennaria fallax*)

Catfoot
(*Gnaphalium obtusifolium*)
Pearly Everlasting
(*Anaphalis margaritacea*)

CATFOOT
Gnaphalium obtusifolium L.   Plate 200

Quite similar to the preceding species, but usually more slender, the inflorescence more open and spreading, the leaves less woolly, narrowing somewhat to the sessile base, and the stem not winged.

In open, often in sandy, places. Flowering July to October.

PEARLY EVERLASTING
Anaphalis margaritacea (L.) C. B. Clarke   Plate 200

White-woolly, erect, many-stemmed perennial up to 1 m. tall, branching at the summit, having a basal rosette only when young. Flower heads numerous, white with a yellowish center, globose, up to 1 cm. wide, not changing appreciably on drying, borne in somewhat leafy corymbs at the summit of the stem, the branches of the corymb white and covered with long, appressed, white hairs. Corolla tubular, threadlike; pappus of long bristles; involucre dry, the bracts paperish, white, ovate-lanceolate, spreading in age. Leaves alternate, linear-lanceolate, sessile, bright green with some hairs on upper surface, densely white-hairy or woolly beneath.

In dry, usually open, gravelly or sandy soil, on road cuts, or sometimes along streams or in woods. Flowering July to September.

Several varieties, distinguishable mostly on leaf characters, have been recognized. The flowers are often dried and used in winter bouquets, either in their natural color or dyed.

Anaphalis lacks the characteristic, somewhat spicy, odor which is detectable even in long-dried specimens of *Gnaphalium*.

ELECAMPANE, FIELD INULA
Inula helenium L.   Plate 201

Stout, woolly, usually unbranched perennial up to 2 m. tall from a thick mucilaginous root. Heads few, large (5–10 cm. broad), terminal on stout peduncles, many-flowered; rays yellow, narrow; disk flowers dingy yellow or brownish; achenes 4–5 ribbed; pappus a single row of bristles; involucre hemispherical, 2–2.5 cm. high, of overlapping bracts, the outer ones leaflike. Leaves large, woolly beneath, the basal ones ovate, 2.5–5 dm. long and 2 dm. wide, petioled, the upper leaves becoming sessile and cordate-clasping.

Along roadsides and fences, in rich clearings, fields, and waste places. Introduced from Europe; escaped from cultivation. Flowering May to August.

COMMON RAGWEED
Ambrosia artemisiifolia L.   Plate 202

Extremely variable, simple to many-branched, smooth to hairy annual up to 3 m. tall. Heads small, inconspicuous, greenish, of 2 kinds, the pistillate heads 1 to a few together, sessile in the axils of the leaves or bracts at the bases of the slender staminate racemes or spikes; staminate flowers 5–20 in a head, bearing copious quantities of powdery yellow pollen which is readily windborne. Leaves both opposite and alternate, petioled, merely pinnately lobed to 2 or 3 times pinnately cut into small segments, thin, smooth on upper surface.

In vacant lots, along roads, in cultivated and waste ground of all kinds; frequently in great abundance, flowering July to October.

PLATE 201
Elecampane (*Inula helenium*)

PLATE 202

Common Ragweed
(*Ambrosia artemisiifolia*)

Common Cocklebur
(*Xanthium italicum*)

401

PLATE 203
Cup-plant (*Silphium perfoliatum*)

402

PLATE 204

Prairie-dock (*Silphium terebinthinaceum*)

403

The genus name means "food of the gods," but the pollen of these plants is the main cause of fall hay fever for millions of people. This plant causes so much distress that many communities conduct eradication drives, and many newspapers give the ragweed-pollen count daily during the hay fever season. Its virtual absence is a great boon to the resort regions of northern Michigan, where countless people go in August and September to escape the pollen.

Great Ragweed, *A. trifida* L., also occurs in Michigan, but to a more limited extent. It is much more important farther south, where, in low ground along streams and in rich openings, it may make a dense forest of plants up to 15 or 18 feet tall. The Perennial Ragweed (*A. coronopifolia*) is found in drier areas.

COMMON COCKLEBUR

Xanthium italicum Moretti   Plate 202

Coarse, weedy, usually many-branched annual up to 1.5 m. tall. Heads unisexual; staminate heads uppermost, many-flowered, the flowers tubular, greenish; pistillate heads with 2 flowers consisting of a pistil and a slender, threadlike corolla, enclosed by an ovoid, prickly involucre; fruit a brown spiny bur with 2 incurved beaks, up to 3 cm. long. Leaves alternate, thick and large, cordate-ovate, coarsely dentate, very rough, long-petioled.

In low wet ground, along lakes and streams, on flood plains, and in cultivated ground and waste places. Flowering September to November.

The seedlings and young leaves of this species are said to be highly poisonous to stock. Cockleburs are thought to be American in origin, but they were well established in Europe within 50 years of Columbus' discovery of America, and are now cosmopolitan in distribution. Some authors recognize more than a dozen species of *Xanthium* in northeastern United States; others recognize only two, quite variable, species.

CUP-PLANT, INDIAN CUP

Silphium perfoliatum L.   Plate 203

Stout, coarse, rough perennial up to 2.5 m. tall, the 4-angled stems leafy, branched above, the juice resinous, Heads numerous, large (5–7 cm. broad), yellow; rays 20–30, pistillate and fertile; disk about 1 cm. broad, the flowers sterile, the style not cleft; achenes (of the rays) flat, broad-obovate, surrounded by a wing; involucre broad and rather flat, the outer bracts smooth, spreading, leaflike, the inner bracts similar to the chaff of the receptacle. Leaves rough, coarsely toothed, opposite and (at least the upper leaves) joined by their bases or petioles, often forming a cuplike structure.

In moist soil in prairies, rich woods, and thickets, along river banks, and in low ground. Flowering July to September.

PRAIRIE-DOCK

Silphium terebinthinaceum Jacq.   Plate 204

Differing from the preceding chiefly by having most of the leaves near the base of the plant; neither the leaf bases nor the petioles are joined.

404

Black-eyed Susan

Orange Hawkweed

In fields and waste places, along roads, mostly in dry open ground.

Flowering July to September.

OX-EYE, FALSE SUNFLOWER

Heliopsis helianthoides (L.) Sweet   Plate 205

Nearly smooth perennial up to 1.5 m. tall. Heads showy, yellow, few to several; rays 8–15, 1.5–4 cm. long, pistillate, persisting on the achenes and becoming papery; disk conical, 1–2.5 cm. wide, the flowers fertile; pappus of 2–4 obscure teeth or lacking; involucral bracts in 2 or 3 rows, the outer ones leaflike and spreading. Leaves opposite, ovate-lanceolate to ovate, toothed, petioled, 3-ribbed, rough.

In open woods and thickets and on banks. Flowering July to September.

Ox-eye differs from the true sunflowers by its more conical disk; the rays are persistent on the achenes, and the disk and ray flowers are fertile. In the sunflowers the disk is quite flat, the rays drop off, and only the disk flowers are fertile.

Rudbeckia

1. Leaves entire; plants coarsely hairy .   .   .   . *R. hirta,* Color Plate 15
1. At least some leaves 3-lobed or pinnately cut; plants hairy
   to glabrous 2
   2. Leaves usually 3-lobed; disk dark purple;
      heads on short peduncles .   .   .   .   .   . *R. triloba,* Plate 206
   2. Lower leaves usually pinnately cut; disk greenish-yellow
      to grayish; heads on long peduncles .   .   .   . *R. laciniata,* Plate 206

BLACK-EYED SUSAN

Rudbeckia hirta L.   Plate 207; Color Plate 15

Rough-hairy, erect biennial or short-lived perennial up to 1 m. tall, simple or sparsely branched. Heads solitary or few on hairy peduncles; rays 8–26, usually orange-yellow or orange, but variable and sometimes red or red-tipped, or with a purple or brown spot at base, 2–4 cm. long; disk hemispheric to ovoid, purple or brown, rarely yellow, 12–20 mm. wide; achenes 4-angled, smooth, flat on top; bracts of the involucre leaflike, spreading or reflexed, and much shorter than the rays. Leaves alternate, thick, variable in shape, the basal ones mostly oblanceolate, 1–3 cm. broad, entire, petioled, the upper leaves linear-lanceolate to oblong or ovate, mostly sessile.

In fields, clearings, meadows, along roadsides, mostly in disturbed or waste ground. Flowering July to September.

THREE-LOBED CONEFLOWER

Rudbeckia triloba L.   Plate 206

Smooth to hairy, leafy, branched annual or biennial (rarely short-lived perennial) up to 1.6 m. tall. Heads on short peduncles, showy, about 5 cm. wide; rays yellow or the base orange to brown; disk blackish-purple, soon ovoid; involucre of leaflike, soon drooping bracts. Lower stem leaves usually 3-lobed, pointed at apex, coarsely toothed.

In fields, thickets, and open woods. Flowering June to October.

PLATE 205
Ox-eye (*Heliopsis helianthoides*)

TALL CONEFLOWER

Rudbeckia laciniata L.

Plate 206

Smooth, coarse, glaucous, erect perennial up to 3 m. tall. Heads solitary on long peduncles, showy; rays yellow, soon reflexed; disk dull greenish-yellow, up to 2.5 cm. in diameter, at first hemispherical to globular, but elongating and becoming columnar in fruit. Lower leaves pinnate with 5–7-cut or 3-lobed leaflets; petioled; upper leaves similar or 3–5 parted or uncut, sessile.

In rich, low ground. Flowering July to September.

The cultivated variety, *hortensia* Bailey, is a well-known garden flower under the name Golden-glow. It has many more ray flowers.

PRAIRIE CONEFLOWER

Ratibida pinnata (Vent.) Barnh.

Plate 207

Hoary perennial up to 1.5 m. tall. Heads several or solitary; showy; rays 5–10, pale yellow, drooping, 2.5–6 cm. long; disk elliptic, grayish, the receptacle having an aniselike odor when crushed, the chaffy bracts subtending the ray and disk flowers and enclosing the 4-sided achenes; involucre a single series of a few small, spreading bracts. Leaves at or near the base of the plant, alternate, pinnately divided into 3–7 lanceolate segments.

In dry soil. Flowering June to August.

Helianthus

1. Annuals; flowers large, disk red-purple to dark brown,
   flat or nearly so, large, usually over 4 cm. broad . . . *H. annuus,* Plate 208
1. Perennials; disk yellow (sometimes browish yellow), convex
   or obtusely conic; usually not over 3.5 cm. broad 2
   2. Leaves mostly basal; flowering stems having only 1–3
      pairs of small, opposite leaves; bracts of involucre
      tightly appressed . . . . *H. occidentalis,* Plate 209
   2. Leaves borne along flowering stem; outer bracts of
      involucre spreading at tips 3
3. Leaves mostly folded together and curving back;
   peduncles short . . . . *H. maximiliani,* Plate 210
3. Leaves flat or nearly so; peduncles moderately long 4
   4. Leaves sessile or on very short petioles (not over 5 mm.
      long), opposite, spreading horizontally . . . *H. divaricatus,* Plate 209
   4. Leaves having definite petioles 5
5. Leaves broadly lanceolate to ovate, at least ⅓ as
   wide as long 6
5. Leaves lanceolate or narrower, more than 3 times as
   long as wide . . . . *H. giganteus,* Plate 212
   6. Plants not producing tubers; leaves thin, veins thin and
      inconspicuous; bracts of involucre green . *H. decapetalus,* Plate 212
   6. Plants producing tubers; leaves thick and hard, veins prominent;
      bracts of involucre dark at base . . . . . *H. tuberosus,* Plate 211

COMMON SUNFLOWER

Helianthus annuus L.

Plate 208

Erect, simple to many-branched annual up to 5 m. or more tall. Heads large, 5–7 cm. wide or wider, the rays orange-yellow, the disk rather flat, dark brown to purple; achene obovate, thick, slightly compressed, whitish to

PLATE 206

Three-lobed Coneflower   Tall Coneflower
(*Rudbeckia triloba*)   (*Rudbeckia laciniata*)

grayish with dark lines; involucre of wide-spreading, rather broad bracts with tapering tips. Leaves mostly alternate, heart-shaped to elliptic-ovate, long-petioled, 3-nerved, toothed, rough on both surfaces.

In old fields, along fences, and in waste places, mostly as an escape from cultivation. Flowering August and September.

As is true of most of the sunflowers, nearly all parts of this plant have some use. It is said that the plants make good fodder, the silage having about 90 per cent of the food value of corn silage. The young heads may be boiled and eaten; the seeds contain considerable oil which may be expressed and used in cooking, the residue making a good food for cattle and poultry; the seeds themselves are extensively used for poultry and bird feeding, and are sometimes prepared to be eaten like peanuts. The Huron Indians used the oil obtained by boiling the ground-up meal for cooking and as a hairdressing. A floss may be obtained from the stalks; the pith is light and has been used in life preservers.

SUNFLOWER
Helianthus occidentalis Riddell   Plate 209

Slender, erect, smooth to hairy perennial up to 1.5 m. tall, branching only at the inflorescence, almost leafless above. Heads generally few, yellow, 2–4 cm. wide, the rays 10–16; achenes 4-sided, pappus soon falling, of 2 thin, chaffy scales. Leaves mostly at the base of the plant, opposite, ovate to oblong-lanceolate, tapering to the winged petiole, entire, wavy, or crenate; stem leaves 1–3 pairs, small, lanceolate or ovate, sessile or short-petioled.

In dry soil, sandhills, abandoned fields, pine plains, and on rocky banks. Flowering August and September.

MAXIMILIAN'S SUNFLOWER
Helianthus maximiliani Schrad.   Plate 210

Stout, rough perennial up to 3 m. tall, unbranched up to the inflorescence, the lower part often leafless or nearly so. Heads yellow, up to 10 cm. wide, borne on short peduncles in slender racemes, the rays 15–30, 2–3 cm. long; involucral bracts loosely spreading, narrowly lanceolate, pointed. Leaves numerous, alternate, lanceolate, point-ed at apex, somewhat folded together upward (troughlike) and curled backward (somewhat like peach leaves), sessile or on short petioles.

Along roads and railways, on rich prairies and in waste ground, mostly in sandy or dry soil. Flowering July to October.

WOODLAND SUNFLOWER
Helianthus divaricatus L.   Plate 209

Glabrous, often glaucous perennial up to 2 m. tall, simple or branching above. Heads few, bright yellow, sessile or on short peduncles, 3–6 cm. broad, the rays narrow, about 2.5 cm. long, the disk about 1 cm. broad; involucre of somewhat recurving bracts. Leaves opposite, sessile or nearly so, spreading at right angles to the stem, ovate to lanceolate, rounded at the base and tapering to a long point at the apex, 3-nerved, green and rough above, pale beneath.

In dry woodlands, thickets, openings and on roadsides. Flowering July to September.

409

PLATE 207

Black-eyed Susan
(*Rudbeckia hirta*)

Prairie Coneflower
(*Ratibida pinnata*)

410

PLATE 208
Common Sunflower (*Helianthus annuus*)

411

PLATE 209

Woodland Sunflower
(*Helianthus divaricatus*)

Sunflower
(*Helianthus occidentalis*)

412

TALL SUNFLOWER
Helianthus giganteus L.   Plate 212

Rough or hairy-stemmed perennial up to 3 m. tall. Heads 1 to a few, the rays 1.5–2 cm. long, the disk about 2 cm. broad. Leaves alternate (the lower ones sometimes opposite), lanceolate, shallowly toothed or nearly entire, pinnately veined, 1–3 cm. broad.

In damp or rich thickets, swamps, and other moist places. Flowering July to October.

SUNFLOWER
Helianthus decapetalus L.   Plate 212

Smooth-stemmed perennial, simple or branched above. Heads small, the rays 8–12, 2–2.5 cm. long, the disk about 1.5 cm. broad; involucre of spreading bracts. Leaves opposite (upper stem leaves sometimes alternate), ovate, coarsely toothed to entire, 3-nerved, thin, green both sides, glabrous or nearly so.

In open woods or thickets. Flowering late July to September.

JERUSALEM ARTICHOKE
Helianthus tuberosus L.   Plate 211

Stout, somewhat hairy perennial up to 3 m. tall, the elongate rootstocks producing fleshy edible tubers. Heads several to numerous, 1.5–2.5 cm. wide, rays 10–20, 2–4 cm. long; bracts of the involucre usually rather dark, at least at the base. Lower leaves opposite, ovate or broadly lanceolate, 3-veined at the base, 10–25 cm. long, 4–12 cm. wide, petioles mostly 2–8 cm. long, winged.

Along streams, in damp thickets, borders of woods, and moist open ground. Flowering August to mid-October.

The edible tubers are formed only as the days become shorter. They were eaten extensively by the Indians. This species was introduced into England early in the seventeenth century and is still cultivated in parts of this country.

COREOPSIS, TICKSEED
Coreopsis lanceolata L.   Plate 213

Glabrous, erect or sprawling, many-stemmed, sparsely branched perennial up to 1 m. tall, leafy only near the base. Heads showy, bright golden-yellow, 3–5 cm. wide, upright on long slender peduncles 2–4 dm. long; ray flowers usually 8, in a single marginal row, long, conspicuous, 4–7 lobed at apex, narrowed to the base; disk flat, the flowers numerous, yellow; achenes flattened, oblong; receptacle with some long thin chaff which falls off with the achenes; involucre of 2 series of about 8 bracts, the inner ones broad, closely appressed, the outer ones spreading, leaflike.

In dry, sandy or rocky soils. Flowering May to July.

This attractive plant is frequently used in the garden. It is common in the upper part of the Lower Peninsula and along the sand dunes on the Lake Michigan shore of the Upper Peninsula.

PLATE 210

Maximilian's Sunflower (*Helianthus maximiliani*)

414

PLATE 211
Jerusalem Artichoke (*Helianthus tuberosus*)

415

PLATE 212

Sunflower
(*Helianthus decapetalus*)

Tall Sunflower
(*Helianthus giganteus*)

416

TALL COREOPSIS

Coreopsis tripteris L. Plate 213

Smooth perennial with solitary leafy stems up to 3 m. tall, freely branched above. Heads several or numerous, about 3.5 cm. broad, having an anise-like odor; rays usually 8, rounded at tip or with low round teeth; disk flat, the flowers yellow, becoming brown; involucre of 2 series of 8 bracts, the outer ones leaflike and spreading, the inner ones broader, membranous, appressed. Leaves opposite, petioled, mostly 3- or 5-foliolate, the leflets oblong-lanceolate to linear, stalked, the margin entire; upper leaves often simple and sessile.

In open woods, borders of woods, and thickets, on prairies. Flowering July to September.

BEGGAR-TICKS, TICKSEED SUNFLOWER

Bidens coronata (L.) Britt. var. tenuiloba (Gray) Sherff Plate 214

Glabrous, slender annual or biennial 3–15 dm. tall. Heads yellow, borne on long, slender peduncles; rays golden-yellow, spreading, longer than the outer bracts of the involucre; disk flowers yellow, with purple-black anthers; achenes wedge-shaped at base, blunt at apex and tipped with 2 stiff, sharp, barbed awns, the barbs pointing backward; involucres of 2 series of bracts, the outer series of usually 8 (6–11) linear, blunt, leaflike bracts. Leaves pinnately divided into 3–7 lanceolate or linear, pinnately cut to coarsely toothed divisions.

In bogs, swales, and other wet places. Flowering August to October.

Several other species of Beggar-ticks occur in Michigan. They are all notable for the tenacity with which the fruits stick to clothing.

STICK-TIGHT

Bidens cernua L. Plate 214

Annual up to 1.8 cm. tall, sometimes decumbent and rooting. Heads erect at flowering time, nodding in fruit; discoid or radiate, the rays bright yellow. Achenes curved, olivaceous, the margins somewhat winged, awns with backward pointing barbs. Leaves linear, lanceolate, or oblong, sessile or united at the base (rarely petioled). Highly variable species.

In wet places, springs, and pools. Flowering August to October.

SNEEZEWEED, FALSE SUNFLOWER, SWAMP SUNFLOWER

Helenium autumnale L. Plate 215

Aromatic, resinous perennial up to 2 m. tall. Heads yellow, borne on long peduncles; ray flowers 10–20, deep yellow, soon drooping, 3-notched at apex, usually fertile; disk a darker yellow, depressed-globose, achenes ribbed; involucre small, the bracts reflexed. Leaves thin, alternate, oblong-lanceolate, usually toothed, 5–15 cm. long, up to 4 cm. wide, the decurrent base continued as wings on the stem.

In swamps, wet meadows, along streams, on shores and in rich thickets. Flowering August to November.

SNEEZEWEED

Helenium nudiflorum Nutt. Plate 215

Quite similar to the preceding species, but the plants tending to be shorter, the ray flowers usually sterile, golden yellow over-all or purplish at the base;

PLATE 213

Tall Coreopsis
(*Coreopsis tripteris*)

Coreopsis
(*Coreopsis lanceolata*)

the disk brown or purplish, globose; leaves smaller, firm, less numerous and more erect, usually entire or nearly so.

In moist ground along roads and in waste places. Flowering June to October.

Common Yarrow, Milfoil

Achillea millefolium L.   Plate 216

Strong-scented perennial up to 1 m. tall from a creeping underground rootstock, the flowering stems usually simple below the inflorescence, glabrous to cobwebby (covered with entangled hairs). Heads small, in compound, stiffly-branched flattish-topped corymbs, usually white but sometimes pink to rose-purple. Rays few, small, the heads resembling small 5-petalled flowers; involucral bracts in 3–4 series. Basal leaves very finely 2-pinnately cut and finely dissected; upper leaves similar, but gradually decreasing in size upward.

Along roads and railways, in fields, open woods, dryish hillsides, and waste places. A common weed introduced from Europe. Flowering June to October.

During the Middle Ages this plant was held in high esteem for its supposed curative powers.

Mayweed, Stinking Chamomile, Dogfennel

Anthemis cotula L.   Plate 217

Ill-scented, simple or freely branching annual up to 9 dm. tall. Heads solitary and terminal, the ray flowers white, sterile, 6–10 mm. long, the disk yellow, convex; pappus none, receptacle chaffy. Leaves very finely pinnately dissected into narrow, pointed segments.

Along roadsides and in waste places. Flowering June to October.

Corn Chamomile, *A. arvensis* L., is quite similar, but the heads tend to be slightly larger and the leaves less finely dissected, the ray flowers are fertile, and the plants are not ill-scented.

Ox-eye Daisy, White Daisy, Field Daisy

Chrysanthemum leucanthemum L. var.
pinnatifidum Lecoq & Lamotte   Plate 217

Smooth, erect, simple or sparingly branched, many-stemmed perennial up to 1 m. tall, often growing in colonies. Heads solitary at the ends of branches, 2–5 cm. wide, flattish; rays 14–20, white, long, spreading, 2–3-toothed at apex; disk yellow, the receptacle low, convex, naked; achenes striate; involucre of small, overlapping, compact bracts with dry margins. Basal leaves often forming compact rosettes, oblanceolate or spatulate, usually pinnately cleft or coarsely and irregularly toothed, petioled; middle and upper stem leaves becoming smaller, less deeply cut, sessile and usually somewhat clasping at base.

In fields and meadows, along roadsides. A common weed, introduced from Europe. Flowering June and July.

This attractive weed often virtually takes over run-down meadows and pastures. Cattle seldom browse these plants, but when they do the milk has an unpleasant taste. The Ox-eye Daisy is a very attractive cut flower, and one does not have to worry about diminishing the supply.

PLATE 214

Stick-tight
(*Bidens cernua*)

Beggar-ticks
(*Bidens coronata*)

420

PLATE 215

Sneezeweed
(*Helenium autumnale*)

Sneezeweed
(*Helenium nudiflorum*)

421

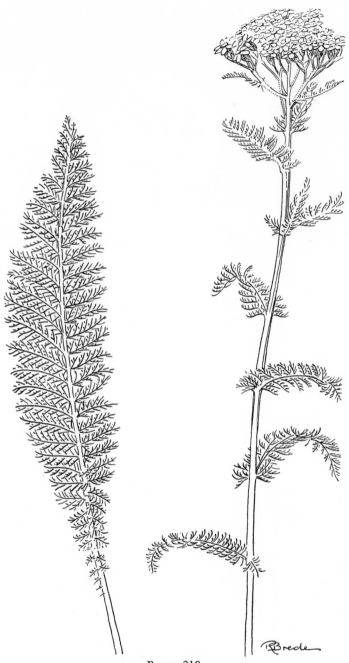

PLATE 216
Common Yarrow (*Achillea millefolium*)

422

PINEAPPLE-WEED
Matricaria matricarioides (Less.) Porter   Plate 217

Low-growing, weedy annual with the odor of fresh pineapple, at least when bruised. Heads without rays, erect, terminal, greenish to yellowish, somewhat resembling acorns in their cups—the disk being conical and the involucre of short, overlapping papery bracts. Leaves 2–3 times pinnately divided into very narrow segments.

Along roads and railways, in fields and dry waste land. Flowering all summer.

COMMON TANSY, GOLDEN-BUTTONS
Tanacetum vulgare L.   Plate 218

Smooth, erect, strongly aromatic, bitter and acrid perennial up to 1.5 m. tall, branching only at the inflorescence. Heads numerous (20–200), yellow, mostly without rays or with a few small obscure ones, hemispheric, 5–10 mm. broad, borne in flat-topped terminal corymbs. Involucre of dry overlapping scales. Leaves very numerous, alternate, deeply and finely 1–3 times pinnately divided into toothed linear-oblong segments, the lower divisions of the leaves often smaller than the upper; basal leaves up to 3 dm. long and half as wide.

In fields, along roads, shady shores, and waste places. Introduced from Europe. Flowering July to September.

This species was cultivated in western Europe during the Middle Ages for its supposed medicinal properties. It is poisonous, and there are records of deaths due to drinking too much tea made from the leaves. Animals may be poisoned by this species, but because of the bitter taste they seldom eat it.

LAKE HURON TANSY
Tanacetum huronense Nutt.   Plate 218

Very similar to Common Tansy, but somewhat shorter; long-hairy to woolly throughout; the heads fewer (1–30) and larger (the disk 1.3–2 cm. broad).

In sands and gravels of lake shores and on river banks. Flowering June to August.

PALE INDIAN-PLANTAIN
Cacalia atriplicifolia L.   Plate 219

Smooth, glaucous perennial up to 2 m. tall. Heads numerous, without rays, whitish, rather large, borne in short, broad, more or less flat corymbs. Flowers 5 or more to a head, the corolla deeply 5-lobed; pappus of numerous soft hairlike bristles; receptacle usually with thickish hairs in the center; involucre narrowly cylindric, the bracts usually 5, erect in a single row, 7–12 mm. long. Leaves alternate, irregularly toothed and shallowly lobed, the lower leaves very large, kidney-shaped or slightly heart-shaped, palmately veined, pale beneath, the upper leaves smaller and rhombic to ovate.

In dry soil in open woods and thickets. Flowering late June to September.

WORMWOOD
Artemisia caudata Michx.   Plate 219

Slightly aromatic, grayish biennial, usually with a single stem up to 1 m. tall rising from the first year's rosette. Heads small, very numerous, crowded in narrow, elongate, green to bronze, terminal leafy panicles 1.5–7.5 dm.

Plate 217
Ox-eye Daisy
(*Chrysanthemum leucanthemum*)

Mayweed   Pineapple-weed
(*Anthemis cotula*)   (*Matricaria matricarioides*)

424

long. Flowers all tubular, 14–25 in a head, yellowish; involucre of thin, green, dry-margined bracts. Leaves of the rosette numerous, grayish-downy, 2–3 times pinnately divided into very long, narrow, almost threadlike seg- ments; stem leaves similar but smaller, numerous.

On dry plains, prairies, and sandy beaches. Common on the sandy beaches of the Great Lakes. Flowering August and September.

Like the ragweeds, which they greatly resemble, the wormwoods have windborne pollen.

GOLDEN RAGWORT, SQUAW-WEED
Senecio aureus L.   Plate 220

Erect perennial up to 16 dm. tall, freely branched above, the rootstocks and basal offshoots horizontal, creeping, usually bearing distinct tufts of leaves. Heads golden-yellow, 2–3 cm. wide; ray flowers 8–15, pistillate; disk flowers perfect; achenes smooth, the pappus white, of numerous, soft hairlike bristles; receptacle flat, naked; involucre of linear, pointed greenish bracts. Basal leaves heart-shaped to nearly round, toothed, long-petioled, often purplish below; lower stem leaves more or less lyrate, short-petioled; upper leaves pinnately cut and sessile.

In wet meadows, swampy ground, and moist thickets. Flowering May to August.

The genus *Senecio* is one of the largest known; over 1200 species have been described. *S. aureus* is quite variable, and at least 5 varieties have been named.

RAGWORT
Senecio pauperculus Michx.   Plate 220

Slender perennial up to 6 dm. tall. Heads usually 1–8, rarely more than 20, deep yellow; rays few, usually conspicuous; involucre bell-shaped, the bracts often purple-tipped. Basal leaves oblanceolate to oblong-elliptic, tapering to the petiole, crenate or toothed, up to 10 cm. long; stem leaves usually pinnately cut, but sometimes undivided, the upper leaves reduced and often sessile.

In gravel, rocky places, on sandy lake shores and dunes, on cliffs, or in bogs and peaty places. Flowering late May to September.

COMMON BURDOCK
Arctium minus (Hill) Bernh.   Plate 221

Coarse, weedy biennial up to 1.5 m. tall. Heads lavender to rose-purple, occasionally white, sessile or borne on short peduncles, solitary or in racemes; flowers all tubular; involucre subglobose, the bracts green, numerous, closely appressed at the base but with long, stiff, pointed, hooked ends, forming a spiny bur in fruit. Leaves broadly ovate, mostly heart-shaped at base, veiny, thin, serrate to entire, green above, gray below, large, up to 7.5 dm. long, hollow-petioled.

In waste land. Introduced from Europe; now a widespread weed. Flowering July to October.

Almost everyone knows the tenacity with which the dry burs stick to clothing. The bristles are so strong that small birds lighting on a cluster of burs may be held fast by the strong, sharply curved hooks, and die of exhaustion before they can free themselves.

PLATE 218

Lake Huron Tansy
(*Tanacetum huronense*)

Common Tansy
(*Tanacetum vulgare*)

426

PLATE 219

Wormwood
(*Artemisia caudata*)

Pale Indian-plantain
(*Cacalia atriplicifolia*)

PLATE 220

Golden Ragwort
(*Senecio aureus*)

Ragwort
(*Senecio pauperculus*)

Cirsium

1. Plants grayish, owing to white-woolly hairs; growing on
   shores of the Great Lakes . . . .*C. pitcheri*, Plate 223
1. Plants green; not usually growing on shores of the Great Lakes . . . 2
   2. Upper stems and branches having broad, prickly-margined
      wings extending from leaf bases . . . . . *C. vulgare*, Plate 222
   2. Stems and branches not having wings 3
3. Flowering stems rising from a basal rosette; involucre
   2–3.5 cm. high . . . . *C. muticum*, Plate 223
3. Flowering stems rising from a deep rootstock, no rosette
   present; involucre 1–2 cm. high . . . . *C. arvense*, Plate 222

PITCHER'S THISTLE
Cirsium pitcheri (Torr.) T. & G.   Plate 223

Stout, erect, white-woolly, prickly biennial up to 1 m. tall from a basal rosette. Heads cream-color, solitary or several in a raceme; flowers all alike, the corolla tubes deeply 5-lobed; involucre ovoid, about 2.5 cm. high, the bracts overlapping in several series, bristle-tipped. Rosette leaves white-woolly, long-petioled, cleft to the midrib into a few, remote, elongate linear segments which may be spiny at the tip or merely rounded, up to 3 dm. long; stem leaves similar but smaller and partly clasping or slightly decurrent at base, the segments about 5 mm. wide, the margins inrolled, sparingly prickly.

On sandy shores and dunes of Lakes Michigan, Superior, and Huron. Flowering May to September.

BULL THISTLE, COMMON THISTLE
Cirsium vulgare (Savi) Tenore   Plate 222

Coarse, prickly biennial with conspicuously spiny-winged stems up to 2 m. tall. Heads discoid, purple, several or solitary at the tips of short prickly-winged branches; involucre ovoid to subglobose, 3–4 cm. high, the bracts lanceolate to linear, tipped with rigid spines. Leaves of the first year pale, woolly or webbed beneath, green above, forming basal rosettes, pinnately cut, the larger ones with the lobes again lobed or toothed, the lobes and teeth with long, strong spines, the stem leaves of the second year similar.

In fields and pastures, along roadsides, and in waste places. Naturalized from Europe. Flowering June to September.

SWAMP THISTLE
Cirsium muticum Michx.   Plate 223

Stout, erect, prickly biennial up to 3 m. tall. Heads reddish-purple to rose-purple, several to many, medium-sized; involucre sticky and cobwebby (covered with entangled hairs), the bracts not tipped with spines. Leaves deeply pinnately cut into lanceolate segments, spiny, densely covered with matted wool beneath when young, becoming smooth and green on both sides.

In swamps, low woods, thickets, and meadows. Flowering July to September.

CANADA THISTLE
Cirsium arvense (L.) Scop.   Plate 222

Prickly, erect perennial up to 1 m. tall from creeping, freely-branching, and sprouting roots. Heads unisexual, pinkish-purple or white, numerous,

429

PLATE 221
Common Burdock (*Arctium minus*)

430

about 2.5 cm. in diameter, the staminate heads globose and with projecting corollas, the pistillate heads more oblong, the corollas shorter, and the pappus long and conspicuous; involucral bracts appressed, short-pointed but not spiny-tipped. Leaves alternate, oblong to lanceolate, and deeply pinnately cut, toothed, very prickly, at first often woolly beneath but finally green on both sides, the lower leaves up to 3 dm. long, petioled, the upper leaves shorter and sessile; no rosette formed.

In cultivated and waste ground. This common weed was introduced from Europe; not, in spite of its name, from Canada. Flowering June to August.

SPOTTED STAR-THISTLE, KNAPWEED

Centaurea maculosa Lam.   Plate 224

Tough, wiry, grayish-green, usually bushy, many-branched, spreading biennial or short-lived perennial up to 15 dm. tall. Heads numerous, terminal on the branches, rose-purple, rose, or at times white, slightly fragrant, 2–3 cm. wide, falsely radiate; flowers all tubular with long narrow lobes, the outer ones, the largest, sterile, the inner flowers shorter and perfect; involucre ovoid, of numerous rows of strongly ribbed, overlapping bracts, the bracts with short, dark, pinnately cut tips, the inner bracts the longest. Leaves alternate, grayish-green, sessile; principal stem leaves deeply pinnately cut into long, linear segments, the upper leaves smaller; leaves of the short flowering branches linear.

In fields, along roadsides, and in waste places. Introduced from Europe. Flowering July to August.

This weed is spreading rapidly. Our familiar garden Cornflower or Bachelor's Button is *Centaurea cyanus* L.

WHITE STAR-THISTLE, KNAPWEED

Centaurea diffusa Lam.   Plate 224

Shorter (1–6 dm.), stiffer, and more erect than the preceding species. The heads are smaller, very numerous, white, creamy, roseate, or sometimes rose-purple; all flowers with corollas the same length; involucral bracts pinnately cut and spiny-tipped.

In fields and along roadsides. Introduced from Europe. Flowering July to September.

CHICORY

Cichorium intybus L.   Plate 225

Erect, stiffly branching biennial or perennial up to 1.2 m. tall from a long, stout, fleshy root; juice milky. Heads showy, blue (rarely pink or white), 2–5 cm. in diameter, opening in the morning, closing in the afternoon or in cloudy weather, solitary or 2–3, sessile in the axils and terminal on the stem and short, thick branches. Flowers all ligulate, the outer flowers with corollas about 2.5 cm. long, the inner flowers shorter (falsely radiate); involucre double, the outer bracts 5, broad and spreading, the inner bracts 8–10, narrower, erect. Basal leaves spreading, spatulate, pinnately cut to merely sharply toothed, the divisions directed backward; stem leaves greatly reduced, toothed or entire.

Along roads, in fields and waste places. Introduced from Europe. Flowering June to October.

This species is most attractive when the heads are expanded; it often grows in large patches and makes a striking display. It can

PLATE 222

Canada Thistle
(*Cirsium arvense*)

Bull Thistle
(*Cirsium vulgare*)

432

PLATE 223

Pitcher's Thistle
(*Cirsium pitcheri*)

Swamp Thistle
(*Cirsium muticum*)

PLATE 224

Spotted Star-thistle
(*Centaurea maculosa*)

White Star-thistle
(*Centaurea diffusa*)

be a troublesome weed, however, and if eaten by cows gives the milk an unpleasant taste. The ground roots are roasted and used as an adulterant in, or substitute for, coffee. Common endive, *C. endivia* L., is closely related.

DWARF DANDELION

Krigia virginica (L.) Willd.   Plate 226

Annual with several flowering stems up to 3 dm. tall from fibrous roots; unbranched, leafy at or near the base only; with milky juice. Heads yellow, solitary at the end of the slender flowering stem. Flowers all ligulate and perfect; bell-shaped involucre of 9–18 bracts which become reflexed in age.

Pappus double, of 5–7 short roundish scales alternating with long bristles. Earliest leaves roundish and entire; later leaves linear to obovate, often pinnately cut, 1.5–12 cm. long, 1–12 mm. wide.

In sterile, dry or sandy soil. Flowering April to August.

YELLOW GOAT'S-BEARD

Tragopogon major Jacq.   Plate 227

Stout, glabrous perennial up to 1 m. tall; juice milky, soon brown. Heads yellow, large, solitary at the ends of branches, the peduncles enlarged upward. Flowers all ligulate, the rays of the central flowers about half as long as those of the outer flowers, the rays 5-lobed at the end; achenes linear, 2.5–4 cm. long, borne in large globose

heads; pappus of numerous long, plumose bristles attached to the long beak of the achene; involucre simple, usually of 8 bracts, the bracts longer than the flowers and becoming 4–7 cm. long in fruit. Leaves grasslike, alternate, linear, entire, clasping, parallel-veined.

Along roadsides and in waste places. Flowering May to July.

Like the other species of *Tragopogon* found here, this one is native to Europe but is now widely naturalized in North America. The roots are edible and are frequently used in soups or as a vegetable. The tops are sometimes eaten as greens. The Indians used the coagulated juice for chewing-gum. The heads close up shortly after being picked and also when the sun sets and during cloudy weather.

YELLOW GOAT'S-BEARD

Tragopogon pratensis L.   Plate 227

Quite similar to the preceding species, but generally larger and more robust, the peduncle slenderly cylindric throughout, scarcely enlarged even in fruit, the involucre about as long as

or shorter than the flowers, elongating to 1.8–3.8 cm. in fruit, the achenes 1.5–2.5 cm. long.

Along roadsides, in fields and waste places. Flowering May to August.

PURPLE SALSIFY, OYSTER-PLANT

Tragopogon porrifolius L.   Plate 227

Similar in general aspect to the 2 preceding species, but readily distinguished by the purple flowers. The peduncle is thickened below the head.

In waste places and fields, along roads and railways. Flowering May to July.

PLATE 225
Chicory (*Cichorium intybus*)

436

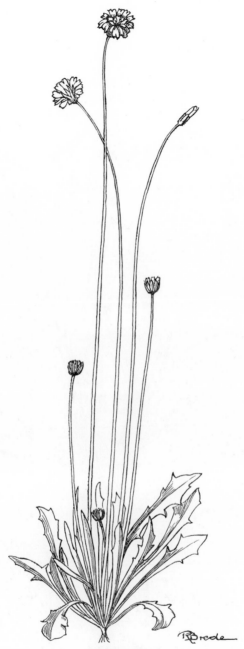

PLATE 226
Dwarf Dandelion (*Krigia virginica*)

437

PLATE 227
°Purple Salsify (*Tragopogon porrifolius*)
Yellow Goat's-beard (*Tragopogon major*)
°Yellow Goat's-beard (*Tragopogon pratensis*)

°Young fruiting heads only shown.

438

DANDELION

Taraxacum officinale Weber

Plate 228

Ever-present, rosette-forming perennial 5–50 cm. tall from a deep tap root; juice copious, milky. Heads numerous, opening only in sunshine, bright golden-yellow, 2–5 cm. wide, solitary at the ends of the naked, hollow, flowering stalks. Flowers 150–200, all ligulate and perfect, the outer flowers the longest; involucre double, the inner bracts the longer, becoming erect after flowering, then reflexed and exposing the globular head of brown to straw-colored achenes; each achene crowned with a fine, pale, parachutelike pappus. Leaves basal, horizontal or ascending, narrowed to the slender, usually slightly winged, petiolelike base, oblanceolate, usually coarsely and irregularly wavy-toothed or pinnately cut, sometimes nearly entire, 6–40 cm. long.

Abundant in lawns, grasslands, open ground, and disturbed places. Introduced from Europe. Flowering April to September.

The leaves of dandelions are a well-known early spring green. They can be served either boiled or raw. Dandelion wine (made from the blossoms) is a favorite with some people.

RED-SEEDED DANDELION

Taraxacum erythrospermum Andrz.

Plate 228

Quite similar to the preceding species in general aspect, but the leaves more dissected, usually cut almost or quite to the midrib into narrow, widely spaced lobes; the terminal lobe typically quite slender and not much larger than the lateral lobes; several small lobes usually present between the larger ones; the achenes red to purplish at maturity.

In thin, dry soil of fields, pastures, and lawns, along roadsides and in other disturbed areas. Native of Eurasia now established in North America, but much less common than the preceding species. Flowering April to July.

FIELD SOWTHISTLE

Sonchus arvensis L.

Plate 229

Coarse, glandular to smooth perennial up to 12 dm. tall, creeping extensively by underground rootstocks; the stems leafy below, almost naked above; juice milky. Heads bright yellow, 3–5 cm. wide, resembling dandelions, several on long peduncles in an open corymb. Flowers all ligulate; involucre 2.5 cm. high, of uniformly colored, overlapping bracts of 3 lengths; achenes oblong, the pappus copious, of very soft, white, simple bristles which usually fall off together. Leaves lanceolate, the upper leaves deeply pinnately cut, with backward-pointing segments spiny-toothed, up to 3 dm. petioled; upper leaves small, entire, clasping.

In fields and waste places, along roads, and on gravelly shores. Introduced from Europe; now a widespread weed. Flowering July to October.

WILD LETTUCE

Lactuca canadensis L.

Plate 229

Glaucous, usually glabrous, leafy-stemmed biennial up to 3.5 m. tall, with basal rosette from a tap root; juice milky. Heads yellow, sometimes

PLATE 228
Dandelion
(*Taraxacum officinale*)

Red-seeded Dandelion
(*Taraxacum erythrospermum*)

440

becoming purplish in age, borne in open, elongate panicles; flowers 12–20 in a head, all ligulate; achenes flat, 1–3 nerved on each face, contracted to a long, threadlike beak which bears a short-lived, very soft, copious white pappus of hairlike bristles; involucre green or tinged with purple, urn-shaped, the bracts of unequal length, closely appressed, in 2 or more series.

Leaves glabrous, or slightly hairy beneath, numerous, alternate, variable, unlobed to wavy-pinnate with lanceolate to oblong segments that are broader at the base, the upper leaves usually lanceolate and entire, sessile, clasping.

In thickets, open woods, borders of woods, and waste places. Flowering July to September.

Prickly Lettuce, *L. scariola* L., is an annual or biennial. It has only 5–7 flowers in a head, the leaves are spiny-toothed, and the achenes have 5–7 nerves on each face. Garden Lettuce, *L. sativa* L., often escapes from cultivation and may be found along roads and in waste places, but does not usually persist.

The Indians used the fresh white latex of Wild Lettuce to treat warts.

WHITE RATTLESNAKE-ROOT, WHITE LETTUCE
Prenanthes alba L.   Plate 230

Glaucous, smooth perennial up to 1.5 m. tall; juice milky, copious. Heads nodding, slenderly cylindric, whitish or greenish, tinged with rose or pale purple, closing at night and in cloudy weather, borne in loose terminal panicles; flowers 8–15 in a head, all ligulate and perfect, fragrant; the styles with the 2-cleft stigmas extending well beyond the rays to produce a ragged appearance; involucre cylindrical, of 6–8 long, purplish-tinged bracts and many much smaller triangular bracts;

pappus of rough, brown to deep reddish-brown bristles on short, columnar, beakless achenes. Leaves alternate, variable, the lower ones more or less triangular, often 3–5 lobed, the base heart-shaped or hastate, the margin wavy-toothed, the petioles long, wing-margined; upper leaves much smaller, more or less oblong, often with angular teeth or small lobes, the petioles short.

In rich woodlands and thickets. Flowering August and September.

TALL RATTLESNAKE-ROOT
Prenanthes altissima L.   Plate 230

Somewhat taller than the preceding species (up to 2 m.) the heads usually 5–6-flowered and borne in a long, leafy, open panicle; the involucre of 5 principal bracts; the pappus

creamy-white to bright yellow-brown; the leaves often unlobed, the petioles winged, or not.

In moist woods. Flowering July to October.

ORANGE HAWKWEED, DEVIL'S PAINT-BRUSH
Hieracium aurantiacum L.   Color Plate 16

Erect, stiffly-hairy perennial up to 6 dm. tall from a basal rosette; juice milky. Heads orange-red to deep orange, few, in loose, more or less flat-topped terminal clusters, the pedicels and involucres thickly clothed

with black glandular dots. Flowers all ligulate and perfect, the outer row or two with longer rays; involucre of 2 or 3 rows of nearly equal, pointed bracts; achenes black, columnar, tapering to the base; pappus a single series

PLATE 229

Field Sowthistle
(*Sonchus arvensis*)

Wild Lettuce
(*Latuca canadensis*)

442

PLATE 230

White Rattlesnake-root
(*Prenanthes alba*)

Tall Rattlesnake-root
(*Prenanthes altissima*)

PLATE 231

King Devil
(*Hieracium florentinum*)

Rattlesnake-weed
(*Hieracium venosum*)

of nearly equal, brittle, rough bristles. Leaves mostly in a basal rosette (occasionally 1 or 2 on a scape), oblong or oblanceolate, 5–13 cm. long, green and long-hairy on both sides; vigorous, leafy stolons are frequent.

In fields and open woods, along roads, and in waste places. Introduced from Europe; now a troublesome weed. Flowering June to August.

RATTLESNAKE-WEED

Hieracium venosum L.

Plate 231

Erect perennial with a solitary stem up to 1 m. tall from a basal rosette, the stem many-branched above; juice milky. Heads numerous, yellow 15–40-flowered, in open panicles; involucre cylindric with a single series of long, narrow bracts and a few short outer ones. Leaves all basal, oblong-spatulate, 2.5–12 cm. long, distinctly marked with reddish-purple along the veins.

In open woods and clearings, usually in sandy or poor soil. Flowering May to September.

KING DEVIL

Hieracium florentinum All.

Plate 231

Slender, smooth or hairy, many-stemmed perennial up to 1 m. tall from basal rosettes, the leafless stems many branched above. Heads yellow, 3–75, on glandular-hairy peduncles in a corymb. Flowers all perfect and ligulate; pappus of many bristles; achenes columnar, narrowed at the base; involucre with black glandular hairs. Leaves all basal, narrowly oblong or spatulate, thick, entire, pale green, narrowed to a winged petiole.

In fields, meadows, and clearings, along roadsides. Naturalized from Europe. Flowering May to August.

This very aggressive weed has become very common in the tip of the Lower Peninsula and in the Copper Country within the last few years. Flowering at the same time as Orange Hawkweed, Ox-eye Daisy, and some of the ragworts, it adds color to wasteland, particularly in late June.

SELECTED REFERENCES

MANUALS

FERNALD, MERRITT LYNDON
> 1950. Gray's Manual of Botany, eighth edition. New York: American Book Company.

GLEASON, HENRY ALLAN
> 1952. The New Britton and Brown Illustrated Flora of the Northeastern United States and Adjacent Canada, 3 vols. New York: New York Botanical Garden.

GLEASON, HENRY ALLAN, AND ARTHUR CRONQUIST
> 1963. Manual of the Vascular Plants of Northeastern United States and adjacent Canada. Princeton, New Jersey: D. van Nostrand Company.

SPECIAL GROUPS TREATED FOR MICHIGAN

BILLINGTON, CECIL
> 1949. Shrubs of Michigan, second edition. Bloomfield Hills, Mich.: Cranbrook Institute of Science.

BUCHHOLTZ, K. R., *et al.*
> 1954. Weeds of the North Central States. Urbana, Illinois. Agricultural Experiment Station Circular 718. (Available as North Central Regional Publication No. 36, Michigan Agricultural Experiment Station, East Lansing, Michigan.)

CASE, FREDERICK W., JR.
> 1964. Orchids of the Western Great Lakes Region. Bloomfield Hills, Michigan: Cranbrook Institute of Science.

GROWING WILDFLOWERS

BIRDSEYE, CLARENCE AND ELEANOR G.
> 1951. Growing Woodland Plants. New York: Oxford University Press.

HULL, HELEN S.
> 1952. Wildflowers for Your Garden. New York: M. Barrows & Company.

STEFFEK, EDWIN F.
> 1954. Wildflowers and How to Grow Them. New York: Crown Publishers.

TAYLOR, KATHRYN S., AND STEPHEN H. HAMBLIN
> 1963. Handbook of Wild Flower Cultivation. New York: The Macmillan Company.

TAYLOR, NORMAN
> 1955. Wildflower Gardening. Princeton, N. J.: D. Van Nostrand Company.

GLOSSARY

Achene. A small, dry, hard, 1-seeded fruit.

Alternate (leaves). Borne singly at a node, first on one side of the stem, then on the other.

Annual. Living a single season.

Anther. The pollen-producing part of the stamen.

Apex. Upper end or tip (of leaf, petal, etc.).

Appressed. Lying flat and close against.

Aril. A fleshy, often bright-colored, appendage to a seed.

Auricle. Ear-shaped appendage or lobe.

Awn. Slender, usually stiff, terminal bristle.

Axil. Angle formed between the leaf and stem, or branch and stem.

Axillary. In an axil.

Beak. A projection ending in an elongated tip.

Bearded. Bearing long or stiff hairs.

Berry. A fleshy fruit having a thin skin or outer covering, the seeds surrounded by the pulp.

Biennial. Living only two years and flowering the second year.

Bisexual. Having both stamens (male organs) and pistils (female organs).

Bract. A small leaf, often scalelike and usually subtending a flower or inflorescence.

Bracted. Having bracts.

Bulb. Underground leaf-bud with fleshy scales.

Calyx. The outer, usually green, portion of the flower.

Capitate. Headlike; arranged in a head, or dense cluster.

Capsule. A dry fruit composed of several cells, opening at maturity.

Carpel. A simple pistil, or one member of a compound pistil.

Chaff. The scales or bracts on the receptacle of many composite flowers.

Chlorophyll. The green coloring matter of plants.

Ciliate. Fringed with hairs.

Clasping. Partly surrounding another structure at the base, *e.g.,* as a leaf surrounds a stem.

Clavate. Club-shaped; gradually thickened upward.

Compound. Composed of 2 or more similar parts united into one whole. *Compound leaf,* one divided into separate leaflets.

Connective. The part of a stamen that joins the two anther cavities.

Cordate. Heart-shaped, the broadest part at the base.

Corm. The enlarged, solid, bulblike base of some stems.

Corolla. The second or inner set of floral parts, composed of separate or united united petals; usually conspicuous by its size and/or color.

Corona. A crownlike structure on inner side of the corolla, as in narcissus, milkweed, etc.

Corymb. A flat-topped or convex flower cluster, the outer flowers opening first.

Crenate. Having much-rounded teeth.

Cuneate. Shaped like a wedge.

Cyathium. Cuplike involucre around the flowers in Euphorbia.

Cylindric. Shaped like a cylinder.

Cyme. A convex or flat flower cluster, the central flowers unfolding first.

Decumbent. Stems in a reclining position, but with the end ascending.

Decurrent. Extending downward (applied to leaves in which the blade is extended as wings along the petiole).

Dentate. With sharp teeth.

Diadelphous (referring to stamens). Combined in two, often unequal, sets.

Dicotyledon or *dicot.* Plant with 2 seed-leaves or cotyledons. In practice usually recognized by the net-veined leaves, the parts of the flower in 4's or 5's, the fibers of the stem in a ring.

Disk. Central part of the head of many composite flowers.

Disk-flower. In composite flowers, the tubular flowers in the center of the head, or comprising the head.

Dissected. Cut or divided into narrow segments.

Drupe. A fleshy fruit with a single hard stone in the center, such as the peach, plum, or cherry.

Ellipsoid, Elliptic. Oval in outline, widest at the middle and narrowed about equally at the ends.

Entire. With a continuous, unbroken margin; without teeth, scallops, or lobes.

Fertile. Capable of normal reproductive functions. A fertile anther produces pollen; a fertile flower produces fruit.

Filament. The stalk of the stamen.

Filamentous. Threadlike.

Flexuous. Curved alternately in opposite directions.

Foliate. Having leaves, leaved, as 3-leaved.

Foliolate. Having leaflets.

Follicle. A dry fruit developed from a single ovary, opening by a slit along one side.

Fruit. The seed-bearing product of a plant; the ripened ovary with such other parts as may be attached to it.

Glabrous. Smooth, in the sense of lacking hairs (not necessarily smooth to the touch).

Glaucous. Covered with a fine bluish or whitish bloom.

Globose, globular. Spherical or nearly so.

Glutinous. Gluelike, sticky.

Hastate. Shaped like an arrowhead, but with the basal lobes pointed outward.

Herbaceous. Soft, not woody; leaflike in color or texture.

Hip. The fleshy, ripened fruit of the rose.

Hood. A cap-shaped or hood-shaped structure formed by the sepals and petals in orchids.

Horn. An incurved pointed projection.

Hypanthium. A cuplike receptacle that bears the flower parts on its upper margin.

Inferior. Lower or below (an inferior ovary is one that is seemingly below the calyx segments).

Inflorescence. A flower cluster.

Involucral. Belonging to an involucre.

Involucre. A whorl of small leaves or bracts below a flower or flower cluster.

Irregular (flower). Showing inequality in the size, form, or union of its similar parts.

Keel. The two fused lower petals of the flower of the pea family.

Keeled. Having a central ridge.

Lanceolate. Shaped like a lance-head (much longer than wide, widest near the base and tapering to the apex).

Leaflet. One of the divisions of a compound leaf.

Legume. A fruit from a simple ovary, opening along 2 sides; e.g., a pea pod.

Ligulate. Furnished with a ligule (applied to the ray flowers in the composites).

Ligule. A straplike organ.

Limb. The expanded part of a corolla of united petals.

Lip. The upper or lower division of an irregular corolla or calyx, as in the mints. The characteristic (and apparently lower) petal of an orchid is called the lip.

Lobe. A partial division of a leaf or other structure.

Lyrate. Pinnately cut, with a large, rounded lobe at apex, but with the lower lobes small.

Membranous. Thin and somewhat transparent, like a membrane.

Midrib. The central rib or vein of a leaf.

Monocotyledon or *monocot.* A plant with 1 seed-leaf (cotyledon). In practice usually recognized by the parallel veins of the leaves, the flower parts in 3's or 6's, the fibers of the stem scattered (not in a ring).

Naked receptacle. Without scales or bracts.

Nectar. A sweet, often fragrant liquid.

Nectariferous, or *Nectiferous.* Producing or having nectar.

Nectary. Any place or organ where nectar is secreted.

Nerve. A principal, unbranched vein.

Net-veined. Having veins forming a network or reticulum.

Node. A point on a stem where leaves, branches, or buds are attached.

Nutlet. A small hard, 1-seeded fruit.

Ob–. Prefix meaning inverted, e.g., *obovate,* meaning ovate but with the broadest part toward the apex.

Oblong. Having the length two to three times the width, the sides nearly parallel.

Obtuse. Blunt or rounded at the end.

Opposite (leaves). A pair of leaves arising from the same node and on opposite sides of the stem; of stamens, inserted in front of the petals, and thus opposite or across from them.

Ovary. The part of the pistil that produces seeds.

Ovate. Egg-shaped, the broadest part basal.

Palmate. Having parts diverging from a common base, as the fingers from a hand.

Panicle. A loose, elongate, flower cluster with compound branching.

Papilionaceous. Having a standard, wings, and a keel and resembling a butterfly, as in a pea flower.

Pappus. The calyx in the Compositae, consisting of hairs, bristles, awns, or teeth at the top of the ovary or achene.

Parallel (venation). Parallel-veined; having veins rising at base of a leaf and continuing to apex in a nearly parallel manner.

Parasite. A plant that gets its nourishment from another living plant to which it is attached.

Parted. Cut or lobed more than halfway to the middle or base.

Pedicel. The stem of a single flower in a flower cluster.

Peduncle. The stem or stalk of a single flower, or of a cluster of flowers.

Perennial. A plant that is able to live year after year.

Perfect (flower). Having both stamens and pistils.

Perfoliate. Having the stem apparently passing through the leaf.

Perianth. The flower envelope, consisting of the calyx and the corolla (if present).

Petal. One of the parts of the corolla.

Petiole. The stem or stalk of a leaf.

Pinnate. Like a feather, having the parts arranged in two rows along a common axis.

Pistil. The seed-bearing part of the plant, produced in the center of the flower.

Pistillate. Provided with pistils.

449

Plumose. Featherlike, with fine, soft hairs along the sides.

Pod. A simple, dry fruit which opens when ripe; a legume.

Pollen. The spores (male) produced by the anthers.

Prostrate. Lying flat on the ground.

Pubescent. Hairy, the hairs soft.

Punctate. Covered with dots or pits.

Raceme. A flower cluster with pedicelled flowers borne along a somewhat elongated common axis, the lower flowers opening first.

Ray. One of the branches of an umbel; a strap-shaped flower in a head in which tubular disk flowers are also present.

Receptacle. The end of a flower stalk upon which the flower parts are borne, or the enlarged end of the peduncle upon which the flowers are borne in the composite family.

Recurved. Curved downward or backward.

Reflexed. Bent downward or backward.

Regular (flower). Having all members of each kind similar in size and shape, e.g., the petals all alike.

Reticulate. Like a network.

Rhombic. Somewhat diamond-shaped.

Rib. A primary or prominent vein of a leaf.

Rootstock. (also called *rhizome*). A prostrate or underground stem, usually rooting at the nodes.

Rosette. A cluster of leaves in circular form, usually at the base of a plant.

Rotate (corolla). Wheel-shaped, having a short tube and widely spreading limb, as in the forget-me-not.

Runner. A horizontal, aboveground stem that may root and develop new plants.

Sagittate. Shaped like an arrowhead.

Salverform. Having a slender tube (relatively long) and widely spreading limb.

Scape. A leafless, flowering stalk arising from the ground or from a very short stem bearing basal leaves.

Seed. A mature ovule which can germinate and give rise to a new plant.

Sepal. One of the parts of the calyx or outer floral envelope.

Sessile. Lacking a stalk or stem.

Sheath. A tubelike part which surrounds another part, as a leaf may sheathe a stem.

Shrub. A plant, shorter than a tree, with several to many woody stems which do not usually die at the end of the growing season.

Simple. Not compound; composed of a single piece or unit.

Sinus. The indentation between two lobes.

Solitary. Single.

Sordid. Dirty white, dingy.

Spadix. A spike of flowers on a fleshy axis.

Spathe. A large, often showy bract enclosing or subtending a flower cluster (usually a spadix).

Spatulate. Shaped like a spatula, oblong with a long, somewhat tapering base, the apex rounded.

Spike. An elongated flower cluster with sessile or nearly sessile flowers borne along a common axis.

Spur. A hollow, somewhat pointed projection.

Stamen. The part of the flower that bears the pollen.

Staminate. Having stamens.

Staminode. A sterile stamen; a stamen that does not bear pollen.

Standard. The upper, enlarged petal of a pea flower.

Stem. The major supporting system of a plant to which buds, leaves, and flowers are attached.

Sterile. Unproductive, as a flower without a pistil, or a stamen without an anther.

Stigma. The part of a pistil upon which pollen germinates.

Stolon. A basal branch rooting at the nodes to produce new plants; a runner.

Stoloniferous. Bearing or producing stolons.

Style. The portion of the pistil between the ovary and stigma.

Sub–. Prefix meaning somewhat or slightly, e.g., *subcordate,* meaning somewhat heart-shaped.

Subtend. To extend under, as a bract or involucre subtends a flower or flower cluster.

Succulent. Juicy or fleshy in texture, usually resistant to drying out.

Superior (ovary). Placed above the point of attachment of the other flower parts.

Tendril. A slender, almost threadlike, twining structure.

Throat. The part in a corolla or calyx where the tube and limb come together.

Tooth, teeth. Small, sharp-pointed projection or projections.

Tuber. A thickened, fleshy, modified, underground stem having numerous buds or eyes, e.g., the Irish potato.

Tubercle. A small, swollen, and usually hardened structure.

Tubular. Shaped like a tube.

Tufted. Forming clumps.

Twining. Winding spirally.

Umbel. A flower cluster with all the pedicels arising from the same point.

Undulate. Having a wavy margin or surface.

Unisexual. Of one sex, either staminate or pistillate only.

Urn-shaped (corolla). Having an enlarged, globular base, narrowed at the neck, and with a small limb.

Vein. A thread of visible fibrovascular (transporting) tissue.

Venation. Character or pattern of the veining.

Whorl. A group of three or more similar parts in a circle around a stem.

Wing. A thin expansion of tissue, e.g., along a petiole; a lateral petal, as in a pea flower.

INDEX

Figures preceded by an asterisk indicate principal page reference.

454

457

463